ALPS.

a
a; S.W. Dauph.—

inosa)
olia)
cula)
nosa)
cens (daonensis)
osa, minima

ma
ima
nsis)
nsis, minima?)

la)

abilis)
a, tyrolensis

34—Breonie	}	hirsuta, minima, glutinosa (auricula?)
35—Tuxer Zillertal		
36—Kitzbühler	}	auricula, minima, glutinosa (clusiana)
37—Steins Meer		
38—Hohe Tauern	}	hirsuta, minima, glutinosa
39—Deferegger		
40—Kreuzeck	}	auricula, minima, glutinosa (wulfeniana)
41—Carnic		
42—Julian		auricula, wulfeniana
43—Camnic		auricula, wulfeniana (villosa)
44—Karawanken		auricula, wulfeniana (minima, villosa?)
45—Gurktal		glutinosa, minima, villosa
46—Styrian East Carnic		minima, glutinosa (villosa, wulfeniana)
47—Low Tauern		minima, glutinosa (villosa)
48—Dachst. Tot. Geb.	}	auricula, minima, clusiana
49—Austrian		

with best wishes
George Smith

PRIMULAS

of

Europe and America

by

G. F. Smith, B. Burrow and D. B. Lowe

Hon. Editor: J. E. GOOD, Ph.D.

ISBN 0 900048 41 7

First Published 1984

© The Alpine Garden Society
Lye End Link, St. John's
Woking GU21 1SW
Surrey, Great Britain

Printed by
L. Baker (Printers) Ltd.
71 Lombard Street, Birmingham B12 0QU

CONTENTS

Dust Jacket: *Primula allionii*   *Photo: G. F. Smith*

LIST OF COLOUR PLATES AND THEIR AUTHORS

1. *Primula palinuri* Petagna: a specimen in cultivation.
   Photo: G. F. Smith
2. *Primula auricula* L.: on the Hochturm in the Northern calcareous Alps of Austria. *Photo: H. Taylor*
3. *Primula auricula* L.: Southern Alps. *Photo H. & W. Bevington*
4. *Primula marginata* Curtis: habitat—north-facing cliffs in the Maritime pre-Alps. *Photo: G. F. Smith*
5. *Primula marginata* Curtis: Maritime pre-Alps; in flower at the end of March at 700 m. *Photo: G. F. Smith*
6. *Primula latifolia* Lapeyr.: specimen in cultivation.
   Photo: G. F. Smith
7. *Primula carniolica* Jacq.: specimen in cultivation (N.B. the corolla colour is rather lighter in life). *Photo: D. B. Lowe*
8. *Primula hirsuta* All.: Pyrenees; the rounded leaves are typical for the region. *Photo: H. & W. Bevington*
9. *Primula daonensis* Leyb.: above the Tonale Pass in the Central Alps. Note the wedge-shaped leaves. *Photo: G. F. Smith*
10. *Primula pedemontana* Thomas (*ex* Gaudin): specimen in cultivation. Note the rust-coloured leaf margins. *Photo: C. Banham*
11. *Primula villosa* Wulfen.: specimen in cultivation.
    Photo: G. F. Smith
12. *Primula spectabilis* Tratt.: habitat—stony meadows in the Lake Garda region. *Photo: C. Greenfield*
13. *Primula spectabilis* Tratt.: Lake Garda region.
    Photo: C. Greenfield
14. *Primula glaucescens* Moretti: Brescia pre-Alps. *Photo: H. Taylor*
15. *Primula wulfeniana* Schott: Cimolais, Eastern Dolomites.
    Photo: G. F. Smith
16. *Primula clusiana* Tausch.: Wiener Schneeberg, at the eastern limit of the Alps. *Photo: H. Taylor*
17. *Primula allionii* Lois.: limestone cliff habitat in the Roya Valley, north of Nice. *Photo: G. F. Smith*
18. *Primula allionii* Lois.: pendent plant in the Roya Valley; this attractive habit is untypical. *Photo: G. F. Smith*
19. *Primula allionii* Lois.: colour variations in the Roya Valley. Note the conglomerate limestone. *Photo: G. F. Smith*
20. *Primula allionii* Lois.: a lovely tuffet in the Roya Valley.
    Photo: J. Jermyn
21. *Primula integrifolia* L.: habitat in the Glarus Alps.
    Photo: G. F. Smith
22. *Primula integrifolia* L.: Pyrenees. *Photo: H. & W. Bevington*
23. *Primula tyrolensis* Schott: specimen grown by Eric Watson.
    Photo: G. F. Smith
24. *Primula kitaibeliana* Schott.: specimen in cultivation.
    Photo: G. F. Smith
25. *Primula minima* L.: Dolomites. *Photo: G. F. Smith*

26. *Primula glutinosa* Wulfen: Gurktal Alps, Austria.
    Photo: G. F. Smith
27. *Primula deorum* Velen.: Rila Mountains, Bulgaria.
    Photo: G. F. Smith
28. *Primula deorum* Velen.: habitat in the Rila Mts. Note the boggy ground, and the accompanying *P. farinosa* L. subsp. *exigua* (Velen.) Hayek.
    Photo: G. F. Smith
29. *Primula angustifolia* Torr.: habitat on Pikes Peak. Crumbling granite at 3500 m. (12,000'), above Colorado Springs.
    Photo: M. Collins
30. *Primula angustifolia* Torr.: Pikes Peak.   *Photo: M. Collins*
31. *Primula parryi* A. Gray: Bighorn Mountains, Northern Wyoming. Habitat on north side of limestone cliffs, 2500–3000 m. (8–9000').
    Photo: B. A. Mech
32. *Primula parryi* A. Gray: Bighorn Mts.   *Photo: B. A. Mech*
33. *Primula cusickiana* A. Gray: habitat in the Wallowa Mountains of Oregon.
    Photo: R. J. Poff
34. *Primula cusickiana* A. Gray: Wallowa Mts.   *Photo: J. Lunn*
35. *Primula rusbyi* Greene; specimen in cultivation.
    Photo: G. F. Smith
36. *Primula ellisiae* Pollard *et* Cockerell: a pale form in cultivation.
    Photo: G. F. Smith
37. *Primula suffrutescens* A. Gray: specimen in cultivation.
    Photo: G. F. Smith
38. *Primula cuneifolia* Ledeb. subsp. *saxifragifolia* (Lehm) Sm. *et* Forr.: Thompson Pass, Alaska.   *Photo: R. Redfield*
39. *Primula cuneifolia* Ledeb. subsp. *saxifragifolia* (Lehm) Sm. *et* Forr.: Thompson Pass, Alaska.   *Photo: R. Redfield*
40. *Primula tschuktschorum* Kjell.: McKinley National Park, Alaska.
    Photo: S. Walker
41. *Primula nutans* Georgi (=*sibirica* Jacq.): the shore of Altafjord, Norway.   *Photo: H. Taylor*
42. *Primula borealis* Duby: Nome, Alaska.   *Photo: R. Redfield*
43. *Primula stricta* Hornem.: small specimen in cultivation; this species can vary considerably in size.   *Photo: B. Burrow*
44. *Primula mistassinica* Michx: specimen in cultivation; note the root offset on the left.   *Photo: M. Collins*
45. *Primula magellanica* Lehm. (=*decipiens* Duby): habitat in the Falkland Islands.   *Photo: T. V. Callaghan*
46. *Primula magellanica* Lehm.: specimen in cultivation.
    Photo: B. Burrow
47. *Primula incana* Jones: specimen in cultivation. *Photo: B. Burrow*
48. *Primula halleri* Gmelin: specimen in cultivation (N.B. the corolla colour is rather lighter in life).   *Photo: G. F. Smith*
49. *Primula farinosa* L.: on Ingleborough, Yorkshire, England.
    Photo: B. Burrow

50. *Primula algida* Adam: in the Caucasus.   *Photo: B. Burbidge*
51. *Primula auriculata* Lam.: specimen in cultivation.
Photo: B. Burrow
52. *Primula scotica* Hook.: Sutherland; corolla colour a little too red.
Photo: G. Wheeler
53. *Primula scotica* Hook.: Sutherland; nearer to the true colour.
Photo: A. J. Clement
54. *Primula luteola* Ruprecht: specimen in cultivation.
Photo: B. Walker
55. *Primula juliae* Kusn.: specimen in cultivation. *Photo: B. Burrow*
56. *Primula amoena* M. Bieb.: at high altitude in the Caucasus.
Photo: G. Barrett
57. *Primula renifolia* Volg.: specimen grown by A. Willis.
Photo: J. Dixon
58. *Primula vulgaris* Hudson: in the wild, England. *Photo: G. Wheeler*
59. *Primula elatior* (L.) Hill: Pyrenees.   *Photo: H. & W. Bevington*
60. *Primula veris* L.: in the wild, England.   *Photo: G. Wheeler*
61. *P.* × *miniera* (and *P. allionii* Lois.): *P.* × *miniera* is above and to the right, *P. allionii* below and to the left. 1200 m., Roya Valley.
Photo: G. F. Smith
62. *P.* × *vochinensis* Gusmus × *P. wulfeniana* Schott (left) and *P. wulfeniana* Schott (right): back crossing of hybrids with a parent can cause identification problems (see p. 174).
Photo: G. F. Smith
63. *Primula* × *juribella* Sünd.: near the Rolle Pass, Dolomites.
Photo: G. F. Smith
64. *Primula* × *miniera*: grown on from a branch of the plant in Plate 61.   *Photo: G. F. Smith*
65. *Primula* × *bowlesii* Farrer: Petit Mont Cenis. *Photo: G. F. Smith*
66. *Primula* × *muretiana* Monitzi: specimen in cultivation.
Photo: H. Taylor
67. Unknown, probably a hybrid: W. Alps.   *Photo: H. Taylor*
68. *Primula* × *floerkeana* Schrad.: Pfitzscher Joch, near the Brenner Pass.   *Photo: G. F. Smith*
69. *Primula* × *crucis* Bowles: Maritime Alps.   *Photo: S. Mayr*
70. *Primula allionii* 'Anna Griffith': specimen in cultivation.
Photo: B. Burrow
71. *Primula* 'Fairy Rose': specimen in cultivation. *Photo: B. Burrow*
72. *Primula* 'Margaret': specimen in vultication. *Photo: D. B. Lowe*
73. *Primula* 'Joan Hughes': specimen in cultivation.
Photo: J. E. G. Good
74. *Primula* 'Old Red Dusty Miller': specimen in cultivation.
Photo: B. Burrow
75. *Primula vulgaris* double white: specimen in cultivation.
Photo: K. Haywood
76. *Primula* × *pubescens* Hort. 'Rufus': specimen in cultivation.
Photo: A. Evans

ACKNOWLEDGEMENTS

We wish first of all to thank Mrs. Judy Burrow for her enthusiastic participation throughout the work, and in particular for her tireless transatlantic correspondence, which brought in so much valuable information on the American species.

We also wish to thank the very large number of friends, too many for all to be named, who helped us generously in so many ways. Of these however we would like particularly to mention Mr. E. K. Balls, Mr. and Mrs. Gilbert Barrett, Mr. and Mrs. Harold Bevington, Ms. Maryann Collins, Mrs. Kath Dryden, Mrs. Margaret Earle, Mr. Alf Evans, Mrs. Connie Greenfield, Mr. Ralph Haywood, Mr. Fritz Kummert, Ms. Jay and Ann Lunn, Mr. Siegfried Mayr, Mrs. Betty Ann Mech, Mrs. G. Parker, Mr. R. J. Poff, Mr. David Riley, Dr. V. Satava, Mr. D. Schummel, Mr. and Mrs. Michael Stone, Mr. and Mrs. Henry Taylor, Mr. Frank Tindall, Mrs. Sally Walker, Mr. J. Wilkinson, Mr. A. Willis, Dr. D. P. Winstanley, and Mr. K. R. Wooster.

Last, but not least, we thank Dr. John Good for his patient and invaluable help in tidying up the final manuscript.

INTRODUCTION

Practically every garden has primulas in it, and the chances are high that they will have descended from ancient cultivars derived from Cowslips, Primroses, and their hybrids. The most widely cultivated are the numberless varieties of Polyanthus, which provide such bright and glowing colours in springtime, and even in late winter. Of more recent origin are the Juliana and related hybrids, which have gained great popularity, with *Primula* 'Wanda' in the lead. The Pubescens hybrids, also of ancient lineage, are likewise popular. All of these may be called European. Over the last hundred or more years, they have been joined by several groups of Asian primulas—the Candelabras, *Primula sikkimensis, Primula polyneura*, and the many varieties of *Primula denticulata*. This Guide describes and discusses, even if somewhat superficially, these general gardening plants where they are of European origin; it concentrates however mainly on species and natural hybrids which have so far been mainly the province of the specialist and alpine plant enthusiast. The species and natural hybrids have not gained much ground in general gardening, largely because most of them are difficult to maintain in the open garden, are prone to certain pests and diseases, have short flowering periods, and, on top of it all are, with notable exceptions, not free-flowering.

The text begins (Chapter 1) with a brief presentation of the relevant aspects of the botanical classification of the European and American species, followed by a synoptic view of their geographical distribution (Chapter 2). The Alps are a special case, with so many species, of which up to five may occur in one area: mainly to assist identification in the wild, we have tabulated the regional distribution of the Auriculastrum species in the Alps, and included a map in which the Alps are subdivided into natural regions (inside cover). Another map indicates the distribution of the Parryi Section and of *P. suffrutescens* in N. America (p. 10).

Chapter 3 gives a full description of each species, in alphabetical order except for certain very rare or unattractive species, which are described along with closely related, better known species. For each species, the occurrence, habitat, and anatomic description are given, accompanied by a line drawing; where appropriate, references to the excellent articles and illustrations in *Curtis's Botanical Magazine* are cited—many main Municipal and University libraries as well as the big Botanical Gardens have complete, or partial sets, of this famous periodical. An outline of the species in the Subgenus Sphondylium (Verticillata) of S.W. Asia has been included because it is close to the European Region.

Chapter 4 attempts to deal with the complex question of the identification of European and American primulas in the wild: it is obvious that a scheme for the identification of these primulas in the Garden, which would have to take into consideration Asiatic species, as well

5

as horticultural cultivars and hybrids, would be well beyond the scope of this guide.

Chapter 5 tries to tackle the thorny problem of the natural hybrids; fortunately these are numerous only in the Primula (Vernales) and Auriculastrum Sections. It is noteworthy that virtually no natural hybrids are reported from America: this may be because the species are thinly scattered. We have included schematic presentations of the natural and of the artificial hybrids, which allow a clear overall view of what is to be found and what is *not*: we are indebted to Mr. F. Kummert for the conception of this type of diagram, and permission to publish. This is followed by a discussion of each hybrid and by a few hints on their identification in the wild.

Chapter 6 presents a systematic descriptive treatment of the vast area of horticultural cultivars and hybrids. Here of course we have had to be selective, and we have concentrated mainly on those plants which are reasonably widespread in cultivation: the descriptions have had to be brief, for we have been directed to concentrate mainly on the wild species and hybrids.

Finally, Chapter 7 describes fully the cultivation of primulas, with sections on propagation, soil mixtures, fertilisers, and pests and diseases.

There is a glossary of botanical terms, with an accompanying set of diagrams, and lists of synonyms for species and hybrids: most of these names are obscure and only the most significant ones have been included in the general index.

All the many references throughout the text to the *Quarterly Bulletin of the Alpine Garden Society* are abbreviated *Bull.*, followed by the year of issue, volume (in italics), and page numbers. All other references will be found in the bibliography on p. 236.

CHAPTER 1

CLASSIFICATION OF PRIMULA SPECIES

A new classification of the Genus Primula was proposed by P. Wendelbo in 1961, and an outline of the scheme was given by R. B. Cain in the *Bull.*, 1964, *32*, 290. This scheme seems to have been generally accepted, as it makes better sense than the previous one from the evolutionary point of view. The essence of the scheme is to divide the Genus into seven quite distinct subgenera: the further subdivision into Sections then obviously brings together those which are most closely related. The abbreviated table below presents the information relevant to European and American Species (Subgenera IV, V, and VI are exclusively Asiatic).

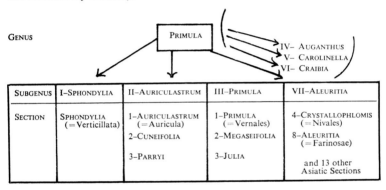

SUBGENUS	I–SPHONDYLIA	II–AURICULASTRUM	III–PRIMULA	VII–ALEURITIA
SECTION	SPHONDYLIA (=Verticillata)	1–AURICULASTRUM (=Auricula)	1–PRIMULA (=Vernales)	4–CRYSTALLOPHLOMIS (=Nivales)
		2–CUNEIFOLIA	2–MEGASEIFOLIA	8–ALEURITIA (=Farinosae)
		3–PARRYI	3–JULIA	and 13 other Asiatic Sections

The names in brackets are the older, more familiar ones. So in Europe we have the entire Auriculastrum Section of Subgenus II, the entire Subgenus III, many Species in Section Aleuritia (Farinosae) of Subgenus VII, and a couple of Species in Section Crystallophlomis (Nivales) of Subgenus VII.

In America we have the entire Parryi Section of Subgenus II, a couple of Species in the Cuneifolia Section of Subgenus II, many Species in the Aleuritia (Farinosae) Section of Subgenus VII, and a couple of Species in the Crystallophlomis (Nivales) Section of Subgenus VII.

(See also—Dr. R. B. Cain, the Genus Primula, a review of its diversity and origin, *Bull.*, 1967, *35*, 128.)

CHAPTER 2
DISTRIBUTION OF PRIMULAS
IN EUROPE AND AMERICA

Primulas can be found almost anywhere in the northern Hemisphere outside the Tropics. *In Britain* the most widespread are the Primrose and the Cowslip; the Oxlip, so common in many parts of Continental Europe, is alas limited to a few small areas in S.E. England; *P. farinosa*, the Bird's eye primula, is to be found in the northern Pennines, the few scattered localities in Scotland have not been confirmed since the 1930's; last but not least, our only endemic, the lovely *P. scotica*, occurs exclusively along the north coast of Scotland and in the Orkneys.

In Continental Europe the Primrose, the Oxlip, and the Cowslip are quite widespread; in addition to these, the Caucasus has the closely related *P. amoena*; from Thrace eastwards, the Primrose begins to take on a range of colours other than sulphur-yellow; three other related Caucasian endemics are *P. juliae, P. renifolia* and *P. megaseaefolia; P. farinosa* occurs in most corners of Europe, but only in certain well defined and mostly widely separated areas—the Alps form the largest area of occurrence which includes much of the lowland to the north down to the Danube, other areas are to be found round the Baltic Sea, in the Tatras, the Pyrenees, and Bulgaria; *PP. stricta* and *scandinavica* are to be found in the Scandinavian Mts., and *P. stricta* joins *P. nutans* as the two circumarctic species; *P. halleri* (*longiflora*) occurs in the Alps, mainly in the eastern half, and in the Carpathians; *P. algida* replaces *P. farinosa* in the Caucasus, where there are several other species in the Aleuritia (Farinosae) Section, notably *P. luteola* and *P. glacialis* (*auriculata*); the Auriculastrum Section, with its widely divergent species, essentially forms the glory of the Alps, the richest area in Europe for primulas (see map opposite); away from the Alps, *P. auricula* spreads down the Apennines and also into the northern Carpathians; *PP. latifolia, hirsuta* and most abundantly *P. integrifolia*, are to be found in the Pyrenees; *P. minima* pops up here and there east and southeast of the Alps, mainly in the southern Carpathians, but also in northern Greece and Bulgaria; it is interesting to note that the one very isolated occurrence of *P. glutinosa* is in central Bosnia, half way between the Alps and the Rila Mts. in Bulgaria, the home of the closely related and gorgeous *P. deorum*, one of the few Auriculastrum species not to be found in the Alps. The others not in the Alps are *P. kitaibeliana* in the Dinaric Alps of Yugoslavia, *P. apennina* in the N. Apennines, and *P. palinuri*, that odd species from southern Italy.

The Sphondylia (Verticillata) primulas of the Near East are possibly ancestral to *P. palinuri* and more distantly to the Auriculastrum Section.

The Section Parryi in the Subgenus Auriculastrum is exclusively North American, and is almost entirely located in the western half of

8

CLUSIANA.

AREA OF THE MAIN ALPINE CHAIN

GLUTINOSA

MINIMA

VILLOSA

INTEGRIFOLIA

LATIFOLIA

TIROLENSIS

GLUTINOSA

WULFENIANA

MINIMA

GLAUCESCENS

SPECTABILIS

CARNIOLICA

PEDEMONTANA

LATIFOLIA

MARGINATA

VILLOSA

LATIFOLIA
ALLIONII

APENNINA

P. hirsuta

P. auricula

SECTION AURICULASTRUM
IN THE ALPINE REGION.

the U.S.A. (see map on p. 10). The most widespread species by far in this Section is *P. parryi*, which can be found dotted about and locally quite abundant on the main Cordillera well away from the Pacific coast; next in abundance is *P. angustifolia*, which is concentrated in Colorado; at the southern end of its distribution, *P. parryi* is replaced in New Mexico by *P. ellisiae*, then in S.W. New Mexico by *P. rusbyi*, which also has one or two tiny locations in Mexico; *P. cusickiana* occurs in Idaho and eastern Oregon in the N.W. of the U.S.A.; the remaining three species, *PP. maguirei, nevadensis*, and *capillaris* are extremely rare and localised, the first in N. Utah, and the other two in Nevada.

P. suffrutescens is in the Section Cuneifolia, also in the Subgenus Auriculastrum, and it occurs along the Sierra Nevada of Central California; in America *P. cuneifolia* is limited to Alaska, with its main occurence in N.E. Asia.

The remaining American species are all in the Subgenus Aleuritia. The only representative of the Section Crystallophlomis (Nivales) is the Alaskan *P. tschuktschorum*, which also occurs on the Siberian side of the Bering Sea. The Section Aleuritia (Farinosae) is well represented: the two main species are *P. mistassinica*, which stretches right

9

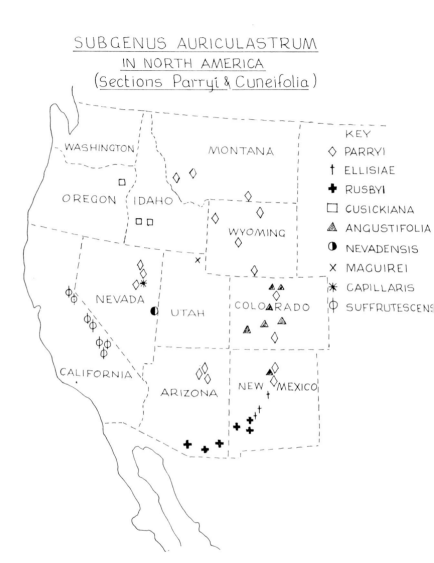

SUBGENUS AURICULASTRUM
IN NORTH AMERICA
(Sections Parryi & Cuneifolia)

KEY

◇ PARRYI
† ELLISIAE
✚ RUSBYI
☐ CUSICKIANA
🔺 ANGUSTIFOLIA
◑ NEVADENSIS
✕ MAGUIREI
✳ CAPILLARIS
φ SUFFRUTESCENS

across the north of N. America, where it replaces *P. farinosa* L., and then *P. incana*, which is found up and down the main Cordillera from E. Alaska to Colorado State; *P. mistassinica* is replaced by *P. intercedens* round the shores of the Great Lakes; *P. laurentiana*, botanically close to *P. scandinavica*, has a fairly wide distribution in maritime Eastern Canada, reaching Maine in the U.S.A.; *P. egaliksensis* stretches along the arctic coast of the Continent, with one or two other areas further south; *P. borealis* is another maritime-arctic species, with the main occurrence round the shores of the Bering Sea; finally from N. America, there are the very rare and highly localised *P. specuicola* in S. Utah and *P. hunnewellii* from Arizona, known from only one incomplete herbarium specimen.

The only primulas in S. America are at its southernmost tip, in S. Patagonia, Tierra del Fuego, and the Falkland Islands; the main one is *P. magellanica* (*P. decipiens*), and the other, probably not to be separated as a species, is *P. comberi*; their affinity is to *P. incana*.

Subdivision of the Section Auriculastrum

The subdivision of this Section into clearly defined subsections has proved to be impossible, and the several schemes proposed all have exceptions. The most widely used subdivision is that of Schott (*Die Sippen Österreichischer Primeln*, 1851). Schott's scheme sets up seven subdivisions, and does no more than put similar species together, and does not imply phylogenetic relations.

1—*Euauricula*, which means "closest to auricula", includes *auricula* and *palinuri*. These in many ways very different species come together largely because of the yellow corolla colour.

2—*Brevibracteata*, that is with short bracts, includes the somewhat disparate *carniolica*, *latifolia*, and *marginata*. The main common characteristic of these three is a farinose corolla; the short, broad bracts they share with the Erythrodrosum subsection; in addition, these three have colourless glandular hairs.

3—*Erythrodrosum*, which means "red glandular", contains *apennina*, *daonensis*, *hirsuta*, *pedemontana*, *villosa*. These five primulas are indeed very closely related to one another, and are characterised by yellowish to reddish glandular hairs; in addition they have short bracts, and are totally efarinose.

4—*Arthritica*, the meaning in the original Latin is "gouty", which is not easy to associate with the four species *clusiana*, *glaucescens*, *spectabilis*, and *wulfeniana*: this very closely related quartet has somewhat leathery leaves with cartilaginous margins; they have longish to long bracts, and are efarinose.

5—*Rhopsidium*, derived from a Greek word for shrub, probably refers to the long branching rhizomes of *allionii*, *integrifolia*, *kitaibeliana*, and *tyrolensis*; this is a somewhat diverse group of efarinose plants, with colourless glandular hairs, and non-cartilaginous leaf margins.

6—*Cyanopsis*, which means "blue appearance", includes *deorum* and *glutinosa*; these two probably closely related plants share a deep corolla colour with much blue in it; they are in addition efarinose, and have stiff, upright, narrow leaves.

7—*Chamaecallis*, which means small and beautiful, contains only the lovely *minima*.

P. algida

12

CHAPTER 3

DESCRIPTIONS OF THE SPECIES IN ALPHABETICAL ORDER

In this chapter each of the species is described, alongside a line drawing of a representative specimen. Distribution maps show occurrence in the wild, insofar as this is known: much remains to be determined, even for some of the commonest species. + on the maps indicates an individual site or record of occurrence, while cross-hatching denotes the extent of the range(s). Of course, it must not be assumed that a species will occur throughout its range—most will be severely limited in occurrence by the availability of suitable habitat. While the maps are of necessity small scale, and hence give only very approximate locations, it is hoped that, in combination with the descriptions of Distribution in the text, they will enable the reader to find the primulas he seeks.

Little known and very rare species are included under better known, closely related species, or at the end of the chapter.

Primula algida Adam   (Algidus is Latin for cold)
Photo. *Bull.*, 1971, *39*, 288

This species is intrinsically so variable that it can be said to be polymorphic (e.g. see *P. darialica* Ruprecht). In spite of the fact that the literature contains three named varieties, and that before it was separated from *P. farinosa*, it came under six varietal names in that species, it does not seem possible to uphold division into varieties.

DISTRIBUTION—Throughout the Caucasus, in the mountains of E. and N.E. Turkey, N. Iran, the Pamir and Altai. In these regions it replaces the very closely related *P. farinosa* L. ALTITUDINAL RANGE—

Continued on page 147   See **Plate 50**

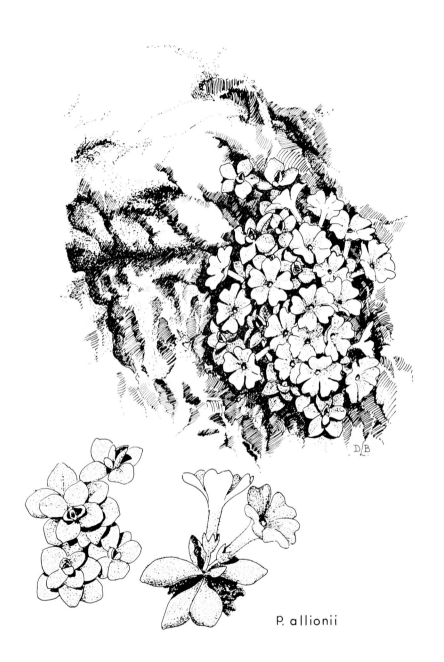

P. allionii

Primula allionii Loiseleur   (Commem. Allioni, botanist, 1705–1804)

This very beautiful species is a great favourite in cultivation, where it is nearly always given alpine house treatment. Pans smothered in bloom are a regular feature of early spring shows. The variable character of its flower has given rise to a crowd of cultivars, a list of which, with brief descriptions and comments, is given on p. 179.

DISTRIBUTION—Occurs in two areas between Cuneo and Nice; the main area lies in France, south of the Col de Tende, and corresponds to the Roya valley system, an area roughly 20 km. × 10 km. The lesser area is in Italy, north of the Col de Tende, and is the region between Entracque and Roaschia, an area about 3 km. × 5 km. Within these areas the occurrence is highly local, corresponding with suitable rock types and exposures (see HABITAT). Although it is probably among the least abundant of the European species, it is thriving and well ensconced in its many cliff homes, mostly totally inaccessible to *Homo sapiens* ssp. *topiarius*, so that it cannot be regarded as an endangered species: one of us (GFS) now knows of six quite distinct areas of occurrence, which were discovered in the course of only four days' searching in March, 1983. ALTITUDINAL RANGE—700–1900 m. HABITAT—A strictly saxatile species: it prefers shady and moist environments, and is rarely found on south facing sites; it seems it grows only in a Breccia (conglomorate) made up of limestone lumps cemented by a tufa-like material. Most of the plants grow in the open, but many may be found in caves formed by the weathering of the conglomorate. Quite large cushions, up to 22 cm. across, or even more, can be found not infrequently in the wild, though the vast majority of individuals are small tuffets: a colony in full flower is a most thrilling sight. In the wild it flowers in early March at 700–800 m., early April at 1200–1500 m., and later still at the highest altitudes. RHIZOME—Fairly stout, can become

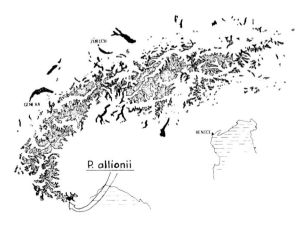

P. allionii

Continued on page 147   **See Plates 17–20, 61, 70**

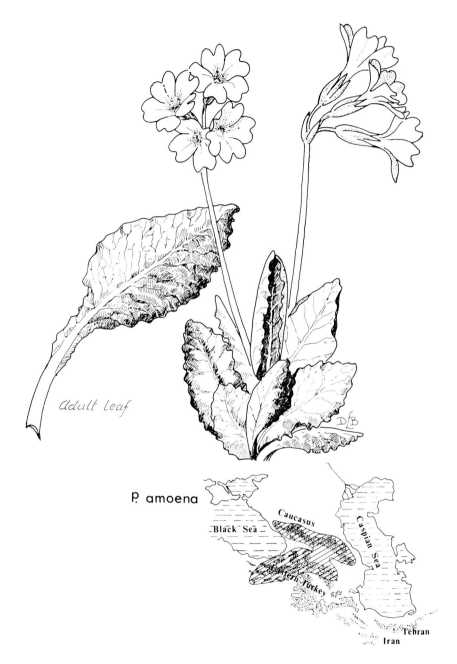

Adult leaf

P. amoena

Black Sea
Caucasus
Caspian Sea
North Turkey
Tehran
Iran

Primula amoena M. Bieb. (Delightful to look at)
(See *Curtis's Bot. Mag.*, 3252, 9593)
Very closely related to *P. elatior* (L.) Hill, it differs mainly in the
violet-blue to purple corolla. It is regarded by some taxonomists as
P. elatior subsp. *meyeri* (Rupr.) Valentine and Lamond. Like *P. elatior*,
it varies considerably in form, especially leaf shape. It is not common
in cultivation, though relatively easy to grow.

DISTRIBUTION—Throughout the Caucasus and in the adjoining
Pontic Mountains in N.E. Turkey. To confuse the issue somewhat,
variants named *meyeri* and *kusnetzovii* are given specific rank in the
Flora of the U.S.S.R. ALTITUDINAL RANGE—Very wide, 900–4000 m.
HABITAT—From peaty, earthy banks to quite rocky terrain. At high
altitude (around 3000 m.) Gilbert Barrett found it mostly growing
among largish boulders, as if appreciating the shelter they offered.
RHIZOME—Short and stout, bearing fleshy roots. LEAF ROSETTE—
Upright when immature becoming open rosulate. LEAF—5–16 cm. by
2–4 cm.; petiole usually half as long to as long as the blade, membraneously winged; blade shape varies considerably and is sufficiently
constant in particular regions to allow a division into varieties (see
below)—the blade may be elliptic, ovate, obovate, or spathulate, round
tipped or obtuse, usually tapering towards the petiole, sometimes truncate or nearly cordate; margins irregularly crenate or denticulate;
upper surface bright green, lower usually densely covered with white
wool, but sometimes nearly glabrous; midrib and lateral nerves deeply
impressed above and very prominent below. PEDUNCLE—5–15 cm.,
hirsute. UMBEL—Usually one-sided, 2–18 flowers (mostly 6–10).
BRACTS—2–8 mm., linear-lanceolate, hairy. PEDICELS—5–40 mm.,
more or less erect. CALYX—Tubular, strongly ridged, 8–12 mm., cut to
$\frac{1}{4}$–$\frac{1}{3}$ into ovate to lanceolate ciliate lobes. COROLLA—Exannulate,
violet-blue to lavender-blue, to purple, with yellow eye; albinos are
known; tube narrow, as long as to 2×calyx; limb flat to shallow-
funnel shape, 1·5–2·5 cm. across, with obovate deeply emarginate
lobes. CAPSULE—Longer than calyx. SEEDS—Resemble those of *P.
elatior*.

VARIETIES—(a) with white wool on leaf undersurface
> var. *kasbek* Kusn.: blade tapers into petiole, margin
> minutely denticulate; N. and S. Caucasus.
> var. *sublanata* Kusn.: blade tapers into petiole, margin
> grossly double toothed. N. and S. Caucasus, Lazistan
> (E. and S.E. of Batum).
> var. *grandiflora* Kusn.: blade abruptly contracted at base,
> but not cordate. N. Caucasus.
> var. *hypoleuca* Kusn.: blade cordate. S. Caucasus.
> (b) essentially hairless on leaf undersurfaces
> var. *intermedia* Kusn.: blade tapers into petiole, many-
> flowered. N., N.W. and S. Caucasus.
> var. *meyeri* Kusn.: blade abruptly contracted at the base,
> few-flowered. N., N.W. and S. Caucasus. See **Plate 56**

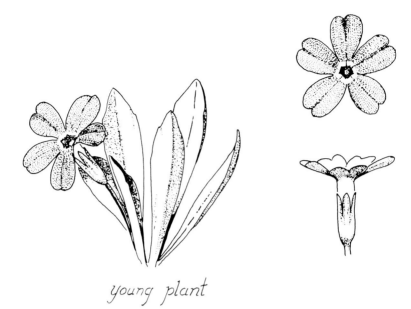

young plant

P angustifolia

Primula angustifolia Torr.   (Narrowleaved)

This is a small efarinose species. Wright-Smith and Fletcher consider *P. brodheadae* Jones, which occurs in South Idaho, to be a robust form of *P. angustifolia*, whereas several American authors regard *P. brodheadae* to be a form of *P. cusickiana*. All three are taxonomically very close to one another.

DISTRIBUTION—Colorado and Northern New Mexico, S. Idaho. ALTITUDINAL RANGE—2400–4200 m. HABITAT—Rocky slopes and meadows in relatively dry conditions. RHIZOME—Very stout for the size of the plant. LEAF—Upright, oblanceolate to lanceolate, round tipped and usually curled inwards along the longitudinal axis; blade 0·5–7 cm. long by 0·3–1 cm. wide, tapering to a slightly winged petiole which may be equal in length to the blade, but is usually shorter, and is sheathing at the base; leaf margin entire or remotely denticulate; midrib not very prominent. PEDUNCLE—Slender, 0·5–10 cm. tall, usually single flowered, but may bear a spreading UMBEL of 2–4 flowers (normal in the form *brodheadae*); flowers borne just above the leaves. BRACTS—Linear to lanceolate, 1–6 mm. long. PEDICELS—Very slender, 3–10 mm. long. CALYX—Tubular, 5–8 mm. long, cut to the middle into lanceolate lobes. COROLLA—Exannulate, flat to shallow funnel shaped, rosy lilac to purply pink with a clear yellow eye surrounded by a white halo; albinos may occasionally be found in a normal population; the variety *helenae* from New Mexico has a white corolla with a yellow eye; tube as long as calyx or a little longer; limb 7–20 mm. in diameter with obovate, slightly to moderately emarginate lobes which are often overlapping. CAPSULE—Ovate-cylindrical, 3–5 mm. long, shorter than the calyx. SEED—Relatively large (about 1 mm. in diameter), irregularly quadrate and angular.

See Plates 29, 30

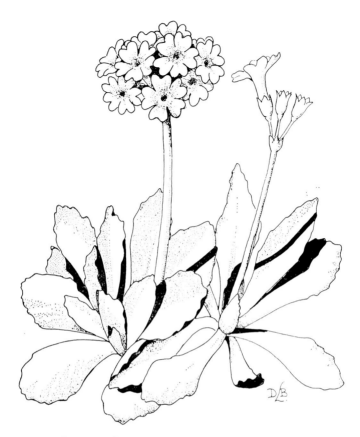

P. apennina

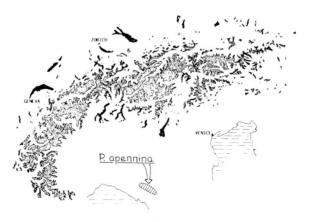

Primula apennina Widmer (From the Italian Apennines)
(See *Curtis's Bot. Mag.*, 1954–5, *170*, 224)

This species, which has a limited distribution in the northern Apennines, is the most recently named (1891) and least well known in the Auriculastrum section. It had been identified as *P. hirsuta* All. by Arcangeli and *P. villosa* Wulfen by Parlatore. Examination of freshly collected material by Widmer led her to the conclusion that here was a new species, and this diagnosis has survived into the recent *Flora Europaea*. This species is very rare in cultivation. It is, however, easy, hardy, and, in spite of Farrer's lack of enthusiasm for it (*The English Rock Garden*, Vol. II, 111), attractive.

DISTRIBUTION—Parmese Apennines near Lago Verde and on Monte Orsaro north of La Spezia, from which it has most frequently been collected; it is also found in the Tusco-Emilian Apennines (the Mommio, Corfino, and Palodina Alps, and on Monte Vecchio). ALTITUDINAL RANGE—Always above 1400 m. HABITAT—Rock fissures and humus pockets on cliff ledges, mostly on north facing sandstone cliffs. RHIZOME—Short, clothed in persistent withered foliage near growing tip. LEAF ROSETTE—Openly rosulate. LEAF—2·5–6·5 × 1–2·5 cm., elliptic, obovate or broadly oblanceolate; apex rounded or obtuse; blade narrowing gradually or abruptly into winged petiole; margins almost entire or with 3–15 irregular and shallow dentations in the upper half; surfaces and margins thickly beset with very short glandular hairs, 0·05–0·15 mm. long; glands fairly large, yellow in young leaves, often orange brown in mature leaves; midrib and nervature distinct only on lower surface; petiole very short to as long as blade, winged. PEDUNCLE—1–9 cm., just longer to twice as long as leaves; quite thick, 2–2·5 mm., covered in tiny glandular hairs as are all green parts of inflorescence. UMBEL—Symmetrical, 1–8 flowers, up to 12 in cultivation. BRACTS—1–4 mm., rotundate to ovate-oblong, obtuse, with wide translucent margin. PEDICELS—3–10 mm. long, relatively stout (1 mm.). CALYX—4–7 mm., conical-bell shaped, cut to $\frac{1}{3}$ into broadly ovate to triangular blunt lobes, adpressed in fl., spreading slightly in fruit. COROLLA—Exannulate, lilac to magenta pink with a white eye; tube 20–23 mm., 2–3 × calyx; limb flat to shallow saucer shaped, 18–25 mm. in diameter, with obovate emarginate lobes which can be overlapping. CAPSULE—About $\frac{3}{4}$ length of calyx.

P. auricula

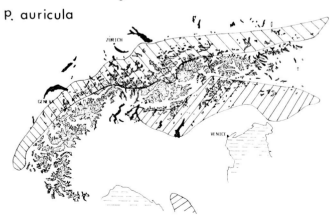

Primula auricula L.
(Small ear—in many regions
folk name is Bear's ear)
(See *Curtis's Bot. Mag.*, 6837)

This species occupies a special position in the Auriculastrum Section as one of only two to be yellow flowered (the other is *P. palinuri* Petagna). A quite variable species, at its best very beautiful. Though very amenable to cultivation, it is not as widely grown as it deserves. Its hybrids with *P. hirsuta* All. and *P. villosa* Wulfen have, over a long period of time, produced a wide range of attractive cultivars known collectively as the 'Pubescens hybrids', which are among the most popular and widely grown of garden primulas, (see page 184).

DISTRIBUTION—There are four main regions of occurrence: the entire sweep of the western and northern calcareous Alps and Prealps from the Dauphiné all the way to the Wiener Wald just west of Vienna; the southern calcareous Alps and Prealps from Lake Como eastwards to Slovenia; the Apennines from La Spezia to north of Naples; the Tatra and Fatra mountains of Czechoslovakia. The isolated occurrences outside these main regions can be divided into two categories: a large number not too far removed from the main regions—Valdieri in the Maritime Alps, the upper Val d'Isère, the Simplon region, several in the high and low Tauerns, near the Mur river north of Graz, as well as several in the Jura mountains; then there are a number of quite interesting occurrences, almost certainly relict areas from a period when the general distribution was much wider than today's—in the Black Forest region (one on the Belchen at around 1200 m. and the other in the Höllental Gorge at 600 m.), one in the Danube gorge north of Munich, several on the moors just north of that city, and two in the mountains near the Danube Iron Gates on the Roumanian-Yugoslav border. ALTITUDINAL RANGE—Normally to be found from 1000–2500 m. (3000–8000′) the extremes being 250 m. and 2900 m. HABITAT—Nearly always found in limestone regions, where it usually colonises rock faces, less frequently stony meadows. RHIZOME—Stout,

Continued overleaf Continued overleaf See **Plates 2, 3**

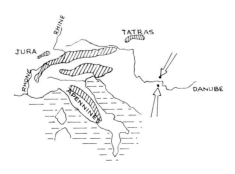

23

freely branched. LEAF ROSETTE—Varies from flat to rosulate. LEAF—
Thick and fleshy, 1·5–12 cm. long, 1–6 cm. wide, from suborbicular
to lanceolate, with obtuse or round tips; most frequently obovate;
grey-green to dark green surfaces appear to be hairless but bear tiny
colourless glandular hairs which, in some variants, may be visible;
leaves efarinose to very farinose; margins entire, to denticulate,
to even sharply dentate, narrowly cartilaginous, bearing a variable
density of 0·05–0·5 mm. long glandular hairs; blade merges gradually
or abruptly into a broad winged petiole, which may be almost absent
to about equal in length to the blade. PEDUNCLE—1–16 (25) cm. tall,
frequently farinose, bearing a one-sided UMBEL of 2–30 flowers.
BRACTS—Ovate to transversely ovate, more or less papery. PEDICELS—
Farinose, 5–25 mm. long. CALYX—Usually farinose, bell shaped, 2–7·5
mm. long, cut to the middle into obtuse or acute lobes. COROLLA—
Pale to deep yellow, exannulate; tube 7–13 mm. long, about 3 × calyx;
limb funnel shaped to almost flat, 15–25 mm. in diameter, with a
powdering of farina at the throat, giving it a white eye; throat also has
a covering of colourless glandular hairs; petals obovate, deeply
notched, generally overlapping; corolla frequently scented. CAPSULE—
Spherical, usually just longer than calyx.

Most authors have divided this variable species into two subspecies
and several varieties.

Subsp. *bauhini* (Beck) Lüdi is taken by Wright-Smith and Fletcher to
represent the typical form. This is itself very variable, especially
with respect to presence or absence of farina, and size and shape
of leaf. It is characterised by having very short cilia, around
0·1 mm. on its leaf margins and lemon yellow, scented flowers.
Further divisions lead to:

var. *albocincta* Widmer (forma *marginata* Stein) which has
particularly dense farina round the margins of the leaves.
forma *nuda* Widmer which is efarinose except for corolla
throat and inner side of calyx lobes.

var. *monacensis* Widmer refers to the plants growing on the
moors north of Munich, in which the leaves are narrowly
oblong.

var. *widmerae* Pax refers to the Black Forest plants, which have
narrow, thin-textured leaves.

var. *serratifolia* (Roch.) Lüdi, occurring around the Iron Gates
of the Danube, in which the leaves are very markedly
serrate dentate.

Subsp. *ciliata* (Moretti) Lüdi (subsp. *balbisii* (Lehm.) Widmer) which
is the less widespread main subspecies: it is only found in Italy,
being absent from the areas north of the Alpine watershed. It is
characterised by being always efarinose, and by having long
(0·5 mm.) cilia on the leaf margins; the rounded leaves have a
short petiole, and the deep yellow flowers are scentless.

var. *obristii* (Stein) Beck is intermediate between the two subspecies: it resembles *ciliata*, but is scented and has a
farinose calyx and pedicel.

Valentine and Kress, in *Flora Europaea*, state that in *P. auricula*
size, leaf shape, indumentum, dentation, farina, and odour vary so
much, occasionally even within a single population, that it is difficult
to delimit subspecies. We would totally agree with this view for, in our
own relatively limited experience, we have seen "ciliatas" growing
within yards of "albocinctas", and individuals with toothed leaves and
others with entire leaves growing in the same valley. This would seem
to lead to the conclusion that this species is *polymorphic*. It would be
very interesting to examine this point experimentally by growing on as
many seedlings as possible from a single capsule collected from a plant
in the wild, growing where variation is evident. The term subspecies is
usually applied to geographically distinct populations which are
anatomically essentially homogeneous, and differ from other neighbouring, but separate, populations. Broad regional differences in the
genetic make-up of *P. auricula* however do exist, which for example
result in the absence of "ciliata" types in the northern and western
Alps. There are also regions, e.g. the Dolomites, in which variation
is almost absent.

P. auriculata aggregate
incl. glacialis & archibaldii.

Primula auriculata Lam. (With small ears, referring to the bract shape)
(See *Curtis's Bot. Mag.*, 392, 9104)

This variable aggregate has been divided by Schwarz (*Bull.*, 1970, *38*, 376) into four species.

> *P. auriculata* Lam. is reserved for the main part of the plants growing in N. Iran (c.f. Green, *Asiatic Primulas*, p. 96).
>
> *P. archibaldii* Schwz., a new name for another race in N. Iran; both these are efarinose.
>
> *P. glacialis* Adam, a name given in 1819 and meaning "frozen", is resuscitated for the Caucasian variant.
>
> *P. dealbata* Schwz. occurs in the Mt. Elbrus region of the central Caucasus. The specific epithet means "whitewashed", referring to the dense covering of farina.

The description which follows is for *P. glacialis* Adam:

DISTRIBUTION—Alpine regions of the southern flank of the Caucasus, also throughout montane Turkey. HABITAT—Wet conditions, very near to running water (*P. rosea* Royle is in the same subsection). LEAF ROSETTE—Scantily farinose, overwintering as an oval bud enveloped by scales, developing into typical Farinosa type rosette. LEAF—Broadly oblong-lanceolate, 12–30 cm. long and 2·5–4 cm. wide, rounded or obtuse at the apex, narrowing into a broad, flat petiole which is $\frac{1}{3}-\frac{1}{2}$ the length of the blade; margins are very sharply serrate-dentate. PEDUNCLE—8–60 cm. tall, bearing a compact symmetrical or globular UMBEL of 8–20 flowers. BRACTS—Lanceolate, markedly swollen at the base. PEDICELS—2–6 mm. long. CALYX—Campanulate, 5–7 mm. long, cut to $\frac{1}{2}$ to $\frac{1}{3}$. COROLLA—Lilac with a pale greenish throat, 9–12 mm. in diameter; tube 2–3 × calyx; lobes broadly obovate, deeply emarginate. CAPSULE—Ovate to globose, about as long as calyx.

P. dealbata differs from *P. glacialis* in having broader leaves with no petiole, in being very farinose, and in having larger flowers which are white with lilac petal tips. All grow well in cultivation if given a rich deep root run with shelter from strong sun.

See **Plate 51**

P. bayernii

Primula bayernii Rupr.   (*P. nivalis* var. *bayernii* (Rupr.) Rgl.)
(Commem. Bayern, botanist)

This is a vigorous white nivalid primula which is rarely seen, although it is in cultivation.

DISTRIBUTION—West-Central Caucasus from Mt. Elbrus to Mt. Kasbek. ALTITUDINAL RANGE—Between 1800 and 3000 m. HABITAT—Very wet conditions in meadows or consolidated moraine. FORM—A robust primula, rootstock girded with white-farinose scales, 2–3 mm. long. LEAF ROSETTE—Upright. LEAF—8–10 cm. by 2·5–4cm., elliptic to oblanceolate; apex obtuse or rounded; cuneate at the base; thin textured and efarinose on both surfaces; margins denticulate, white farinose, though sometimes efarinose; midrib prominent below, white farinose; petiole broadly winged, short to half the length of the blade. PEDUNCLE—12–15 cm., up to 25 cm. in fruit, stout, efarinose or farinose near the apex. UMBEL—Symmetrical, 3–12 flowered. BRACTS—Linear to awl shaped, 10–15 mm., frequently brownish near the base. PEDICELS—10–30 mm., unequal, farinose or efarinose. COROLLA—Annulate, funnel shaped, pure or creamy white, sometimes very faint pink or pale straw coloured; tube up to $1\frac{1}{2}\times$calyx; limb 1·5–2 cm. across with obovate lobes which are entire to deeply notched. CAPSULE—Oblong, up to more than $2\times$calyx.

29

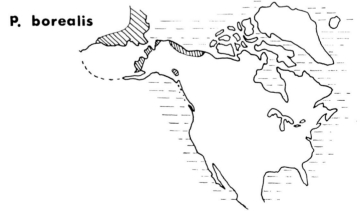

P. borealis

Primula borealis Duby   (Northern)

This is a highly variable plant which, at its best, appears to be very attractive. According to Wright-Smith and Fletcher it is close to *P. mistassinica* Mich. It has been brought back from the wild occasionally, but does not persist in cultivation. This is not very surprising as it is a maritime-arctic species.

DISTRIBUTION—The great majority of its occurrences are on the shores of the Bering Sea and its islands, also the shores of the Arctic Ocean in N.E. Siberia and N.W. North America as far east as the Mackenzie river delta region. Only inland occurrence is in S.W. Yukon. HABITAT—Saline flats along the sea shore. FORM—Efarinose to sparingly farinose. LEAF—Cuneate-obovate to spathulate to rhombic, 4–40 mm. long, 1–10 mm. wide, including petiole; tips rounded to obtuse; blade tapering to winged petiole which may be very short to $2-3 \times$ length of blade; margins irregularly dentate to almost entire; midrib prominent on lower surface, which is sometimes a little farinose. PEDUNCLE—Usually 3–8 cm. tall, but extremes are 1 cm. and 12 cm.; it and all green parts of inflorescence sometimes farinose and often stained purple. UMBEL—1–14 flowered, symmetrical. BRACTS—2–6 mm., linear-awl shaped. PEDICELS—2–15 mm. long, $1-3 \times$ as long as bracts, nearly doubling in length in fruit. CALYX—3–6 mm., campanulate, often swollen at the base and cut to the middle into lanceolate lobes. COROLLA—Annulate, rosy-violet to lilac, not infrequently white; tube usually as long as to twice as long as calyx; limb 7–20 mm. in diameter, i.e. it can be very large in proportion to plant; lobes narrow to broad obovate, emarginate and sometimes overlapping; style sometimes slightly exserted in pin-eyed flowers. CAPSULE—Cylindrical, $1-1\frac{1}{2} \times$ length of calyx.

See **Plate 42**

31

P. carniolica.

Primula carniolica Jacq. (From Carniolia, N.W. Yugoslavia)
(See *Bull.*, 1933–4, *2*, 300, phot, 310)

This very lovely species is not seen as often as it should be in cultivation.

DISTRIBUTION—A relatively small area centred around the town of Idria in N. Slovenia, south of the Julian Alps (N.W. Yugoslavia— Carniolia is the Latinised form of Krain, the name of an ancient Dukedom which included this region). ALTITUDINAL RANGE—900– 1000 m. (3000–3500'). HABITAT—On or near the tops of the limestone hills in light woodland or in stony pasture, frequently in soil pockets on shady limestone rock faces. RHIZOME—Thick, long and branching, bearing fleshy roots. LEAF ROSETTE—Upright when young, flattening out after flowering; the small winter resting bud is surrounded by a few small, green, broadly ovate leaves. LEAF—Blade 2–15 cm. by 1–4·5 cm., obovate to oblong or oblanceolate, gradually tapering at the base; apex rounded or obtuse; texture fleshy; margins narrowly cartila- ginous, entire or slightly and irregularly wavy, sometimes slightly denticulate near the apex, sometimes slightly glandular ciliate; surfaces glabrous, normal to dark glossy green above, lighter below; in cultivation the leaves can be patchily yellow with some form of chlorosis; midrib prominent below; at flowering, juvenile leaves tend to be curled inwards; petiole 1–6 cm., broadly winged, sheathing at base. PEDUNCLE—6–25 cm., stout, erect, smooth, sometimes reddish, holds the umbel well above the leaves. UMBEL—One sided, 1–15 flowers, mostly 2–4. BRACTS—1–5 mm., broadly ovate to lanceolate, apex rounded to acute, texture papery. PEDICELS—3–25 mm., sturdy, erect or semi-pendent. CALYX—2–6 mm., bell shaped, cut to $\frac{1}{3}$–$\frac{1}{2}$ into ovate obtuse, sometimes split lobes. COROLLA—Exannulate, scented, shallow funnel shaped, soft rose to purplish pink, rarely lilac, occasionally white; the only farina on the plant forms a ring round the throat, giving the impression of a white eye; tube 6–10 mm. long, relatively wide, widens further above point of attachment of stamens, and is of same colour as lobes; limb 15–25 mm. across, lobes obovate and deeply notched. CAPSULE—Globose to obovoid, up to 2×calyx. SEEDS—Up to 1 mm., irregularly quadrate, smooth.

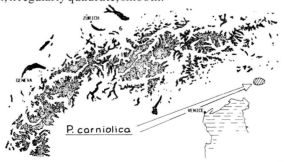

See **Plate 7**

P. clusiana

Primula clusiana Tausch. (Commem. Charles de l'Écluse (Clusius), botanist at Leiden, XVIth C.)

This beautiful primula has been in cultivation for a long time, but no particular cultivar has yet emerged. As is the case with so many European primulas, most clones flower poorly, and it is essential to obtain a floriferous one.

DISTRIBUTION—The northern calcareous alps of Austria, with a minute foothold in Germany, where it may be found in the frontier region between Berchtesgaden and Salzburg. The southern limit follows the Enns valley to Liezen, then goes on to the Mur valley at Leoben, including the Eisenerzer Alpen, follows the river Mürz to Mürzzuschlag, then strikes across to the region of the Wiener Schnee-berg, which forms the eastern limit. The northern limit is defined by the foothills, from Berndorf, by Weidhofen, Gmünden, back to Salzburg. There are only three very small outliers to the south: two in the lower Tauern on Speiereck and in the Taferlscharte, and the third further east on the Hochlautsch near Kapfenberg. In the wild it is widely separated from its close relative, *P. wulfeniana*. ALTITUDINAL RANGE—Generally above the tree line, between 1800 and 2500 m., does not reach great heights and not infrequently occurs at lower altitudes, even down to 600 m. HABITAT—Always in limestone regions, even if frequently in neutral humus; habitat varies from moist rock fissures to stony slopes, to short turf; can form large dense colonies. RHIZOME—Can be quite stout and branched; tightly covered with withered remains of foliage near the apex; bears thick fleshy roots. LEAF ROSETTE—Rosulate and tight. LEAF—1–9 by 0·5–3 cm., oblong to elliptic, ovate, or obovate, stiff and leathery in texture; apex acute, obtuse, or even rounded, tapering gradually at the base; margin entire, narrowly cartilaginous and conspicuously ciliate with tiny (0·25 mm.) colourless glandular hairs; upper surface dark green and shiny, glabrous, lower surface pale grey green, with moderately conspicuous midrib and nervature visible; petiole short and winged. INFLORESCENCE—Covered with colourless glandular (0·25 mm.) hairs. PEDUNCLE—1–5 (11) cm. UMBEL—1–4 (6) flowered, symmetrical, borne clear of the leaves. BRACTS—4–18 mm., generally longer than the pedicels, narrowly linear, oblong or lanceo-late, acute or obtuse, often broadened at the base, frequently purplish. PEDICELS—2–15 mm., stiff and erect. CALYX—8–17 mm., tubular to tubular-bell shaped, sometimes tinged red, cut to between $\frac{1}{3}$ and $\frac{1}{2}$ into ovate lobes which are obtuse or rounded at the apex, lying on the tube or diverging only slightly from it. COROLLA—Exannulate, bright rose, fading to lilac, with a white eye; tube as long as to 2 × calyx, glandular pubescent inside near the throat; limb shallow-funnel shaped, 1·5–4 cm. across, with broadly obovate, deeply notched lobes. CAPSULE—4–7 mm., half the calyx.

See Plate 16

35

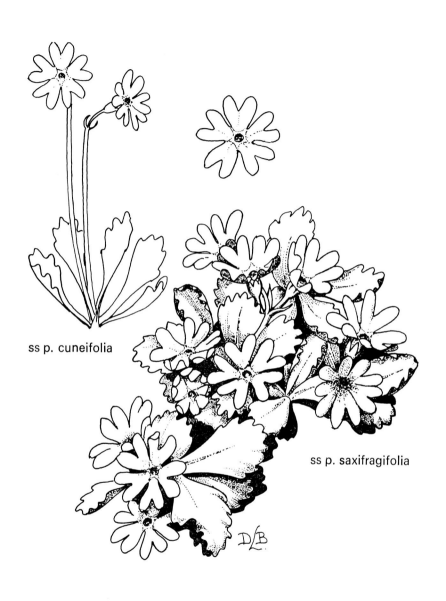

ss p. cuneifolia

ss p. saxifragifolia

P. cuneifolia

Primula cuneifolia Ledeb.   (With wedge-shaped leaves)

DISTRIBUTION—Fairly wide, stretching from Eastern Siberia, Kamtchatka, Northern Japan, to the Aleutian Islands, the coasts of Western and Southern Alaska, and just reaching British Columbia. HABITAT—From wet meadows to crags and bluffs; nearly all the Alaskan occurrences are close to the sea shore. FORM—A glabrous species, with a very short and relatively stout RHIZOME. All green parts in the Alaskan plants are often tinged with dusky maroon to purple. LEAF ROSETTE—Open. LEAF—Including the petiole, 1·5–8 cm. long; blade relatively fleshy, 1–3 cm. long and 0·5–2·5 cm. wide, oblanceolate to obovate, or cuneate, round tipped, tapering gradually into the petiole; coarsely dentate in the upper half; midrib conspicuous; the membraneously winged petiole may be almost absent to considerably longer than the blade. PEDUNCLE—4–30 cm. tall. UMBEL—Discoid to symmetrical, 1–9 flowered (occasionally in cultivation there are two superposed umbels). BRACTS—Awl-shaped, 1·5–5 mm. long. PEDICELS—4–20 mm. long. CALYX—Broadly campanulate, 3–6 mm. long, cut to $\frac{2}{3}$ into acute or obtuse lobes. COROLLA—Annulate, usually heteromorphic, rose red to magenta, with a yellow eye which sometimes has a white margin, albinos are known; tube a little longer than calyx; limb 1–2 cm. in diameter, with narrowly obovate, deeply emarginate lobes, in some forms resembling those of *P. minima*. CAPSULE—Globose to ovoid, a little shorter than the calyx. SEED—1–1·5 mm. in diameter, irregularly quadrate and angled.

Most Alaskan specimens are compact, with usually 5 cm. tall peduncles, and have relatively large homomorphic (?) flowers: they have been brought under subsp. *saxifragifolia* (Lehm.) Sm. *et* Forrest.

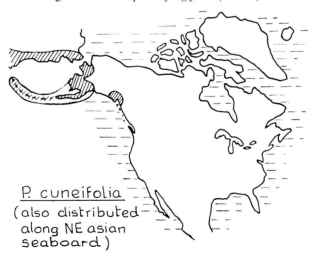

P. cuneifolia
(also distributed
along NE asian
seaboard)

See Plates 38, 39

P. cusickiana

PP. cusickiana + maguirei

OREGON

IDAHO

P. maguirei

UTAH

38

Primula cusickiana A. Gray (*P. angustifolia* var. *cusickiana* A. Gray)
(Commem. Cusick, botanist)

This beautiful species blooms early, surrounded by banks of melting snow, and in the summer is subject to heat and drought. It is rare in cultivation and has the reputation of being very difficult to keep.

DISTRIBUTION—Wallowa Mts. of N.E. Oregon and adjacent Idaho. ALTITUDINAL RANGE—Relatively low altitude, between 1000 and 2600 m. (3000–8000′). HABITAT—Varies from open woodland to moist, even marshy meadows, to stony sub-alpine slopes. RHIZOME—Stout for the size of the plant. LEAF ROSETTE—Mostly upright but can be rosulate, or even flattish in a disordered sort of way. LEAF—Oblanceolate to oblong, rather thick and fleshy, 2–5 cm. long, 0·3–1 cm. wide, obtuse to round tipped; petiole broad winged, hardly separable from blade, variable in length from very short to over half the length of blade, sheathing at the base; margin entire or occasionally bearing a few teeth; midrib fairly conspicuous above and below. PEDUNCLE—3–9 cm. tall, bearing a spreading UMBEL of 1–4 flowers. BRACTS—Lanceolate to ovate, 3–10 mm. long, sometimes toothed. PEDICELS—Often unequal, 1–8 mm. long, may bear a little farina. CALYX—Tubular, green to maroon, 5–9 mm. long, cut to the middle into lanceolate lobes, with five lines of white farina from the sinuses to the base. COROLLA—Exannulate, scented, deep violet, occasionally white, darker round the eye, slightly farinose about the yellow, often starry eye; tube 1–1·5 times calyx; limb shallow funnel shaped, 1–1·5 cm. in diameter with obovate lobes, which can be slightly emarginate, but more often have an irregular, undulate outline. CAPSULE—Ovoid to globose, 4–6 mm. long.

See Plates 33, 34

Primula capillaris N. *et* A. Holmgren (Hair-like, referring to the slender leaves)

This attractive small primula is closely related to *PP. angustifolia*, *cusickiana*, *maguirei* and *nevadensis*. There is no record of it in cultivation.

DISTRIBUTION—Ruby Mts. of N.E. Central Nevada in one locality only, at about 3000 m. (10,000′). HABITAT—Turf on north-facing slopes. RHIZOME—Relatively stout. LEAF ROSETTE—Sparse, upright. LEAF—Very slender, oblanceolate to spathulate, 1–6 cm. long, 1–6 mm. wide; round tipped, narrowing gradually into a winged petiole; margins entire. PEDUNCLE—1·5–6 cm. tall, bearing a one-flowered UMBEL (rarely two-flowered). BRACTS—Ovate to lanceolate, 1–5 mm. long. PEDICELS—2·5–12 mm. long. CALYX—Narrowly campanulate, 3·5–8 mm. long, cut to $\frac{1}{3}$ into lanceolate lobes. COROLLA—Shallow funnel shaped, exannulate, magenta-violet, 2·5–10 mm. in diameter, with obovate emarginate lobes; no eye mentioned; tube yellow, about twice the length of the calyx.

P. maguirei and **P. nevadensis** overleaf

39

P. maguirei L. O. Williams   (Commem. Maguire, the discoverer)

This recently discovered primula (1932) is quite closely related to *P. cusickiana.*

DISTRIBUTION—In and around Logan Canyon in the Wasach Mts. of N.E. Utah; a second location is on sheer limestone cliffs on a high summit in E. Nevada. It is well separated geographically from *P. cusickiana.* ALTITUDINAL RANGE—Relatively low, 1200–1800 m. (4000–6000′). HABITAT—Rocky slopes with a northern exposure, or damp overhanging rocks, or moist crevices in cliffs. LEAF ROSETTE— Open rosulate. LEAF—Relatively thin textured, broadly spathulate, 3–7 cm. long, 8–12 mm. wide, round tipped; margins entire and slightly undulate. PEDUNCLE—Slender, 4–10 cm. tall. UMBEL—1–3 flowered. BRACTS—Usually two, unequal, one is lanceolate to linear-lanceolate and 4–7 mm. long, the other vestigial to 3 mm. long, sickle shaped. PEDICELS—Length not given. CALYX—Tubular-campanulate, 5–6 mm. long, extending to 9 mm. in fruit, cut to about $\frac{1}{2}$ into lanceolate lobes which are farinose on both surfaces. COROLLA—Exannulate; limb 14–25 mm. in diameter, with obovate, emarginate lobes; fresh flower colour not given, but that of herbarium specimens is red or purple; polymorphism is in evidence in that when only one flower is borne, it is much larger than when there are two, and the first to develop in a 2- or 3-flowered umbel is much larger than the subsequent ones. CAPSULE—5 mm. long, cylindrical, much shorter than the calyx.

Primula nevadensis N. Holmgren   (From the State of Nevada)

This species is a close relative of *PP. angustifolia, capillaris, cusickiana* and *maguirei.*

DISTRIBUTION—Very limited, in the Grant and Snake Ranges of east-central Nevada, where it was discovered in 1964. ALTITUDINAL RANGE—Above 3300 m. (11,000′). HABITAT—Limestone outcrops where it is common in crevices and on ridges and open gravelly slopes. LEAF ROSETTE—Upright, taller than the inflorescence. LEAF—Oblanceolate to linear-lanceolate, mostly 5–10 cm. long, 0·6–1 cm. wide; margins coarsely toothed beyond the broadest point, to sometimes entire; tips acute or obtuse, rarely rounded; blade tapers to a winged petiole. PEDUNCLE—3·5–9 cm. tall. UMBEL—Of 2–3, rarely up to 8 flowers. BRACTS—Triangular to lanceolate, of different lengths, the largest 4–8 mm., the smallest 0–3 mm. PEDICELS—5–15 mm. long, sometimes longer. CALYX—Variable, 6–11 mm. long, pale green and farinose to purplish and scarcely farinose, cut to about $\frac{1}{3}$ into triangular lobes. COROLLA—Funnel shaped, violet with a yellow eye; tube yellow to white, 7–10 mm. long; limb 6–11 mm. in diameter, with broadly obovate, emarginate lobes, which are 5–9 mm. long. CAPSULE— Elliptic, 5–6 mm. long, included in the calyx.

P. daonensis

P. daonensis

Primula daonensis Leyb. (*P. oenensis* Thomas)   (From Val Daone)

The earlier name, *P. oenensis*, is derived from the Latin for the river Inn, Oenus, a curious choice given that only a very small fraction of the population of this primula is found in the catchment area of the Inn.

DISTRIBUTION—Somewhat restricted in the south central Alps in the Ortles and Adamello groups, and in the eastern end of the Orobic (Bergamasque) Alps; quite frequent in the Stelvio Pass region on the northern side of its range; the southern limit is in the Valli Giudicarie and Val Daone; the westernmost area is in Valle Seriana south of Sondrio; outside its main range it is found to the north just inside Austria, east of Nauders on the Geisbleisenkopf, and then well to the east in the upper Val Cadino in the S.W. Dolomites. In its distribution area, *P. daonensis* replaces *P. hirsuta* All. ALTITUDINAL RANGE—1500–3000 m. HABITAT—Stony pastures and rock faces, with a strong preference for non-calcareous rocks; near Val Daone, where granite and limestone meet and mingle, Lüdi (in *Hegi*, p. 1771) notes that *P. daonensis* is always on granite, and its companion in that region, *P. glaucescens* Moretti, is always on limestone. RHIZOME—Short and, as is usual in the subsection, clothed in withered leaves at the growing tips. LEAF ROSETTE—Variable, may be compact or loose rosulate; does not tend to form large mats, as does *P. hirsuta*. LEAF—1–8 by 0·5–2 cm., oblong-cuneate (wedge-shaped), to lanceolate-cuneate, to spathulate, sometimes obovate and even suborbicular; apex rounded to truncate (in the wedge shaped leaves), tapering gradually at the base; margin toothed, frequently with larger teeth round the apex, never entire; surfaces sticky, covered with tiny (0·1–0·3 mm.) orange to red glandular hairs; midrib and venation prominent below; petiole very short to as long as blade, winged. PEDUNCLE—1–8 cm., usually overtopping the leaves, stiff and erect, densely covered with tiny orange glandular hairs, as are the remaining green parts of the inflorescence. UMBEL—Symmetrical, 1–7 flowered. BRACTS—Papery, ovate, 1–3 mm. PEDICELS—1–3 (6) mm. CALYX—Bell to tubular-bell, 3–5 mm., cut to $\frac{1}{2}$ into ovate or obtuse lobes, which are adpressed to corolla tube. COROLLA—Exannulate, rose to magenta-crimson with a white eye, flat to shallow funnel shaped; tube 6–11 mm., 2–4 × calyx, white on inner surface; limb 10–20 mm. across, with obovate emarginate lobes. CAPSULE—About the same length as the calyx.

See Plate 9

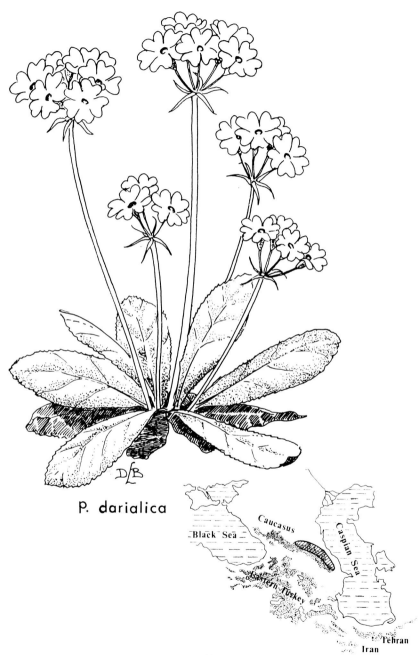

P. darialica

Black Sea

Caucasus

Caspian Sea

Eastern Turkey

Tehran

Iran

44

Primula darialica Rupr.   (From the Darial Valley)

It is important to note that probably *all* plants being sold and grown under this name are in fact not *P. darialica* but some other species, nearly always *P. frondosa* Janka (see p. 61). *P. darialica* is closely related to *P. algida* Adam (see Schwarz, *Bull.*, 1970, *38*, 375; photo. Watson, *Gardeners' Chron.*, 1918, *63*, 234, Fig. 99). *P. ossetica* Kusn. (see below) is probably only a variant of *P. algida* or *P. darialica*.

DISTRIBUTION—*P. darialica* occurs on the north side of the Caucasus in forested subalpine regions east of Mt. Kasbek. ALTITUDINAL RANGE—300–900 m. HABITAT—Moist shady rocks, often in ravines. LEAF ROSETTE—Openly rosulate. LEAF—2–8 by 1–3 cm., obovate, oblong or spathulate, thin textured; apex rounded or obtuse, tapers gradually at the base; margins sharply and regularly denticulate; upper surface efarinose, lower slightly yellowish white farinose or efarinose; midrib and lateral nerves prominent on lower surface; petiole short to equal to blade, winged. PEDUNCLE—2·5–10 (15) cm., slightly exceeding to twice as long as the leaves, sometimes slightly farinose near the apex (all green parts of the inflorescence may also be slightly farinose); Wright-Smith and Fletcher write that it is slender and flexuous, though this is not evident from the one photograph, and these attributes are not given in the *Flora of the U.S.S.R.* UMBEL—Upright to symmetrical, 2–15 flowered. BRACTS—Linear, 3–4 mm., not swollen at the base, becoming reflexed, as in *P. algida*. PEDICELS—4–8 mm., slender, unequal in length and semi-pendent. CALYX—Cup shaped, 3–5 mm., cut to $\frac{1}{2}$ into lanceolate, pointed lobes. COROLLA—Annulate, rose to carmine red, probably with a yellow eye; tube $1\frac{1}{2}$ to $2 \times$ calyx, whitish yellow near the throat; limb flat, 10–14 mm. across, with obovate, deeply emarginate, somewhat overlapping lobes. CAPSULE—Cylindrical and pointed, about $2 \times$ calyx.

Subsp. *farinifolia* (Rupr.) Kusn. occurs in Daghestan, on the northern flank of the eastern Caucasus. It differs from the type mainly in the larger leaves with copious farina on their lower surfaces, the much longer pedicels, and the smaller flowers.

P. ossetica Kusn. (From Ossetien) has been collected only once, in 1890, in alpine meadows at Ossetien in the Central Caucasus. It is a small, slender species with relatively large violet flowers with a yellow eye. Distinctively, the petals are notched almost to the base. There is no report of it having been in cultivation.

P. deorum

Primula deorum Velen.   (Of the Gods)
                            (see *Curtis's Bot. Mag.*, 8124)

This is one of the most recently described of the European species in the Auriculastrum Section, having been discovered in 1889 in the Rila mountains of S.W. Bulgaria. It is a strikingly beautiful species and well deserves its specific epithet. It is not too difficult to grow, but many people find it to be shy flowering; however, when grown at 1800 m. on the Schachen (the Munich Botanic Garden Alpine Garden), mature plants flower regularly. It is efarinose.

DISTRIBUTION—Very restricted, being limited to the Rila mountains south of Sofia, an area not much more than five miles square (c. 6300 ha.). ALTITUDINAL RANGE—About 2000–2600 m., above the tree line. HABITAT—Very wet marshy grassland at flowering time in July; wetness then may be largely due to snow-melt water and the terrain could be much less wet in Autumn. The Rila mountains are non-calcareous. RHIZOME—Very stout, often more than 1 cm. in diameter, bearing thick, fleshy roots. LEAF ROSETTE—Sheaf-like, most leaves being quite erect. LEAF—2–10 (15) cm. by 0·4–2 cm., narrowly oblanceolate to oblong, apex obtuse to acute; texture leathery, surfaces somewhat shiny and glabrous, upper surface slightly pitted; leaf margin entire and cartilaginous; petiole short, winged, and hardly distinguishable from the blade. PEDUNCLE—5–20 cm., more or less dark violet near the apex. UMBEL—Mostly one-sided, 3–10 (18) flowered. BRACTS—3–10 mm., narrowly lanceolate. PEDICELS—2–10 mm., semi-pendent. CALYX—3–6 mm., tubular bell shaped, cut to $\frac{1}{2}$ into triangular or lanceolate lobes. Bracts, pedicels, and calyx are mostly of a dark violet maroon colour and are sticky. COROLLA—Exannulate, funnel shaped, very rich violet-purple to crimson-purple; tube 10–15 mm., narrow, up to 3 × calyx; limb 10–15 mm. across, lobes obovate and shallowly notched; throat bears small glandular hairs. CAPSULE—Generally longer than calyx.

See Plates 27, 28

47

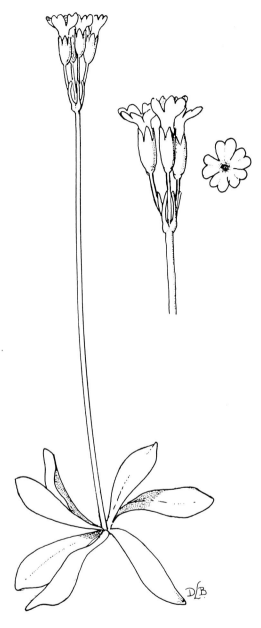

P. egaliksensis

Primula egaliksensis Wormsk. (From Igalik, southern tip of Greenland)

This is a relatively unattractive relative of *P. scandinavica* Bruun.

DISTRIBUTION—Nearly the entire breadth of northernmost N. America, also along the Aleutian chain, the coast range of S.E. Alaska, S.W. Yukon, and two or three small areas along the main Cordillera, one as far south as South Park in Colorado, where it occurs with *P. incana* Jones; in addition there are two small areas in S. Greenland and one in N. Iceland. ALTITUDINAL RANGE—From sea level in the north to around 2400 m. (8000′) in the south. HABITAT—Wet meadows, edges of streams, generally in turfy and peaty areas. FORM—Varying considerably in size; totally efarinose. LEAF—Ovate, elliptic to spathulate, including the petiole 0·5–5 cm. long and 0·2–1·5 cm. wide; rounded at the tip, tapering to a slender petiole which may be equal to or longer than the blade, and sheathing at the base; margin entire or finely remotely denticulate; midrib prominent on lower surface. PEDUNCLE—1–15 cm. tall. UMBEL—Upright with 1–9 relatively small flowers. BRACTS—3–7 mm., lanceolate, broadened and bulging at the base. PEDICELS—Erect, 1–3 times the length of the bracts when in flower, up to 5 cm. long in fruit. CALYX—4–6 mm., tubular, cut to about $\frac{1}{3}$ into often ciliolate lobes. COROLLA—Homomorphic, annulate, usually white, but may be violet to deep lilac; tube yellowish, slightly longer than calyx; limb 5–9 mm. in diameter, with oblong or narrow-cuneate, deeply emarginate lobes. CAPSULE—Cylindrical, $1\frac{1}{2}$–3 × calyx.

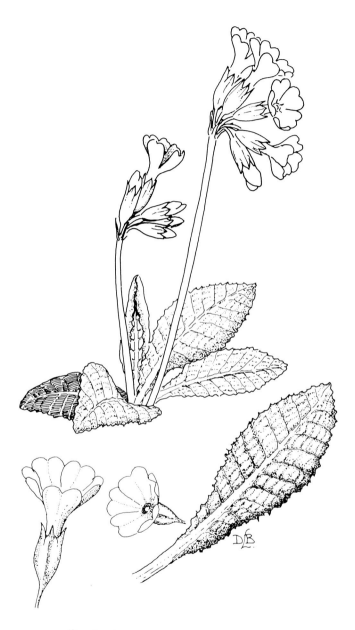

P. elatior.

Primula elatior (L.) Hill   the Oxlip   (More uplifted, taller)

This is a lovely, well known and much loved primula.

DISTRIBUTION—Widely distributed and locally very abundant in central and southern Europe; in the British Isles it is, alas, to be found only in a few small areas in East Anglia where, however, it can be locally quite abundant; indeed Dr. Grey-Wilson believes it may be on the increase; its northern limit is Denmark, with just one locality in southernmost Sweden; further south it is less frequently found in the lowlands, and along the Mediterranean it occurs only in mountain regions. Eastwards it reaches the Carpathians and central Ukraine; southeastwards it reaches the Balkans; after a gap in central and southern Russia and western Turkey, it continues in the Crimea, the whole Caucasian region, eastern Turkey, N. Iran, the Altai and the Urals; the *Flora of the U.S.S.R.*, but not Wright-Smith and Fletcher, extends its area of distribution to the whole of non-arctic Siberia. ALTITUDINAL RANGE—Upper limit in the Alps and Pyrenees usually 2200 m., though it can reach 2600 m. (8500′). HABITAT—Moist meadows and open woodland, especially near rivers and streams; prefers shady places and, in the mountains, north-facing slopes.

Flora Europaea divides the species into five subspecies on a combination of morphological and geographic criteria: the situation is complicated by variations within populations and also by confusion with the relatively frequent *P. veris* × *P. vulgaris* hybrid, which it often resembles.

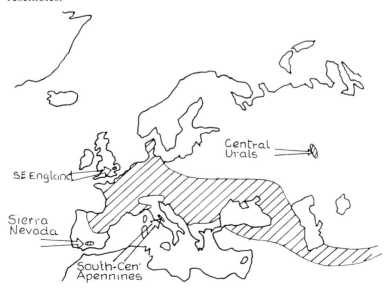

Continued overleaf   See **Plate 59**

51

Subsp. *elatior* (subsp. *genuina* (Pax) Lüdi). This is by far the commonest subspecies in Europe, found throughout the range, but less frequently in the south, where it is largely replaced by subsp. *intricata*. The description that follows relates to subsp. *elatior*.

LEAF ROSETTE—Upright at flowering time, becoming openly rosulate later. LEAF—5–20 by 2–7 cm., ovate to oblong or elliptic, round tipped, usually abruptly contracted at the base, or sometimes gradually narrowing; midrib and nerves impressed above and quite prominent below, giving a very rugose blade, the edges of which are recurved in the juvenile stage; upper surface downy to almost hairless, lower surface quite hairy; margins crenate to denticulate, often quite irregular in outline (erose); petiole about as long as blade, broad, winged, hirsute, sheathing at the base. PEDUNCLE—10–30 cm., stiff and upright, quite hairy (as are all green parts of the inflorescence; hairs $\frac{1}{4}$–$\frac{3}{4}$ mm., rarely 1 mm.). UMBEL—One sided, many flowered. BRACTS—3–6 mm., linear to ovate, somewhat papery. PEDICELS—5–20 mm. CALYX—6–15 mm., narrowly tubular, yellowish, bulges in the middle owing to five prominent greenish ridges, and is cut to $\frac{1}{3}$–$\frac{1}{2}$ into lanceolate pointed lobes. COROLLA—Exannulate, flat to funnel shaped, sulphur yellow, usually odourless; throat markings greenish yellow to orange; tube just longer than, to 2 × calyx; limb 15–25 mm. across; lobes broadly obovate and notched. CAPSULE—Longer than calyx, cylindrical, sometimes tapers towards the tip. SEEDS—1–1·5 mm., ovoid, subspherical to cuboid, dark brown to blackish.

Subsp. *intricata* (Gren. *et* Godron) Lüdi. This is the usual form in the mountains of southern Europe, excluding the Alps but including the Dolomites, the Pyrenees and the Balkans. The leaves always narrow down gradually into the petiole, which forms the main difference from subsp. *elatior*. Other differences include margins which are entire in the young leaves, a *few*-flowered umbel, the smaller limit of 20 mm. for the diameter of the limb, which tends to be flat and is seldom funnel shaped. Hairs are shorter than usual, up to $\frac{1}{2}$ mm.

Subsp. *leucophylla* (Pax) H. Harrison *ex* Wright-Smith *et* Forrest. This occurs in the limestone formations of the eastern Carpathians in Roumania. The leaves differ from those of subsp. *elatior* in that they always narrow gradually into the petiole, are grey tomentose below (fugitively), and the leaf margins are crenulate to entire; in addition the calyx lobes are short.

Subsp. *lofthousei* (H. Harrison) Wright-Smith *et* Forrest. This is limited to the Sierra Nevada in southern Spain. It differs from subsp. *intricata* in having a many-flowered umbel of deeper yellow, saucer shaped flowers which are somewhat smaller.

Subsp. *pallasii* (Lehm.) Wright-Smith *et* Forrest. This is found in the Urals, Siberia, the Altai, and N. Iran. The leaf blade narrows gradually into the petiole and differs from the other subspecies in being glabrous and dentate; in addition the umbel is few-flowered.

Other subspecies, not included in *Flora Europaea*, are:

Subsp. *carpathica* (Fuss) Wright-Smith *et* Forrest. This has rounder leaves than subsp. *elatior* and is included in the latter in *Fl. Eur*.

Subsp. *cordifolia* (Rupr.) Wright-Smith *et* Forrest. This differs from subsp. *elatior* by its glabrous, non rugose, cordate leaves, a petiole which can be twice as long as the blade, and its overall smaller size. It occurs in the Caucasus and Armenia.

Subsp. *pseudoelatior* (Kusn.) Wright-Smith *et* Forrest. This is close to subsp. *elatior*, but its leaves are cordate and pubescent. It occurs in the Caucasus.

Subsp. *ruprechtii* (Kusn.) H. Harrison. This is close to subsp. *leucophylla*, from which it is said to differ by its persistently tomentose leaves. It occurs in the Caucasus and Armenia.

In addition to the above, the literature abounds with names given to particular variations found as individuals in a normal population—the following is a representative list.

forma *acaulis* Petermann, forma *calycina* Schube, forma *colorata* Pax, forma *dialypetala* Petermann, var. *diaphana* Domin, forma *fragrans* (Krause) Pax, var. *lingelsheimii* Pax, forma *mirabilis* Celakovsky, var. *obscura* Harrison (one of the most recently recorded (*Trans. North. Nat. Union*, 1931, *1*, 52) differs from the type by having dark grey-green leaves with pronounced pubescence), forma *perreiniana* (Flügge) Pax, forma *rotundata* Boas, forma *schoenmanniana* Boas, forma *schusteriana* Boas, forma *uniflora* Petermann.

See also Appendix 1.

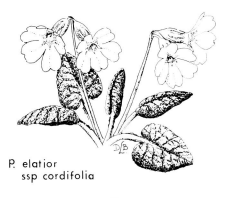

P. elatior
ssp cordifolia

P. ellisiae

young plant

Primula ellisiae Pollard *et* Cockerell   (Commem. Miss C. Ellis, the discoverer)

This species, which is very close to *P. rusbyi* Greene, and indeed was included in the latter by Pax, has done very well in cultivation and is quite widely grown.

DISTRIBUTION—Central New Mexico, apparently restricted to two mountains. ALTITUDINAL RANGE—3000–3300 m. (10,000–11,000′). HABITAT—Moist crevices and ledges on cliffs. RHIZOME—Very short and stout. LEAF—Upright recurvent, oblanceolate to spathulate, efarinose; may have acute to obtuse tips; blade 3–10 cm. long, 1·5–3 cm. wide, with very faintly to conspicuously denticulate margins; midrib conspicuous on both surfaces; petiole up to 5 cm. long but never longer than the blade, broadly winged and sheathing at the base. PEDUNCLE—Sturdy, 10–20 cm. tall, sometimes white farinose near the apex, bearing a one sided UMBEL of 4–8 flowers. BRACTS—Very unequal, ovate to lanceolate, 3–9 mm. long and sometimes white farinose round the margins. PEDICELS—0·5–4 cm. long, white farinose. CALYX—Tubular, 7–13 mm. long, cut to the middle to give lanceolate lobes sometimes fringed with farina, and bearing ten longitudinal ridges alternately broad green to brown and narrow farinose. COROLLA—Annulate or exannulate, rose-violet to rose-magenta occasionally shading towards blue, darkening round the eye, which is yellow; tube yellowish to dusky purple, as long as to $1\frac{1}{2} \times$ calyx; limb shallow funnel shaped, 1·5–3 cm. in diameter, with broadly or narrowly obovate lobes, slightly to deeply emarginate—the flower thus varies quite a lot in appearance. CAPSULE—Ovoid, 5–9 mm. long, shorter than the calyx.

See **Plate 36**

55

P. farinosa

Primula farinosa L. the Bird's eye Primrose   (Floury or mealy)

This much loved species is fairly frequently seen in cultivation but with most people it is short-lived. Not too long ago there was a host of subspecies of *P. farinosa*: most of these have now been either included in subsp. *farinosa*, or separated as distinct species, which has happened to all the North American ones. *Flora Europaea* recognises only two subspecies in Europe: subsp. *farinosa* and the Bulgarian endemic, subsp. *exigua* (Velen.) Hayek. This simple picture has been considerably perturbed by Schwarz (*Wiss. Z. Univ. Jena, Math. Wiss.,* 1968, *17*, 328) who holds the view that the Bulgarian endemic is a subspecies of *P. frondosa* Janka (this we reject, see p. 59), and more importantly and acceptably, limits subsp. *farinosa* to north of a line from the English Channel through central Germany to the central Urals; plants south of this line are included in a new subsp. *alpigena* Schwz.. This division is supported by pollen studies and minor morphological differences. We will follow *Flora Europaea*.

DISTRIBUTION—The most widespread of all primulas, ranging from Europe through Siberia to the Pacific coast, a distance of 6500 miles (10,400 Km.). This range includes Mongolia, but enters China only in Northern Sinkiang. In N. America it is replaced by *P. mistassinica* Michx., a very closely related species. Schwarz (loc. cit.) is of the opinion that the Asian occurrences also represent distinctly different species; the opposite view is expressed by Fedorov in the *Flora of the U.S.S.R.* The main areas of occurrence of *P. farinosa* in Northern Europe are round the central and southern Baltic Sea: in the southern half of Sweden, the central Baltic islands, the whole of Lithuania, Latvia and Estonia, and an area in northern East Germany. In Britain it occurs in North Lancashire and the Pennines of Yorkshire; a few small localities have been indicated for Scotland which have not been confirmed for many years. The largest single area of distribution in Central Europe is the whole of the Alpine region

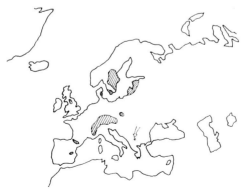

Continued overleaf   See **Plate 49**

and the lowlands to the north of it down to the Danube; smaller areas are the Tatra Mts. in South Poland and Eastern Czechoslovakia, the Juras, the Pyrenees, and the Montes Universales in Spain, some 90 miles N.W. of Valencia. This represents a very disjunct distribution: it is totally absent from Ireland, Iceland, Norway, Finland, Belgium, Holland, Portugal, and Greece, and is absent from most of Spain, France, middle Germany, and peninsular Italy; elsewhere there are very many small isolated occurrences; its presence in the Caucasus is questioned, in any case it must be very rare there. HABITAT—Generally marshy or damp meadows in the lowlands, tolerating drier conditions in upland and alpine meadows; tends to prefer limestone areas; occasionally occurs on rock faces if sufficiently wet. FORM—Generally, of course, farinose, though efarinose individuals do occur. RHIZOME—Fairly stout and short, in time can bear several rosettes. LEAF ROSETTE—Rosulate, with the mature leaves tending to lie flat; winter resting bud small. LEAF—Including the petiole, 1–10 cm. long and 3–20 mm. wide; blade varying from oblanceolate to elliptic to almost ovate, with an obtuse or rounded tip, narrowing into a winged petiole which may be almost absent to as long as the blade; upper surface green, lower nearly always white farinose; midrib and lateral nerves prominent below; margins entire to finely denticulate, frequently rolled back. INFLORESC-ENCE—There may be several per rosette in a strong mature plant; green parts are farinose. PEDUNCLE—Can vary enormously in length, from 2–25 (30) cm., lengthening in fruit. UMBEL—Symmetrical, two to very many-flowered; ten to twenty-five being a good average in strong plants. BRACTS—2–8 mm. long, linear lanceolate to awl shaped, acute, broadened and humped at the base. PEDICELS—2–8 mm. long, greatly lengthening in fruit and becoming erect. CALYX—Tubular to pitcher shaped, 3–6 mm. long, cut to $\frac{1}{3}-\frac{1}{2}$ into ovate to triangular obtuse, rarely acute lobes which are frequently tinged with a dark maroon colour, and lie on the corolla tube; the calyx has five ribs which correspond to the axes of the lobes. COROLLA—Annulate and dimorphic (pin- and thrum-eyed); tube greenish yellow, 5–8 mm. long, equal to or slightly exceed-ing the calyx; limb flat to shallow saucer shaped, 8–16 mm. in diameter, nearly always a shade of lilac-pink, rarely purple or white, always with a yellow eye; depth of colour varying widely even within a small popu-lation; lobes obovate, deeply notched, varying from narrow to broad and slightly overlapping. CAPSULE—Cylindrical, slightly longer than to $2 \times$ calyx. SEED—0·5 mm., ovoid to quadrate angular, minutely vesicular.

Subsp. *exigua* (Velen.) Hayek. This subspecies is to be found above 2100 m. (7000′) on Vitoša, Rila (here in the company of *P. deorum* Velen.), and the northern Pirin, the high mountains south west of Sofia. It grows in wet meadows, especially near streams and pools. Subsp. *farinosa* replaces it at lower altitudes down to 1600 m. on Vitoša and Rila but not on Pirin. It is effectively a smaller and slenderer efarinose version of subsp. *farinosa*, with smaller flowers (7–8 mm. across), fewer per umbel. Though it grows to a larger size in cultivation, it remains distinct in appearance. We have seen it in the wild and grown it over a period of years and it appears to us (*contra* Schwarz and *pro* Jordanov and Peev) to be obviously closer to *P. farinosa* than to *P. frondosa*.

See **Plate 28**

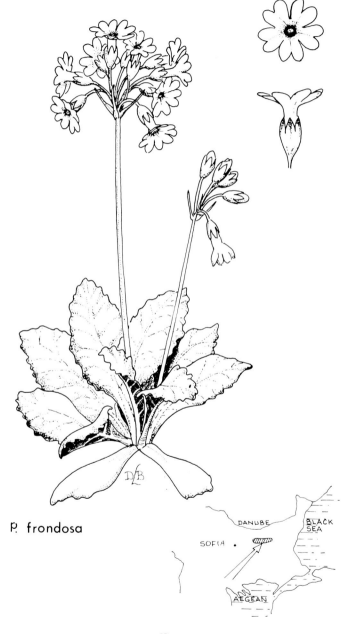

P. frondosa

DANUBE

BLACK SEA

SOFIA

AEGEAN

60

Primula frondosa Janka   (Leafy)

This is a very widely grown and popular primula. It is very close to *P. farinosa* and indeed at one time was included in it. It is much more amenable to cultivation than its very much more widely distributed cousin. It sets seed readily and comes true from it: one of the remarkable features of the Section Farinosae (Section Aleuritia as it should now be called), in Europe and America, is the almost total absence of hybrids.

DISTRIBUTION—Of quite limited occurrence in the wild, being limited to the central Stara Planina, about 145 kilometres (90 miles) east of Sofia. Most sources say that it occurs in Northern Thrace, which was correct a hundred years ago, but is misleading now: at that time the Stara Planina formed the northern frontier of the then much larger province of Thrace in European Turkey. ALTITUDINAL RANGE—900–2000 m. HABITAT—Both above and within woodland, normally on steep humus or rocky slopes, often in rock fissures; avoiding turf—a distinctly different ecology from that of *P. farinosa*. Two varieties have been described recently (Jordanov and Peev, *Izv. Bot. Inst. Sofia*, 1970, *20*, 131): var. *frondosa* with broadly cordate petals and glabrous calyx growing on a siliceous substrate, and var. *jordanovii* D. Peev with narrow Y-shaped petals and hairy calyx, growing on calcareous substrata. RHIZOME—Short and stout. LEAF ROSETTE—There may be several in a tight cluster: open rosulate holding most of the leaves upright; winter resting buds very farinose, beginning to open very early. LEAF—Recurvent when mature, 3–10 (17) cm. long, 1–2·5 cm. wide, spathulate to obovate, rounded at the apex, gradually tapering into the winged petiole, which varies from being shorter than the blade to twice as long; margins sharply denticulate when young, becoming more crenate and crinkled with age; the dull darkish green upper surfaces are essentially efarinose, the lower nearly always thickly coated with white farina; midrib and main veins impressed on the upper surface and very prominent on the lower. INFLORESCENCE—There may be several to a rosette; farinose to efarinose. PEDUNCLE—4–12 cm. long, $1\frac{1}{2}$–3 × leaf length, not lengthening significantly in fruit. UMBEL—Loose, symmetrical to one-sided, of 1–12 (40) flowers. BRACTS—4–5 mm., linear or linear lanceolate, wider at the base but not markedly swollen as in *P. farinosa*; adpressed to the pedicels. PEDICELS—5–35 mm. long, the outer ones semi-pendent and becoming erect in fruit. CALYX—4 mm., tubular-bell shaped, cut to the middle into pointed lanceolate lobes; the midrib of the lobes, the base of the calyx, and even the top of the peduncle may be of a darkish purple colour. COROLLA—Rose-lilac to reddish purple, annulate, pin and thrum eyed, though rarely monomorphic; tube yellow, can be just longer than the calyx to twice as long; limb flat to shallow saucer shaped, 10–15 mm. in diameter; the annulus region can be darker in colour than the rest of the limb; eye narrow, yellow, really corresponds to the end of the tube; lobes obovate and fairly deeply notched, may touch but rarely overlap. CAPSULE—Cylindrical, equals or just exceeds the calyx.

P. glaucescens

Primula glaucescens Moretti   (Bluish or greenish grey)

This attractive species is easy to cultivate, but all too frequently is very shy flowering.

DISTRIBUTION—The westernmost of the Arthritica section, to be found east of Lake Como in the Bergamasque and Giudicarian Prealps: the northern limit runs south of the main crest of the Bergamasque (Orobic) Alps and south of the Adamello Group; the eastern limit is the western flank of the Valli Giudicarie; in its southeastern corner it overlaps with *P. spectabilis* Tratt. ALTITUDINAL RANGE—Very wide, being found from 450–2400 m. HABITAT—A strictly calcicole plant, growing in limestone fissures, on stony slopes and earthy banks, preferring moist, shady, and humusy positions. There is an interesting report of its occurrence at the Cingolo Rosso in Val Daone, where the geology provides a series of alternating granite and calcareous bands: the granite bands contain only *P. daonensis* and the calcareous bands only *P. glaucescens*. RHIZOME—Long, stout, with persistent remains of withered foliage near the apex, and with strong, stout fleshy roots. LEAF ROSETTE—Fairly compact, with the outer mature leaves lying flat on the ground. LEAF—Stiff, leathery, 1–10 cm. long and 0·5–2·5 cm. wide, lanceolate to oblanceolate or oblong, with an obtuse or acute apex; blade tapering gradually to a short, broadly winged petiole; margin cartilaginous and entire, though the cartilaginous edge is minutely crenulate; blade surfaces totally glabrous, shiny but not sticky above; midrib prominent below; specific epithet refers to the bluish green of the leaves, though this in not all too evident. PEDUNCLE—2–12 (15) cm. tall, stout and erect. UMBEL—Symmetrical, of 2–6 flowers. BRACTS—Linear lanceolate, 5–35 mm. long, can be so long as to exceed the calyx; can be reddish in colour. PEDICELS—2–12 (20) mm. long. CALYX—Tubular to tubular-bell shaped, often reddish in colour, 8–20 mm. long, that is can be very long; split to $\frac{1}{3}$ to $\frac{2}{3}$ into linear lanceolate acute lobes which can lie on the corolla tube or diverge from it. COROLLA—Exannulate, varying from pinkish red to lilac, with a whitish eye; tube usually a little longer than calyx, occasionally $2 \times$ calyx; throat and centre of limb covered in tiny glandular hairs; limb 2–3 cm. in diameter, varying from funnel to shallow funnel shaped; lobes obcordate, deeply notched. CAPSULE—6–8 mm., oblong, about half the length of the calyx.

Two subspecies have been defined: subsp. *calycina* (Duby) Pax, which is a more vigorous form with a 2 cm. long calyx and 3 cm. flowers, and is common over most of the range of the species; subsp. *longobarda* (Porta) Widmer, a more gracile form with a 1 cm. calyx and 2 cm. flower, found only at the eastern end of the range, notably on Monte Bondol. Since intermediate forms are found, this division is, according to Wright-Smith and Fletcher, not justified and should be ignored.

See Plate 14

P. glutinosa

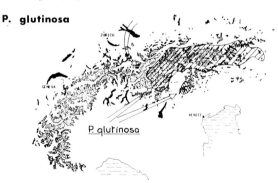

P. glutinosa

Primula glutinosa Wulfen   (Sticky)

In cultivation, *P. glutinosa* is one of the most difficult of the European species: it lingers and fades away and rarely flowers. In the wild it is most beautiful, and it is really worth making the pilgrimage to see it. Hybridisation in the wild with *P. minima* L. occurs so readily that it is sometimes difficult to find the "pure" species; many of the plants seen in cultivation have *minima* in their make-up.

DISTRIBUTION—Lies more or less within that of *P. minima*. It inhabits the main backbone of the Eastern Alps from the Ötztal to the Tauern: the western limit runs from just inside the lower Engadine region of Switzerland, over the Ofen Pass area to the upper Adda valley above Bormio, thence to the Tonale Pass, including the Ortles, the eastern Adamello and Val Genova; the southern limit takes in the Sarentine Alps north of Bolzano, goes east to the Dobbiaco area and the western end of the Carnic Alps, then south of the Drau along the Gailtal Alps right across to the Koralpe, which is the easternmost limit; northwestwards it reaches the Enns valley near Liezen, thence westwards to cross the Salzach river near St. Johann, includes the Kitzbühler and Tuxer Alps, and reaches the Inn valley north of the Ötztal Alps. A relatively small area in the Southern Dolomites takes in Latemar and the Rolle Pass area on volcanic rocks, and goes down to Val Sugana. There are two isolated western outliers near the Rhine above Arosa, and finally a quite disjunct occurrence in the Vranica Mts. in Bosnia, west of Sarajevo. ALTITUDINAL RANGE—Rarely found below 2000 m. and prefers northern exposures, typically in *Vaccinium-Loiseleuria* heaths. It can climb as high as 3100 m. (10,300'). HABITAT—*P. glutinosa* is always found on silicate rocks and avoids limestone; it is generally found in moist or wet clayey grit, in sparse meadows, and in rock fissures; it favours areas where the winter snow lies deep. RHIZOME—Can become stout, long and branched with age; the roots are thick and fleshy. LEAF ROSETTE—Tight and quite erect. LEAF—Leathery, somewhat fleshy, sticky, 1·5–6 cm. long and 0·3–0·8 (1) cm. wide, narrowly oblanceolate to oblong, with an obtuse to rounded apex; blade tapers gradually into the generally short, broadly winged petiole; margin somewhat cartilaginous, finely crenate to denticulate in the upper half, sometimes entire; surface of the blade minutely glandular-punctate, this being the source of the sticky exudate; veining obscure. PEDUNCLE—Stout, erect, 1·5–9 cm. tall. UMBEL—Bears 1–8 quite fragrant flowers. BRACTS—7–13 mm. and a special feature of the species, for they can be quite broadly ovate, even rotundate and overlapping, forming a kind of envelope around the calyces; they are often dark purplish, crinkled in texture, and slightly denticulate round the apex. PEDICELS—Obsolete at flowering, up to 2 mm. at fruiting. CALYX—Bell shaped, glandular, 5–8 mm. long, cut to $\frac{1}{3}$ to $\frac{2}{5}$ into rounded lobes which lie on the corolla tube. COROLLA—Exannulate,

Continued on page 148   **See Plate 26**

65

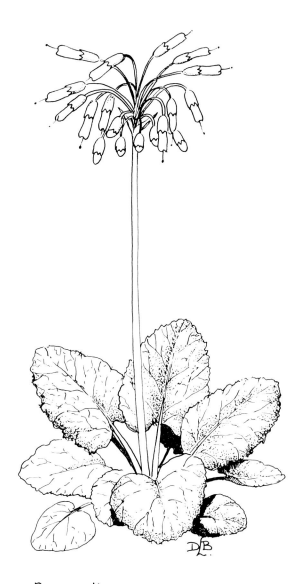

P. grandis

Primula grandis Trautv. (*Sredinskya grandis* (Trautv.) Fed.)   (Tall)

This species stands on the outer edge of the Genus *Primula*. In the *Flora of the U.S.S.R.* it stands outside in the monotypic Genus *Sredinskya*. In the only mention of this plant in the *Bulletin*, Schwarz follows Wright-Smith and Fletcher in placing it in *Primula*. That it is still virtually unknown to amateurs, in spite of the fact that it was in cultivation at the R.B.G., Edinburgh from 1895–1940 and possibly beyond, and in spite of Farrer's poetic praise of it in *The English Rock Garden*, is comment enough.

It is in fact an unattractive plant, with large, broadly ovate leaves, a large and stout 30–60 cm. peduncle which bears an *Allium*-like umbel of 15–40, 1·25 cm. long, pale yellow, tubular flowers; quite unlike a primula. It occurs in the western and northern Caucasus.

P. halleri

Primula halleri J. F. Gmelin (*P. longiflora* All.)

(Commem. Haller, botanist)

This primula, more familiar to many under the now obsolete name of *P. longiflora*, is moderately widespread in cultivation, being reasonably easy to keep and to propagate.

DISTRIBUTION—Widely disjunct, from the western Alps to the Caucasus, chiefly in the eastern half of the Alps: the western limit of this area is around the Maloja Pass at the upper end of the Engadine, thence to the Bergamasque (Orobic) Alps, then eastwards along the foot of the Alps, including Cima Tombea, of course the Dolomites, and on to the Julian and Sanntaler (Steiner) Alps; the eastern limit crosses the Drau at Villach, excludes the Gurktal Alps, and crosses the Tauern

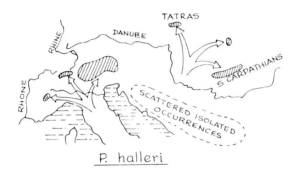

P. halleri

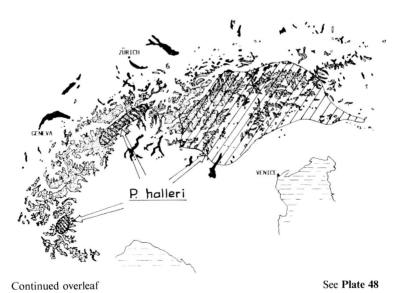

P. halleri

Continued overleaf   See **Plate 48**

Range at around the headwaters of the Mur (30 km. east of the Tauern Tunnel); the northern limit includes the Kitzbühler Alps and runs south of the Inn all the way to the Upper Engadine, crossing the river only in the Julier Pass area. A much smaller area of distribution is found between the Matterhorn and the northern Tessin region and a smaller area still is in the Cottian Alps, in the Monte Viso region. There are also many areas of occurrence east of the Alps, notably the Tatra, the eastern and southern Carpathians in Roumania, scattered areas throughout montane Yugoslavia, for example in the Velebits; the southernmost occurrence in the Balkans is in the Rila and Pirin Mts. in Bulgaria. Finally, it has been reported from the Lesser Caucasus in Armenia. ALTITUDINAL RANGE—1800–2400 m. (6000–8000′), though it can drop to 1000 m. or rise to 2900 m., as around the Stelvio Pass. HABITAT—*P. halleri* likes to grow in sunny stony alpine meadows which are neither very wet nor very dry, thriving best where the humus content is high; also found in moist fissures on rock faces; generally found on limestone though it also occurs in silicate regions, such as the Pennine Alps. RHIZOME—Short, rounded. LEAF ROSETTE—Open, erect. LEAF—Stiff, straight, 2–8 cm. long, 0·5–3 cm. wide, elliptic to oblanceolate or obovate, with an obtuse or rounded apex; blade narrowing gradually into a short winged petiole, which at most is half the length of the blade; margins entire, or seemingly minutely toothed, but the tiny teeth are protuberances at the ends of the lateral nerves; upper leaf surface may be slightly farinose, lower densely covered with creamy farina and bearing the prominent midrib and lateral veins. PEDUNCLE—Stout, 8–18 cm. long, lengthening to 30 cm. in fruit; farinose, particularly near the apex. UMBEL—Of 2–12 (22) flowers, symmetrical or, frequently, one-sided. BRACTS—5–10 mm., narrow, pointed, awl shaped and bulbous at the base. PEDICELS—Slightly farinose, 5–10 mm. long, rarely longer than the bracts, greatly lengthening and becoming erect in fruit. CALYX—Farinose, 8–12 mm. long, tubular-pitcher shaped, widest just below mid-length and prominently five-ribbed; cleaved to the middle into narrow acute or obtuse lobes which lie on the corolla tube. COROLLA—Annulate, lilac to violet with a yellow eye; monomorphic in most of the range, but pin- and thrum-eyed forms do occur in Bulgaria; tube maroony-reddish, 2–3 cm. long and the main distinguishing feature of the species, for it is 2–3 × longer than the calyx; limb flat to shallow saucer shaped, 15–20 mm. in diameter, with deeply notched, obovate lobes; the stamina are set near the apex of the tube, and the style protrudes slightly. CAPSULE—Cylindrical, as long as or a little longer than the calyx.

P. hirsuta

Primula hirsuta All. (*P. rubra* J. F. Gmel.; *P. viscosa* Vill.)   (Hairy)
(See *Curtis's Bot. Mag.*, *14*, 1922)

This is by far the most widespread of the species in the Erythrodrosum Sub-section, occurring in the Pyrenees and a large portion of the Alps. It is a quite variable species, and many forms have been described: Ludi, in Hegi's *Flora von Mittel-Europa*, vol. V, part 3, p. 1768 (1926 Edn.) describes the following: *typica* Pax, *exscapa* (Hegetsch. *et* Heer) Pax, *confinis* (Schott) Schinz *et* Thellung, *ciliata* (Schrank) Schiff, *pallida* Schott, *angustata* Widmer, *serratula* Beauv., *subalpina* Palez, and *rupicola* Palez. The validity of these forms is very much open to question, as variability is very evident within particular populations: the variations occur mainly in the leaves, which may be round to elliptic, long and short stalked, very coarsely to finely toothed; the form, however, appears to be much more constant in the Pyrenees, where leaves are rounded, regularly and strongly toothed, and the umbels have more flowers than average.

DISTRIBUTION—In the Pyrenees it is found from the Pic du Midi d'Osseau in the west to the Maladeta in the central region. Very rare further east. In the Alps it is most abundant in the non-calcareous mountains of Switzerland, the Austrian Tyrol, and adjoining Italian regions, greatly diminishing in frequency of occurrence eastwards and southwestwards of this central area: the eastern limit is in the Gross Glockner region; the southern and northern limits more or less correspond to the transition from silicate to limestone; in the Dolomites it is to be found on the volcanic outcrops; in the southwest it occurs in the Graian and Vanoise Alps, reaching the west Dauphiné

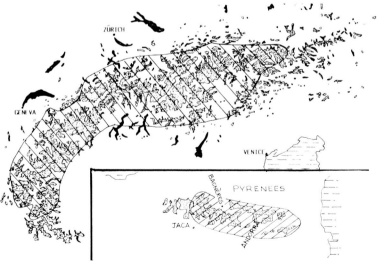

Continued overleaf   See **Plate 8**

and north Cottian Alps in small numbers; exceptionally, it has been reported from the north side of Mont Clapier in the Maritime Alps (Holford, *Bull.*, 1969, *37*, 203). ALTITUDINAL RANGE—Very wide, normally from 1200–2800 m., but has been found on Monte Rosa at 3600 m. (11,750′) and also at 220 m. (700′) in Val Maggia near Lake Maggiore. HABITAT—Though essentially calcifuge, it occasionally occurs on limestone, as on the Grigna above Lake Como, or on the Klausen Pass, between Uri and Glarus in Switzerland; very saxatile, nearly always found in rock crevices: it is a joy to see rows of its bright pink flowers on a cliff when the snow is still lying on the screes and meadows; may also be found on consolidated scree and stony slopes, though much less frequently and then only at high altitudes. FORM—Efarinose and mat-forming. RHIZOME—Stout, branching. LEAF ROSETTE—Rather lax and openly rosulate. LEAF—2–6 (13) cm. long, 1–2 (4) cm. wide, usually roundish in shape but may be rhomboidal, rotundate, obovate, broadly spathulate, elliptic, even oblong; apex rounded or obtuse; blade tapers, usually rather sharply, into a broad winged petiole; margin deeply to finely toothed in the upper half, though sometimes toothing may occur over the whole margin, sometimes only near the tip, rarely teeth may not be very apparent; the teeth may be regular to irregular; leaf surfaces sticky owing to a copious covering of golden, or reddish, sometimes colourless, rarely red, stalked glandular, 0·1–0·5 mm. long hairs; midrib conspicuous below; petiole varying from very short to about equal to the blade in length. PEDUNCLE—From nearly absent to 7 cm. tall, as a rule shorter than the leaves, may be slender or stout, covered in small glandular hairs as are all green parts of the inflorescence. UMBEL—Symmetrical and erect, usually 1–3 flowered, often more, a maximum of 17 having been recorded. BRACTS—1–3 mm. long, papery, broadly ovate and obtuse, one sometimes much longer than the rest. PEDICELS—3–10 (17) mm. long, lengthening in fruit. CALYX—Bell shaped, 3–7 (9) mm. long, cut to $\frac{1}{3}$–$\frac{2}{3}$ into triangular to ovate lobes, which may be acute or obtuse, and generally point outwards. COROLLA—Exannulate, bright pink to mauve, sometimes lilac, rarely white; tube paler in colour than limb, 2–3 × longer than calyx, slightly glandular hairy on its outer surface; limb 15–25 mm. in diameter, with obovate, more or less deeply emarginate lobes, and a white eye; throat beset with colourless glandular hairs. CAPSULE—Subglobose to subcylindrical, usually much shorter than the calyx.

P. incana.

Primula incana Jones (*P. farinosa* subsp. *incana* (Jones) W. W-Smi.
et Forr.)   (Quite grey)
   This relatively small flowered N. American species is very variable
in size. It is closely related to *PP. farinosa, stricta* and *mistassinica.*

DISTRIBUTION—Wide, from eastern Alaska southwards to Colorado
State, roughly following the eastern side of the main Cordillera; an arm
reaches eastwards to southern Saskatchewan, with two isolated
pockets on the S.W. and S.E. shores of Hudson Bay. ALTITUDINAL
RANGE—From sea level in the north to 2000–3000 m. (6000–10,000′)
in the south. HABITAT—Moist or wet conditions, mostly in calcareous
regions. LEAF ROSETTE—Rosulate. LEAF—Elliptic to spathulate,
1·5–8 cm. long, 0·5–2 cm. wide, obtuse or round tipped; margins
usually denticulate, rarely nearly entire; midrib and lateral nerves
prominent on the lower surface, which is usually covered with pale
yellow or white farina; petiole winged, obsolete to as long as the blade.
PEDUNCLE—Stout, erect, having the enormous range of 5–45 cm. in
length, generally farinose towards the apex. UMBEL—Capitate, 2–14
flowers. BRACTS—5–10 mm., linear- lanceolate to linear-oblong,
swollen at the base. PEDICELS—Stiffly erect, farinose, when in flower
shorter than or equal to the bracts. elongating to more than double
their length when in fruit. CALYX—Very farinose, pitcher or bell shaped
7–10 mm. long, 4–5 mm. wide at its widest, cut to $\frac{1}{3}-\frac{1}{2}$ into oblong or
triangular lobes. COROLLA—Annulate, homomorphic, lilac fading
towards the centre, with a yellow eye; tube as long as or a little longer
than the calyx; limb 6–10 mm. in diameter, with oblong or cuneate to
obovate, deeply notched lobes. CAPSULE—Oblong, only slightly
exceeding the calyx.

See **Plate 47**

P. integrifolia

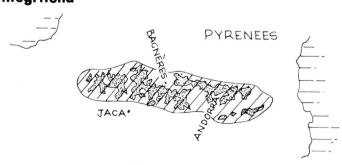

Primula integrifolia L.   (With entire leaves)
                                                   (See *Curtis's Bot. Mag.*, 942)

This distinct species tends, like several others, to be shy-flowering in cultivation.

DISTRIBUTION—Disjunct, in the Alps and in the Pyrenees; widespread throughout the Pyrenees, where in general it has a brighter, pinker colour; in the Alps it occurs in the central region, encompassing in the main the headwaters of the Inn and the Rhine; the northernmost occurrence is in the Säntis group, just south of St. Gallen in N.E. Switzerland; the northern limit goes westwards to include the Glarus and Uri Alps and reaches the Rigi in Canton Schwyz and the Faulhorn south of Lake Brienz; the Lauterbrunnen valley forms the western limit; it does not occur in the high mountains of the Bernese Oberland, but keeps east of the Häslital; the western limit includes the mountains just south of Airolo in the Tessin and reaches Mt. Camoghè near Bellinzona; thence the southern limit follows the north side of the River Adda to its source, and from there crosses the Inn valley near the Swiss-Austrian border and reaches the Arlberg Pass near St. Anton, whence the northern limit goes through the Vorarlberg to reach Säntis. There are two small outliers, one on Pilatus above Lucerne, the other on Mt. Tonale to the S.E. of the main area. ALTITUDINAL RANGE—1500–3000 m. but it is mostly found at 2100–2600 m. HABITAT—Wet peaty conditions and wet turf, mostly on silicate rocks, but not infrequently in limestone regions; tends to prefer situations where the snow lingers longest; hardly ever found on rock faces. FORM—Efarinose. RHIZOME—Stout, branching. LEAF ROSETTE—Open rosulate. LEAF—Soft, green, 1–6 cm. long, 0·5–1 cm. wide, elliptic to spathulate, obtuse to rounded at the apex; margin non-cartilaginous, entire, only

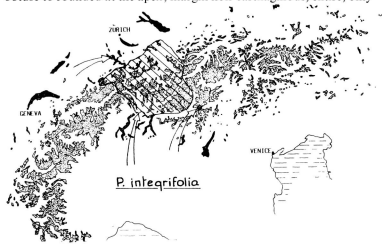

P. integrifolia

Continued overleaf   See **Plates 21, 22**

79

very rarely bearing faint, remote denticulation near the apex, always with a conspicuous fringe of glandular hairs; surfaces somewhat shiny and hairless, or bearing a few small glandular hairs; petiole winged, almost absent at flowering time but lengthening afterwards. PEDUNCLE—Rigid, 1–3 cm. long in flower, up to 7 cm. at fruiting time. UMBEL—1–3 flowered, usually 2, borne just above the leaves. (The green parts of the inflorescence are all densely pubescent with glandular hairs which may be as long as 0·5 mm.) BRACTS—Lanceolate to oblong, 5–10 mm. long, and sometimes have a reddish hue. PEDICELS— 0–2 mm. long, not lengthening in fruit. CALYX—6–12 mm. long, tubular to tubular-bell shaped, often tinged with red, cut to about $\frac{1}{4}$ into obtuse lobes. COROLLA—Exannulate, varying from rose-lilac to magenta-lilac; though sometimes paler round the throat, it does not usually develop a white eye; throat densely glandular hairy with colourless hairs, which sometimes extend onto the petals giving the impression of a white eye; tube cylindrical, often of a darker hue than the corolla lobes, 9–15 mm. long, a little longer to $2 \times$ calyx; limb shallow funnel shaped 1·5–2·5 cm. in diameter, with obovate, sometimes overlapping, deeply notched lobes. CAPSULE—Roundish, $\frac{1}{3}$–$\frac{1}{2}$ the length of the calyx.

P. juliae.

82

Primula juliae Kusnetsow (Commem. Mme. Julia Ludovikovna Mlokossjewicz, the discoverer) (See *Curtis's Bot. Mag.*, 8468).

This delightful small primula was discovered as recently as 1900. It is the key parent in the wide range of 'Juliana' Hybrids of which *Primula* 'Wanda' is the best known, being among the most widely grown of all primulas. The species is easy in cultivation and deserves to be much more widely grown.

DISTRIBUTION—It occurs on both the northern and southern flanks of the Eastern Caucasus in E. Georgia, and in the provinces of Dagestan and Azerbaidjan. HABITAT—Moist rocks in montane forest. FORM—An efarinose, stoloniferous plant, almost disappearing in winter to a small resting bud, which however already begins to open in late January, when the fleshy pinkish bud scales are quite conspicuous. RHIZOME—Long, thin, almost dichotomously branching. LEAF ROSETTE—Open. LEAF—Thin-textured, 2–10 cm. long including the petiole; blade roundish, 0·5–3 cm. long and wide, deeply cordate at the base; margins coarsely crenate; midrib and lateral veins impressed above and prominent below; petiole narrow, usually 2–3 times longer than blade and sheathing at the base. (The petiole and all green parts of the inflorescence are streaked with reddish marks, or almost entirely pinkish). PEDUNCLE—Absent. UMBEL—Arises at the tip of a rhizome branch, usually between two leaf rosettes which will eventually develop into two new rhizome branches. BRACTS—Linear-lanceolate, 3–4 mm. long. PEDICELS—As long as or much longer than the petioles. CALYX—Narrowly tubular, 5–8 mm. long, strongly ridged, cut to $\frac{1}{4}$–$\frac{1}{2}$ into lanceolate lobes. COROLLA—Exannulate, shallow funnel shaped, bright deep bluish magenta, darker and redder round the yellowish eye; tube narrow, yellow, about $2 \times$ calyx; limb 2–3 cm. in diameter with obovate, deeply notched lobes which are not overlapping.

See **Plate 55**

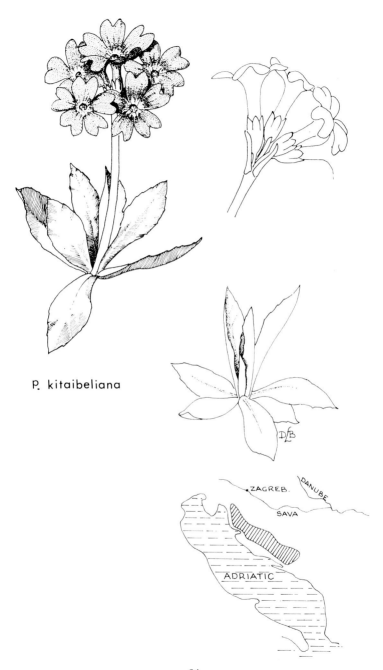

P. kitaibeliana

ZAGREB.

DANUBE

SAVA

ADRIATIC

84

Primula kitaibeliana Schott   (Commem. Kitaibel, botanist)

This relatively little known species is the largest in the Rhopsidium Section, and seems to have *P. integrifolia* L. as its closest relative. In the wild it flowers in May.

DISTRIBUTION—The southern Velebit Mountains of Croatia and in the mountains around Mostar in Herzegovina, notably Prenj, Velež and Cabulja; there is a small northern outlier on Mt. Klek near Ogulin. Its occurrence in these regions is very sporadic and it is only locally very abundant.

ALTITUDINAL RANGE—1000–2000 m., but has been found as low as 350 m.

HABITAT—Quite saxatile, occurring almost exclusively in moist, grassy, mossy pockets on cool, north-facing limestone cliffs. It is, however, missing from the majority of apparently suitable habitats.

RHIZOME—Stout. LEAF ROSETTE—Fairly flat, but the youngest leaves are erect; the winter resting bud is quite prominent, slender and tight. LEAF—Pale green and soft-textured when young; upper surface becoming normal green, sometimes grey green at maturity; the glandular hairs which cover the leaf surfaces exude a distinctive aromatic odour, stated by most authors to be strong, though in our own experience, both in the wild and in cultivation, faint and rather pleasant (Farrer, in his exaggerated style, qualifies it as stinking . . .); the leaves are 1·5–8 cm. long and 0·7–3 cm. wide at flowering time, growing on to a much larger size, up to 12 cm. long by the end of the season; they are elliptic to obovate, obtuse or rounded at the apex, with a very short winged petiole which lengthens in time; margins are not cartilaginous, but thickly beset with 0·3 mm. long glandular hairs, much longer than those on the leaf surfaces; in the upper half of the blade the margins are faintly remotely denticulate, but can also be lightly dentate or entire. PEDUNCLE—Glandular pubescent, 2–5 cm. tall. UMBEL—Symmetrical or slightly one-sided, of 1, usually 2, sometimes up to 5 flowers, borne among the leaves to well above them; scape lengthens after flowering. BRACTS—Linear, 3–6 mm. long, reaching 10 mm. at fruiting. PEDICELS—4 mm., likewise lengthening in fruit. CALYX—Tubular campanulate, 8–12 mm. long, sometimes of a reddish hue, cut to $\frac{1}{3}$–$\frac{1}{2}$ into ovate to oblong lobes, acute to rounded at the apex. COROLLA—Exannulate, bright magenta-rose, to rose, to lilac, with a white eye, which can be strikingly star-shaped; tube as long as or just longer than calyx; limb shallow funnel shaped, 2–2·5 cm. in diameter, with deeply notched obovate lobes. CAPSULE—Roundish, 4–6 mm. long, about $\frac{1}{2}$ the length of the calyx.

See Plate 24

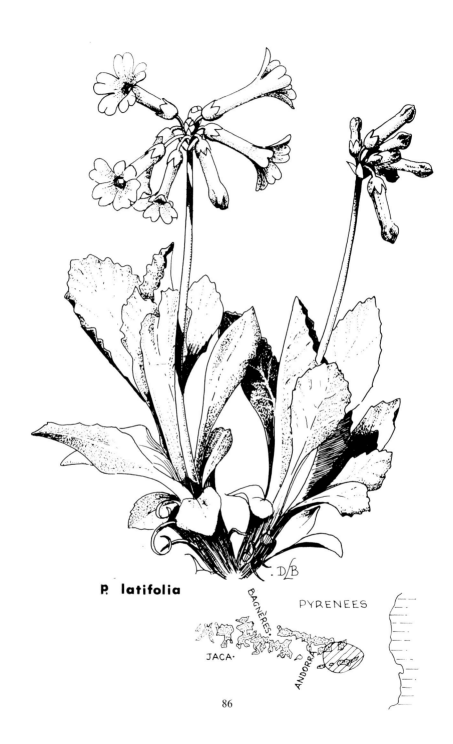

P. latifolia

PYRENEES

BAGNÈRES

JACA

ANDORRA

Primula latifolia Lapeyr. (*P. viscosa* All.)   (Broad-leaved)

This species was long known as *P. viscosa* All., so that many people find the new name confusing: the confusion is increased in the older literature, sometimes in the recent (e.g. *Bull.*, 1976, *44*, 83) by the use of *P. viscosa* Vill. to denote *P. hirsuta* All.

DISTRIBUTION—This essentially calcifuge species has a widely disjunct distribution in the Alps and the Pyrenees: forma *pyrenaica* Pax grows in the Eastern Pyrenees, east of Andorra, and is the most vigorous, with more numerous flowers and larger, more deeply toothed leaves; forma *cynoglossifolia* Widmer (var. *pedemontana* Arch.) grows in two separate areas, one centred on the Graian, North Cottian and Vanoise Alps, reaching the Dauphiné Alps at the Col du Galibier and Lautaret, just reaches the Pennine Alps south of Monte Rosa on the Col di Turlo, and does not go beyond Col de la Croix in the Cottian; the other area is in the Maritime Alps, around Monte Argentera and Mont Clapier, west of the Col di Tenda; forma *graveolens* (Hegetsch. *et* Heer) Pax (which means strong smelling!) grows on the mountains around the upper Engadine and the Adda valley, the northernmost point is near Klosters, the western limit includes the Albula Group and the mountains to the north and west of Chiavenna, the southern limit takes in the non-calcareous backbone of the Orobic (Bergamasque) Alps, then goes north to Bormio, the eastern limit going on to reach the Inn by the Swiss National Park; the entire Bernina Group is of course included. ALTITUDINAL RANGE—Varies from area to area: in Switzerland it is mostly between 2200 and 2700 m.; in the Maritimes it comes down to 1900 m.; we have no data for the Pyrenees. HABITAT—Rock fissures preferred, generally shady and moist; it is also found on

P. latifolia

Continued on page 148   See **Plate 6**

P. laurentiana

Primula laurentiana Fernald   (From the St. Lawrence)

This species is close to *P. scandinavica* Bruun botanically, but is quite distinct from it in appearance. It can reach a relatively large size, and is an attractively proportioned species in cultivation.

DISTRIBUTION—It occurs in maritime Eastern Canada from Labrador to Nova Scotia and in Maine in the U.S.A., that is, broadly in the region around the estuary of the St. Lawrence river. HABITAT— Ranges from calcareous cliffs and ledges, stony hillsides, to freshwater marsh areas. FORM—A farinose, very rarely efarinose species, which may be heteromorphic (pin and thrum) or homomorphic. LEAF ROSETTE—Openly rosulate. LEAF—Oblanceolate to spathulate, may have subacute to obtuse or rounded tips; leaf 1–13 cm. long, including the petiole, and 0·3–3 cm. broad; petiole more or less equals the blade; margin denticulate; upper surface efarinose to slightly farinose, lower surface white farinose, with a prominent midrib. PEDUNCLE—Stout, erect, 1–45 cm. long, farinose mainly near the apex. UMBEL—Symmetrical, of 1–17 flowers. BRACTS—5–14 mm. long, lanceolate to awl shaped, bulging at the base. PEDICELS—Erect, farinose, may be absent to 5 cm. long. CALYX—Pitcher to bell shaped, 5–11 mm. long, 3–6 mm. broad, cut to $\frac{1}{3}$–$\frac{1}{2}$ into lobes which can assume a full range of geometries. COROLLA—Annulate, lilac to pinkish purple with an orange-yellow eye fading to orange, and a yellow tube, which equals or just exceeds the calyx; limb 8–15 mm. in diameter, with obovate emarginate lobes. CAPSULE—Ellipsoid, a little longer than to 2 × calyx.

This species varies enormously in size in the wild, which may well reflect differences in exposure or microclimate.

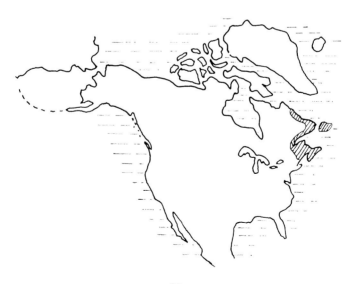

P. longipes

Primula longipes Freyn *et* Sint. (*P. nivalis* Pall. var. *longipes* (Freyn *et* Sint.) Kusn.)   (Long-footed, probably referring to the peduncle)

A vigorous, beautiful, and little known Nivalid. E. K. Balls, who in the 1930's sent back much seed and live material wrote, "one of the loveliest flowers I have ever seen in the wild". Alas, like many Nivalids, it does not persist in cultivation. It is related to *P. nivalis* and close to the Caucasian *P. bayernii* (q.v.).

DISTRIBUTION—N.E. Turkey and adjoining Soviet Adzharistan. ALTITUDINAL RANGE—2000–3350 m. (6500–11,000'). HABITAT—Damp grassy slopes or rocky ledges and crevices, often in running water. RHIZOME—Stout, short. LEAF ROSETTE—Upright to rosulate. LEAF—Blade narrowly obovate, oblong to elliptic, 6–18 cm. by 2–5 cm., thin textured but leathery; tip rounded, obtuse or acute; upper surface efarinose, lower surface farinose; margin crenate-denticulate and often recurved; midrib very prominent on lower surface; petiole broadly winged and sheathing, usually slightly shorter than blade. PEDUNCLE—Very stout and upright, 11–35 (50) cm., densely white farinose. UMBEL—10–15 flowered, one-sided, sometimes two-whorled. BRACTS—Narrowly triangular, shorter than pedicels. PEDICELS—Semipendent, farinose, (5) 15–40 (65) mm., equal or unequal in length, lengthening and becoming erect in fruit. CALYX—Campanulate, 6–12 mm., greenish to purplish, frequently white farinose, cut to $\frac{1}{2}$ into oblong triangular lobes. COROLLA—Annulate, lavender blue to reddish mauve with white eye; tube about equal to calyx; limb 12–22 mm., essentially flat, fragrant; lobes broadly obovate to oblong to nearly round, in some forms slightly emarginate, sometimes overlapping. CAPSULE—2–3 × calyx. SEED—1–1·5 mm., brown, variable in shape, vesicular surfaced.

91

P. luteola

Primula luteola Ruprecht   (Yellowish)

This is a distinctive and attractive yellow-flowered species in the Auriculata subsection of the Farinosae. It was introduced into cultivation in the U.K. around 1867 and has been found to be easy of culture and propagation; it deserves to be much better known.

DISTRIBUTION—A native of the Eastern Caucasus in the province of Dagestan. ALTITUDINAL RANGE—1500–3000 m. HABITAT—Moist meadows, frequently near springs. RHIZOME—Stout, short, bearing bud scales which surround the base of the openly rosulate LEAF ROSETTE. LEAF—Efarinose and glabrous, bright dark green on both surfaces, lanceolate to elliptic to oblanceolate, 10–30 cm. long, including the petiole, and 2–5 cm. wide; they are obtuse or round tipped, tapering gradually into a winged petiole, which is usually about $\frac{1}{3}$ the length of the blade; margins sharply denticulate, recurved. PEDUNCLE—Robust, usually 15–35 cm. tall, white farinose towards the apex. UMBEL—Symmetrical to globular, 10–25 flowers. BRACTS—Linear-lanceolate, 5–7 mm. long, swollen at the base. PEDICELS—Farinose, 10–20 mm. long. CALYX—Campanulate, 5–6 mm. long, farinose within and on the edges of the lobes, cut to $\frac{1}{3}$ into lanceolate lobes. COROLLA—Exannulate, yellow; tube $2 \times$ calyx; limb 15 mm. diameter, shallow funnel shaped, with obovate, deeply emarginate lobes. CAPSULE—Rounded and included in the calyx.

See **Plate 54**

93

P. magellanica (decipiens)

S. AMERICA

FALKLANDS

Primula magellanica Lehmann (*P. decipiens* Duby)

(From the Straits of Magellan)

This is the main primula, maybe even the only primula in South America. The only other species is *P. comberi* W.W-Sm. (see below) which may well eventually be included in *P. magellanica*. There has been confusion over the names *magellanica* and *decipiens*, but all authors now agree that they represent only one species. Fernald (*Rhodora*, 1928, *30*, 74) and Wright-Smith and Fletcher (*Trans. Bot. Soc. Edin.*, 1942–3, *61*, 14) gave precedence to the name *P. decipiens*, which means deceiving, being close to *Farinosa*, but more recently and more convincingly, Lourteig (*Bull. Soc. Argent. Bot.*, 1967, *11*, 140) argues for the earlier name *magellanica*. Botanically it stands closest to the N. American *P. incana* Jones. This species, however named, does well in cultivation, and is not infrequently seen at A.G.S. Shows.

DISTRIBUTION—It comes from the southern tip of S. America, where it occurs in the Tierra del Fuego, south Patagonia, and the Falkland Islands. HABITAT—It grows in wet places. RHIZOME—Thick. LEAF ROSETTE—Openly rosulate. LEAF—Including the petiole, 1–10 cm. by 0·7–2·5 cm., rhombic to obovate to oblanceolate to spathulate; tip obtuse or rounded; margin serrulate-dentate; blade tapering to a petiole which may be very short to about equal to the blade in length: the leaf is efarinose or, more frequently, white or yellowish farinose on the lower surface, on which the midrib and lateral veins are prominent. PEDUNCLE—Usually 5–15 cm. tall, but the extremes are 3 cm. and as much as 50 cm.; it is farinose towards the apex. UMBEL—Few- to many-flowered, tight, symmetrical. BRACTS—Lanceolate, 5–10 mm., swollen at the base. PEDICELS—Farinose, 1–3 mm. long, lengthening in fruit. CALYX—Pitcher to bell shaped, 8–10 mm. long, cut to the middle into oblong to lanceolate lobes. COROLLA—Annulate, homomorphic, sometimes heteromorphic, fragrant, usually white, but may range through cream, lilac, to purple; eye yellow; tube a little shorter than the calyx, or equal to it; limb flat to shallow saucer shaped, 1–2 cm. in diameter, with obovate, deeply emarginate lobes. CAPSULE—Ellipsoid, exceeds the calyx.

See **Plates 45, 46**

P. comberi W.W-Sm.   Commem. Comber, botanist)

This primula occurs in the main Cordillera in southern Argentina at altitudes between 1800 and 2000 m. It grows in peaty soils by the sides of streams and in bogs. Authentic seed was grown at the R.B.G., Edinburgh and cultivated plants persisted for a few years.

It differs from the more widespread *P. magellanica* only in having a corolla tube which is twice the length of the calyx. Furthermore, unlike *P. magellanica*, the corolla of which can range from white through to purple, *P. comberi* is pale lilac only.

Lourteig (*Darwiniana*, 1947, *7*, 558) suggests that *P. comberi* = *P. magellanica*, and that the latter name should be applied to all S. American Farinosae.

P. marginata

Primula marginata Curtis (Margined, referring to the farina on the leaf margins)   (See p. 187 and *Curtis's Bot. Mag.*, 191)

This is a great favourite, one of the chief attractions of which is the great variability in corolla and leaf colour and form.

DISTRIBUTION—The Maritime and Cottian Alps; some sources quote the Dauphiné Alps, but we have not been able to confirm this, in fact it has been difficult to get an accurate picture of the limits of distribution of this very familiar garden primula. The northern limit would seem to be the Col de la Croix in the Cottian Alps, north of Monte Viso, from which the eastern limit follows the foot of the mountains down to the Col di Tenda area and includes Mongioie at the eastern extreme of the Maritimes; the southern limit takes in much of the foothills region south of the main chain, down even to the Cime du Cheiron and the heights north of Menton and Thorenc, includes the Alpes de Provence and turns north near Castellane; the western limit takes in the heights east and north of Digne, then turns N.E. to follow the south side of the Durance valley, then up the Guil torrent, past Aiguilles, to the Col de la Croix; the Col d'Izoard area is probably excluded, though it has been reported from the Orcières region, north of the Durance. Fenaroli in his *Flora delle Alpi* cites a totally disjunct occurrence in the Val d'Ossola in the Simplon region. *P. marginata* is not common in this largish area of distribution, but where it is found it generally occurs abundantly. ALTITUDINAL RANGE—Very wide, 800–3000 m. occasionally down to 500 m. HABITAT—Nearly always on limestone, where its favourite location is a mossy, grassy ledge on the north side of precipitous slopes or cliffs; also found on steep humus slopes in the shade of bushes and trees or growing out of rock fissures. In the lower half of its altitudinal range it is never found in south-facing locations; in the upper half it is more tolerant of exposure to sun. RHIZOME—In combination with the persistent stem grows to 60 cm. (2′) and more and is stout; the

Continued on page 149   See **Plates 4, 5**

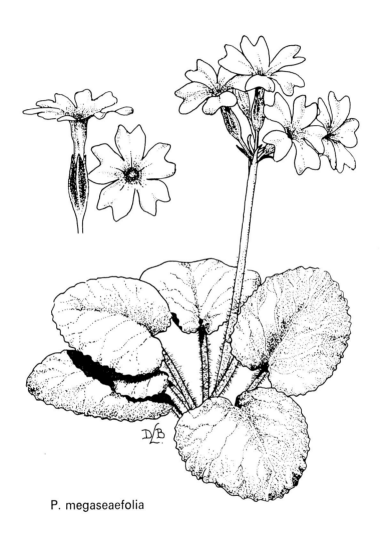

P. megaseaefolia

Primula megaseaefolia* Boiss. (With *Megasea* (*Bergenia*)-like leaves)
(See *Curtis's Bot. Mag.*, 7901)

This species is relatively rare in cultivation. It is very early flowering and apparently needs protection from winter wet.

DISTRIBUTION—Limited, near the Black Sea coast over a distance of about 80 miles in N.E. Turkey and the adjoining province of Batum. ALTITUDINAL RANGE—The few collections range in altitude between 50 and 1100 m. HABITAT—Moist shady gullies in moss among dense shrubs, mostly rhododenrons. RHIZOME—Long, bearing purplish bud scale leaves which are 5–15 mm. long. LEAF—Somewhat leathery, borne in a loose rosette; blade ovate to round, 2·5–15 cm. long, 2·5–12 cm. wide, usually cordate at the base; margins crenate-dentate to nearly entire, teeth slightly mucronate; upper surface dark green and glabrous, lower paler and pubescent along the nerves; midrib and veins impressed above, prominent below; petiole hairy, 1–10 cm. long, tinged with red, sheathing at the base; in the wild the leaves have been observed to lie almost flat on the ground. PEDUNCLE—Stout, usually hairy, reddish. UMBEL—Somewhat one-sided, of 2–9 flowers, or two (rarely even more) superposed umbels. BRACTS—Lanceolate, 5–10 mm. long. CALYX—Tubular and strongly ridged, 10–15 mm. long, cut to $\frac{1}{3}$ into lanceolate lobes. COROLLA—Exannulate, magenta-rose to rosy-pink with a whitish eye and yellow throat; tube yellowish, $1\frac{1}{2}\times$ the calyx; limb almost flat, 15–25 mm. in diameter, with relatively narrow, obovate emarginate lobes. CAPSULE—Oblong, a little longer than the calyx.

*also written megaseifolia.

P. megaseaefolia

P. minima.

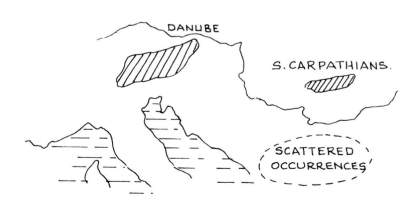

DANUBE

S. CARPATHIANS.

SCATTERED
OCCURRENCES

Primula minima L.   (The smallest)

This well known and beautiful primula is a delight in the wild, but alas for most of us unrewarding in cultivation, because it is usually shy-flowering when away from the mountains.

DISTRIBUTION—Very widely distributed in the eastern half of the Alps, from the Ötztal Group to the Wiener Schneeberg: the western limit passes through the Stubai and Ötztal Alps, by-passes the Ortles, but reaches the Tonale Pass and the adjoining area in the Adda valley, goes through the Adamello to reach the northern Giudicarie and Val Daone; the southern limit takes in most of the Dolomites, including the Bellunese Prealps, and continues to reach the western side of the Julian Alps; it is absent from most of the Julian and Sanntal Alps and from the Karawanken except on Petzen and Mt. Kameni at the eastern extreme; the southern limit crosses the Drau near Villach and includes all the mountains north of the river up to the Kor Alpe where it turns northeast to the Wiener Schneeberg region; thence the northern limit includes all the limestone mountains back to the Karwendel Alps north of Innsbruck. Within this large area there are many regions where the population is very thin and is even zero, and there are others of great abundance, as for example the Dachstein and the Tuxer Gebirge. There are five other very much smaller regions of occurrence along the Carpathians and related mountains; two are on the Czech-Polish border in the Krkonoše, N.W. of Prague, and in the Tatra; two more are in Roumania, the Rodna Alps in the N.E., and the whole 220 km. (150 miles) of the southern Carpathians north of Bucarest; finally there are several scattered points in the Balkans, the Shar Mts. in Yugoslavia near northern Albania, the Stara Planina north of Sofia,

Continued overleaf   See **Plate 25**

101

and the Rila and Pirin Mts. south of Sofia. ALTITUDINAL RANGE—In the Alps, 1700–2700 m., occasionally down to 1200 m. or up to 3000 m. In more northerly regions such as the Krkonoše (Riesengebirge) in Czechoslovakia, normal occurrence begins at 1200 m. HABITAT—It occurs in both silicate and limestone regions but is believed to be essentially calcifuge: the limestone region occurrences are mostly in humus-rich acid soils, as in the Dolomites, where it is never seen growing directly in the limestone: in silicate regions, however, it is found in grit, and even occasionally in rock fissures. Its favourite habitat is flat, humus-rich, sparse meadow, where it can form large mats covered in flowers: beware however of hybrids which often back-cross with *minima* to form large colonies, all the individuals of which may look bafflingly like *minima*. RHIZOME—Can become comparatively stout, long and branching; the roots are long and fleshy. LEAF ROSETTE—Winter resting rosette small, tight, grey-green; summer rosettes usually small and compact. LEAF—Shiny deep green, leathery, 0·5–1·5 (3) cm. long, 3–8 mm. wide, cuneate (wedge shaped) to obtriangulate (broadest at the apex); apex truncate and deeply serrate with 3–9 teeth, which are cartilaginous at the tips; side margins entire; petiole very short, hardly distinguishable from blade. PEDUNCLE—2–8 (30) mm., usually very much shorter than leaves. UMBEL—Single-flowered, rarely two-flowered. BRACTS—Lanceolate, 2–6 (8) mm. long. PEDICELS—Absent at flowering, up to 5 mm. in fruit. CALYX—5–7 (10) mm. long, bell to tubular-shaped, cut to $\frac{1}{3}$ into oblong lobes, rounded and sometimes mucronate at the tip. COROLLA—Exannulate, bright rose-pink, fading to lilac-pink, with a white eye; albinos are known and fairly frequent in some regions, notably the Wiener Schneeberg; tube white, a little longer than to $2 \times$ calyx, glandular-pubescent at the throat; limb 1·5–3 cm. in diameter, flat to shallow funnel shaped, with a very distinct appearance, the lobes being so widely and deeply notched as to be Y-shaped. CAPSULE—Rounded and $\frac{1}{2}$ the length of the calyx.

P. mistassinica.

Primula mistassinica Michx.   (From Lake Mistassini, Quebec)
(See *Curtis's Bot. Mag.*, 2973, 3020)

This is probably the first American primula to be named, having been collected by Michaux in 1792 near Lake Mistassini in Quebec.

DISTRIBUTION—Very wide, right across Canada and in the northeastern States of the U.S.A. adjacent to Canada. In N. America it replaces the Eurasian *P. farinosa* L. which it closely resembles. HABITAT—Wet turfy areas, moist cliffs, or gritty or marshy lake shores, mostly, but not exclusively, in calcareous regions. (See also *P. intercedens* Fernald). FORM—An efarinose or slightly farinose plant in the wild, reasonably farinose in cultivation under glass; unusually for a primula it can form offsets by budding from the roots, a convenient means of propagation. LEAF ROSETTE—Open rosulate. LEAF—Relatively narrow, oblanceolate to spathulate, 0·5–7 cm. long, including the petiole, and 0·2–1·6 cm. wide, obtuse to round tipped; petiole can be obsolete to about half length of blade; margins in the upper part of the blade dentate or denticulate, sometimes subentire. PEDUNCLE—Slender, 3–21 cm. tall. UMBEL—Symmetrical to upright, of 1–10 fragrant flowers. BRACTS—2–6 mm. long, linear awl shaped, thickened at the base. PEDICELS—Slender, 0·5–3·5 cm. long. CALYX—Essentially tubular, 3–6 mm. long, can be farinose, even in the wild; cut to $\frac{1}{2}$ into lanceolate ot oblong lobes. COROLLA—Annulate, heteromorphic, pale pink, lilac, bluish purple or rarely white, with a yellow or orange eye and a yellow tube; tube may be just longer to $1\frac{1}{2}\times$ calyx; limb flat, 0·8–2 cm. in diameter, with obovate to cuneate, emarginate lobes. CAPSULE—$1\frac{1}{2}$–2 × length of calyx. SEEDS—About 0·5 mm. long, smooth and irregularly rounded.

See **Plate 44**

Primula intercedens Fernald   (Coming between)

This primula is found only round the shores of the northern Great Lakes in N. America—lakes Superior, Michigan and Huron. It is very close to *P. mistassinica* Michx. (many botanists* would say a part of it), from which it differs in only two main features: the under surface of the leaves is normally covered with yellow farina, whereas in *P. mistassinica* it is efarinose or, especially in cultivation, lightly covered with white farina; related to this is the bright yellow appearance of the winter resting buds; the second feature is that the seeds are covered with small protuberances and have a reticulate surface, whereas those of *mistassinica* are smooth.

P. intercedens is, at best, a short-lived plant in cultivation.

*Soper, *Bull. Am. Prim. Soc.*, 1972, p. 108; Vogelmann, *Rhodora*, 1960, *62*, 31.

P. nutans

Also very extended distribution in Siberia and Himalayan regions.

Primula nutans Georgi (*P. sibirica* Jacq., and five other synonyms)
(Nodding, though what is nodding is not obvious)
(See *Curtis's Bot. Mag.*, 3167. See also under *P. sibirica* in Roy Green, *Asiatic Primulas*, p. 94).

This attractive species, which deserves to be more frequently seen in cultivation, differs considerably in appearance from other European and American Farinosae, and is placed in a subsection which also includes the lovely Himalayan *P. involucrata*. Its long established name of *P. sibirica* has recently been dropped in favour of *P. nutans*: confusion reigns because for so long the epithet *nutans* has been associated with that delightful and much loved Asiatic in the Soldanelloides Section, now to be called *P. flaccida* Balakr.

DISTRIBUTION—Wide and scattered in montane and northern Asia, in northern Russia, in northernmost Scandinavia near the Barents Sea, at the northern end of the Gulf of Bothnia, in W. Alaska near the Bering Sea, and in S.W. Yukon. HABITAT—Most often seen in wet meadows, generally near the sea shore, even where the tide can reach it. FORM—*P. nutans* is totally efarinose, and varies greatly in size. RHIZOME—Short, thin, bare. LEAF ROSETTE—Upright-rosulate. LEAF—Including the petiole, 1–12 cm. long; blade somewhat fleshy, oblong, to ovate, to orbicular, 1·5–5 cm. long, 0·5–1·5 cm. wide, rounded at the apex, tapering gradually or contracting abruptly into a narrow-winged petiole, which is usually equal to the blade but sometimes is 2–4 times as long; margins entire or obscurely denticulate; midrib conspicuous on the lower surface. PEDUNCLE—2–30 cm. tall. UMBEL—Upright, of 1–10 flowers. BRACTS—Oblong, tend to become yellowish, 5–12 mm. long and having small fleshy outgrowths (auricles) at the base. PEDICELS—Upright, 0·5–4·5 cm. long. CALYX—Tubular, 5–8 mm. long, strongly ribbed, often marked with reddish stripes, divided to $\frac{1}{3}$ into lobes which bear small cilia on their margins. COROLLA—Annulate, lilac to pinkish purple with a yellow eye; tube just exceeds the calyx or up to $2\times$ as long; limb flat, 10–20 mm. in diameter with obovate to cuneate, deeply emarginate lobes; style in pin-eyed flowers and stamens in thrum-eyed flowers exserted. CAPSULE—Generally $1\frac{1}{2}\times$ the calyx.

See **Plate 41**

P palinuri

Primula palinuri Petagna

(From Cape Palinuro)
(See *Curtis's Bot. Mag.*, 3414)

This unusual and interesting yellow-flowered primula has a very limited distribution in the wild, has adopted a specialised marine habitat quite unique in the Auriculastrum Section, and has anatomical characters which seem to place it between Auriculastrum and Sphondylia (Floribundae). In spite of its Mediterranean origin it is quite hardy in the British Isles and easy to grow; some people find it attractive especially when grown in the open on a wall or a scree. In the wild it flowers from February to April.

DISTRIBUTION—Along some 60 kilometres (40 miles) of the west Calabrian coast south of Salerno, from Cape Palinuro round the Gulf of Policastro to the promontory Scalea. HABITAT—High up on sea cliffs, only in friable sandy tufa or in pockets of pure sand; it does not occur inland; like a desert plant, it sheds its leaves in the hot dry summer season, and concentrates its vegetative activity in the wet winter months. STEM—Thick, woody, protrudes well clear of the surface. LEAF—Fleshy, frequently somewhat wavy, including the petiole 3–20 cm. long and 1·5–7 cm. wide, broadly spathulate to oblong-ovate, round tipped, efarinose, glabrous to finely pubescent; margin slightly cartilaginous, acutely and unequally dentate and often erose; the leaves are said to be fragrant; petiole winged, short in the young leaf, lengthening as the leaf matures. PEDUNCLE—Stout, erect, 8–25 cm. tall. UMBEL—One-sided, of 3 to as many as 40 nodding scented flowers. BRACTS—A feature, for they are leaf-like, ovate to oblong, 8–25 mm. long and 3–10 mm. wide, slightly to densely farinose. PEDICELS—5–20 mm. long and very white farinose. CALYX—5–10 mm. long, bell shaped, may be baggy or clasping, densely farinose, cleaved to the middle into triangular acute lobes. COROLLA—Scented, deep yellow, narrow funnel shaped, annulate (contrasting with all the other primulas in this Section) and white farinose at the throat; tube cylindrical, 2–3 × calyx; limb 5–10 mm. long, broadly ovate, notched, frequently failing to unfold fully and giving an untidy aspect to the flower. CAPSULE— Rounded, about as long as the calyx; SEEDS—1–1·5 mm., oblong.

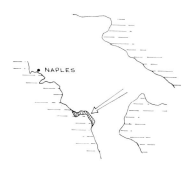

See **Plate 1**

P. parryi

Primula parryi A. Gray   (Commem. Dr. Parry, botanist)
                                          (See *Curtis's Bot. Mag.*, 6185)

This vigorous and attractive primula has been in cultivation since 1856: it does well but can be erratic in its behaviour, sometimes dying suddenly for no apparent reason.

DISTRIBUTION—The most widespread species in the group, being found if infrequently in most of the mountain areas of the western U.S.A. ALTITUDINAL RANGE—2700–4200 m. (9000–14,000'); the upper limit gets lower at higher latitudes, and is around 3000 m. (10,000') in Montana. FORM—Usually a tall, efarinose, somewhat viscid plant. RHIZOME—Stout. LEAF ROSETTE—Various in aspect the whole way from flat to upright. LEAF—Most often upright, recurvent, leathery, frequently somewhat contorted; 6–33 cm. long, 1–6 cm. wide—a very large size range—obovate to oblong, to oblanceolate, with acute to obtuse tips; petiole winged, very short and not much differentiated from blade; margins entire or finely denticulate, the surfaces covered with short capitate glands; midrib strong and conspicuous. The whole plant emits a strong pungent odour, variously described from aromatic to like carrion. PEDUNCLE—Stout, erect, 8–40 cm. tall. UMBEL—Usually one-sided, of 3–20 strongly scented flowers, most of which face sideways. BRACTS—Glandular, ovate to oblong-lanceolate, 5–15 mm. long; overlapping at the base, sometimes denticulate. PEDICELS—Most umbels are made of a mixture or erect and pendent pedicels of different lengths from very short to 10 cm. long. CALYX—Very conspicuously glandular, often purplish, tubular, 8–15 mm. long, cut to $\frac{1}{2}-\frac{1}{3}$ into narrow pointed lobes. COROLLA—Exannulate, can be of various shades of bright magenta to reddish purple, with a yellow eye surrounded by a dark halo; tube yellowish, as long as or just exceeding the calyx; limb 1·5–3 cm. in diameter, with broadly ovate, slightly emarginate to sometimes entire lobes. CAPSULE—Oblong, 7–11 mm. long, included in the calyx. SEEDS—Relatively large (2 mm. × 1 mm.). It has been suggested that the species is polymorphic.

See **Plates 31, 32**

111

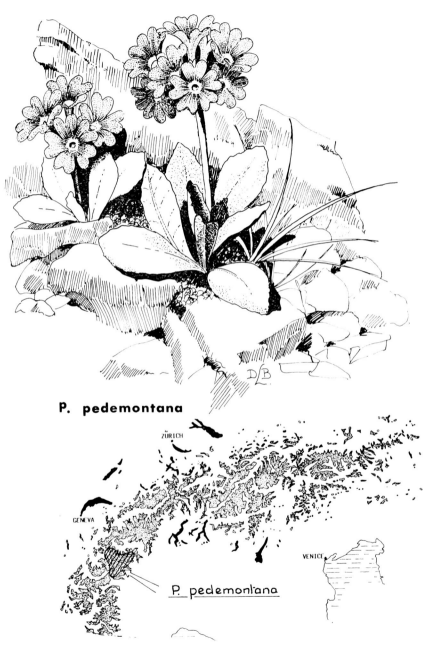

P. pedemontana

ZÜRICH

GENEVA

VENICE

P. pedemontana

112

Primula pedemontana Thomas *ex* Gaudin (From the Piedmont province)   (See *Curtis's Bot. Mag.*, 5794)

DISTRIBUTION—This lovely species occurs in the Vanoise and Graian Alps, its centre of abundance being the region around the Col du Mont Cenis, where hybrids with *P. latifolia* Lapeyr. are fairly frequent. The limits of distribution are not well defined: a westerly location is on Mt. Pourri west of Val d'Isère; to the north it is found in the area of Cogne, south of Aosta, and on the Petit St. Bernard; it does not reach the Mt. Blanc group, and to the south, it probably does not cross the Val di Susa (see *P. villosa*). Its southernmost outlier, cited by Widmer, but doubted by Pax and Knuth, is west of Valdieri in the Maritime Alps. It has recently been reported from the Cordillera Cantabrica, west of the Pyrenees, on the Curavacas, a very disjunct occurrence and given subspecific status (as subsp. *iberica* Losa *et* P. Mons.), but this distinction is doubted by Valentine and Kress in *Flora Europaea*. In most of its range it is only of local occurrence. ALTITUDINAL RANGE— Wide, 1400–3000 m. (4500–10,000′); it would be very interesting to know something of its ecology at the upper altitudinal limit. HABITAT— Normally found in peaty soil on silicate rock in stony or scrubby grassland, often also in rock fissures. FORM—Efarinose. RHIZOME— Stout. LEAF ROSETTE—Openly rosulate. LEAF—Obovate, to oblong-lanceolate, to spathulate, 1·5–10 cm. long, 1–3 cm. wide; apex obtuse or rounded; blade usually tapering gradually to the winged petiole, which varies from almost absent to equal to the blade; margins normally entire to shallowly dentate in the upper half; upper surface in mature leaves shiny dark green, both surfaces are glabrous, or at the most very sparsely beset with small glandular hairs; these hairs are more frequent on young leaves; the leaf margins however are densely covered, most noticeably on young leaves, with brick red to dark red short-stalked glandular hairs; the glands are relatively large and exude a reddish brown secretion; midrib broad and conspicuous below.

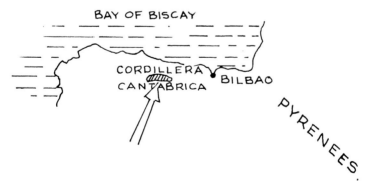

Continued on page 149   See **Plate 10**

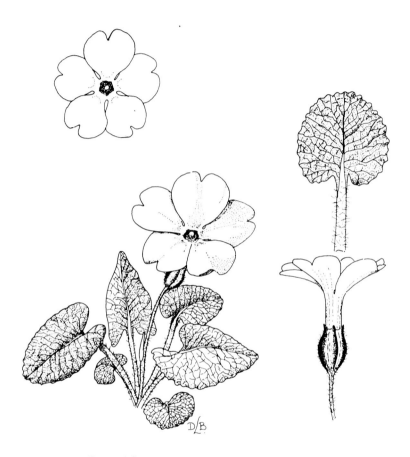

P. renifolia.

Primula renifolia Volg.   (With kidney-shaped leaves)

This species has only very recently come into cultivation in the U.K.; it is closely related to *P. megaseaefolia* Boiss., and is essentially a reduced form of it. Wright-Smith and Fletcher do not accept its specific status, but Fedorov, in *Flora of the U.S.S.R.*, argues strongly for it, but does not give a full description of it; the description given below is a version augmented by estimates made from the line drawing of the species in the *Flora of the U.S.S.R.* and from live specimens grown by D. B. L., Tony Willis, and Geoff Rollinson.

DISTRIBUTION—The north flank of the Western Caucasus, some 60 km. (40 miles) west of Mt. Elbruz, around the Teberda Valley. HABITAT—Rock fissures among pines at the upper limit of the forest at about 2000 m. (6500′). FORM—A small plant, in the wild not more than 10 cm. high. RHIZOME—Short. LEAF—Rounded blade, 3–5 cm. in diameter, cordate at the base and thus somewhat kidney shaped; leaf surface rugose and dull green above, densely white-wooly beneath; margins unevenly crenate-dentate to almost entire; petiole slender, narrowly winged, slightly tomentose and equal to, to more than twice the length of the blade. PEDUNCLE—Slightly hirsute, quite short to about as long as the leaves. UMBEL—Of (1) 2–3 flowers. BRACTS—1–3, lanceolate, small. PEDICELS—Slender, finely hirsute, about 2 cm. long. CALYX—Campanulate or pitcher shaped, cut to $\frac{1}{3}$ into sharply pointed triangular lobes. COROLLA—Blue-violet, with a yellow eye, exannulate; tube greenish yellow, 2–3 × Calyx; limb essentially flat, 2·5–3 cm. in diameter, with obovate emarginate lobes.

See **Plate 57**

P. rusbyi.

Primula rusbyi Greene   (Commem. Rusby, its discoverer)
(See *Curtis's Bot. Mag.*, 7032)

This species is closely related to *PP. ellisiae* Pollard *et* Cockerell and *parryi* A. Gray and is the smallest and the most graceful of the group (in total disagreement with Farrer . . .). It was introduced into cultivation about a century ago, just a couple of years after its discovery, and was quickly awarded a F.C.C. by the R.H.S. It has persisted in cultivation, but is relatively infrequently seen, largely because it rarely sets seed. A high proportion of the plants grown as *rusbyi* are really *ellisiae*: it must be said however that the distinction between the two is not easy to draw.

DISTRIBUTION—S.E. Arizona and S.W. New Mexico, also a few locations much further south in the Mexican mountains. ALTITUDINAL RANGE—2400–3300 m. (8000–11,000'). HABITAT—Damp, shaded habitats on bare rocky ledges on summit slopes. RHIZOME—Stout. LEAF—Erect, efarinose, elliptic to spathulate, acute to obtuse or round tipped; blade 3–8 cm. long, 1–2·5 cm. wide, with entire or denticulate margins; surfaces, especially the lower, glandular; midrib prominent on the lower surface; petiole winged, may be nearly twice as long as the blade, to much shorter, sheathing at the base. PEDUNCLE—6–20 cm. tall, often white farinose near the apex. UMBEL—Frequently one-sided, of 4–12 flowers. BRACTS—Ovate to lanceolate, farinose, 3–8 mm. long. overlapping at the base. PEDICELS—White farinose, 1–3·5 cm. long, CALYX—Tubular to sub-campanulate, 4–8 mm. long, cut to $\frac{1}{3}$–$\frac{1}{2}$ into acute lanceolate lobes, often tinged with purple; there are five distinct white farinose lines leading from the sinuses to the base. COROLLA— Annulate or exannulate, rose red, to magenta, to deep purple, with a yellow eye, usually with a bright crimson ring surrounding the eye; tube pale green, 2–3 × calyx; limb shallow funnel shaped, 1·5–2·5 cm. in diameter, with broadly obovate emarginate lobes. CAPSULE— Oblong, shorter than the calyx.

See **Plate 35**

117

P. scandinavica

118

Primula scandinavica Bruun   (From Scandinavia)

This species is closely related to *P. scotica* Hook., from which it differs mainly in being a significantly larger plant: the sharpest distinction lies in the different chromosome numbers, a point of little value to the amateur.

DISTRIBUTION—Its main occurrence is in the Norwegian mountains in three regions: one inland from Bergen, another just north and east of the Jotunheim Mts., then up to Trondheim, including a portion of western Jämtland in Sweden, and a third from about Lat. 65° 30′ to the Narvik area. ALTITUDINAL RANGE—Upper altitude limit not given. HABITAT—Prefers limestone regions. It is interesting to note that even though in Jämtland it occurs with *P. farinosa*, its ecology is so different that the two species never grow side by side. RHIZOME—Short. LEAF ROSETTE—Openly rosulate, with the youngest leaves quite erect. LEAF—2–3 cm. long, 5–8 mm. wide, narrowly obovate to spathulate, obtuse or rounded at the apex; blade narrows gradually into a winged petiole, which normally is as long as the blade; margins generally denticulate, but may be nearly entire; upper surface lightly farinose, sometimes efarinose, the lower, with prominent midrib and lateral nerves, densely white farinose. PEDUNCLE—4–10 (18) cm. tall, nearly always only one to the leaf rosette. UMBEL—Symmetrical, 2–10 flowered. BRACTS—3–8 mm. long, linear-lanceolate to awl shaped, broadened and bulbous at the base. PEDICELS—Farinose, as long as to 2 × the bracts. CALYX—5–7 mm. long, tubular, ridged, dark hued, more densely farinose inside than outside, cut to the middle into triangular to oblong lobes, which are covered with small glandular hairs, and are obtuse to round tipped. COROLLA—Conspicuously annulate, homomorphic, purplish violet with a yellow eye; tube 8–9 mm., usually 1·5 × the calyx; limb flat, 9–12 (15) mm. in diameter, with deeply notched obovate lobes. The stigma is globose, whereas in *scotica* it is more or less five-lobed. CAPSULE—Somewhat longer than calyx.

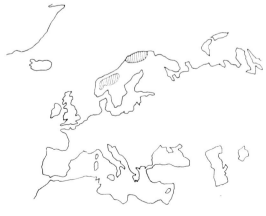

P. scotica.

Primula scotica Hook.   (From Scotland)

This little scented jewel is reasonably well known in cultivation, where it is much admired for the brightness and intensity of colour of its corolla, and for its pleasing proportions. It comes true from seed, which it sets freely. It is very distinct from *P. farinosa*, and is close to the larger *P. scandinavica*.

DISTRIBUTION—Very limited, occuring only on and near the northern shores of Scotland between Cape Wrath and Dunnett Head, and in scattered localities throughout the Orkney Islands. It can be locally quite abundant, but is absent from large sections of its range. HABITAT—It favours moist and sedgy pastures, especially near the sea. FORM—A small plant with a short RHIZOME. LEAF ROSETTE—Openly rosulate, with the youngest leaves erect and the oldest lying flat. The winter resting bud is small and tight. LEAF—1–5 cm. long, 4–15 mm. wide; elliptic, to oblong, to spathulate, with an obtuse to rounded apex, tapering into a winged petiole which can vary in length from almost absent to equal to the blade; margins entire or faintly and remotely crenulate-denticulate; upper surface efarinose and glandular, sometimes farinose, the lower densely covered in white or creamy farina; midrib and lateral nerves prominent below. PEDUNCLE—Very variable in length in the wild, 0·5–6 (10) cm. tall, usually one at a time to each rosette, sometimes two, rarely more; the species frequently flowers twice, even three times, in one season; the peduncle is farinose near the apex, indeed all green parts of the inflorescence are farinose. UMBEL—Erect, of 1–6 (8) flowers. BRACTS—2–5 mm., linear to lanceolate, somewhat broadened and swollen at the base. PEDICELS—1–5 mm., greatly lengthening in fruit. CALYX—4–6 mm., pitcher shaped, divided to $\frac{1}{3}$–$\frac{1}{2}$ into ovate lobes which are obtuse to rounded at the apex and which lie on the corolla tube; each lobe continues as a rib to the base, and the farina lies thickest between the ribs. COROLLA—Tube greenish-yellow, farinose on the outer surface, about $1\frac{1}{2}\times$ the calyx; limb annulate, flat, 5–8 mm. in diameter, dark purple with a yellow eye; corolla colour is remarkably constant, though albinos are known; lobes obovate, deeply notched, can overlap slightly, somewhat farinose on the lower surface; the corolla is homomorphic, with the yellow stamens and the five-lobed stigma visible in the throat. CAPSULE— Oblong, 1–1·5×calyx.

See Plates 52, 53

121

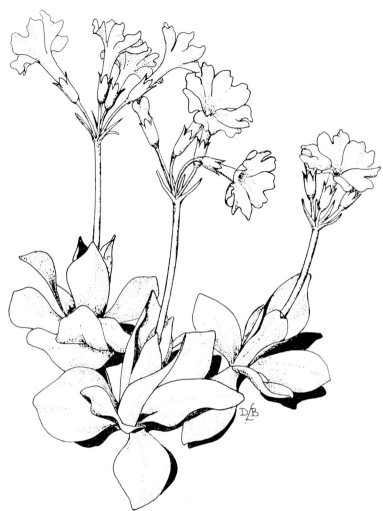

P. spectabilis

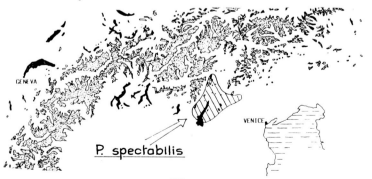

GENEVA

VENICE

P. spectabilis

Primula spectabilis Tratt.   (Remarkable!)

As the name suggests, this primula at its best can be very beautiful. It is widely grown but few see it in all its glory, as many of the forms in cultivation are poor flowerers.

DISTRIBUTION—The Lake Garda region, that is in the Giudicarian, Veronese, and Vicentine prealps, and also in the Brenta Dolomites: the latter form the northernmost area of occurrence; the western limit goes south along the west flank of the Valli Giudicarie to about 10 miles N.E. of Brescia; the southern limit follows the foot of the mountains eastwards up to the river Brenta near Bassano; Monte Grappa, across the river, is the easternmost point in its range; the northern limit then follows the south bank of the Brenta in Val Sugana, crosses the Adige near Trento to reach the Brenta Dolomites. ALTITU-DINAL RANGE—Very wide, 500–2500 m. (1700–8500′), though it is mostly found at 1000–2000 m. RHIZOME—Almost woody, can be quite long; bears many thick fleshy roots. LEAF ROSETTE—Fairly tight, openly rosulate in an untidy way; the outer leaves lie flat. LEAF—Leathery, shiny, the largest in the Arthritica Group (1·5–10 cm. long, 1–4 cm. wide), can vary in shape from broad oval rhomboid, to obovate, to elliptic or oblong, with a rounded, obtuse, to even acute apex; blade, which is often untidily wavy and buckled, narrows into a short petiole which is broadly winged and sheathing at the base; a characteristic feature is that the young leaves at the centre wrap themselves round one another to form an almost cylindrical bunch; margins cartilaginous and entire; surfaces appear glabrous, but actually bear some microscopic glandular hairs; upper surface pitted with tiny depressions which show up as dark dots in oblique light, a key distinguishing feature. PEDUNCLE—2–12 (15) cm. tall, lenthening up to 20 cm. in fruit. UMBEL—Symmetrical, of 1–5 (7) flowers. BRACTS—2–15 mm. long, linear lanceolate, often tinged with red. PEDICELS—Stout, erect, 3–20 mm. long and also lengthening in fruit. CALYX—Often purplish, 3–15 mm. long, tubular to tubular-bell shaped, minutely glandular; cut to $\frac{1}{3}$ into lanceolate to ovate lobes, which may be acute or obtuse and which diverge from the corolla tube. COROLLA—Exannulate, pink or rose, sometimes lilac, with a white eye; albinos are known; tube can be 1–3 times, but is mostly twice as long as the calyx; limb generally shallow funnel shaped, 2–4 cm. in diameter, one of the largest in the Auriculastrum Section; lobes obovate, deeply notched, nearly always crinkled at the edges; throat and undersides of the petals bear very small glandular hairs. CAPSULE—Oblong, $\frac{1}{2}$–$\frac{2}{3}$ the length of the calyx.

See **Plates 12, 13**

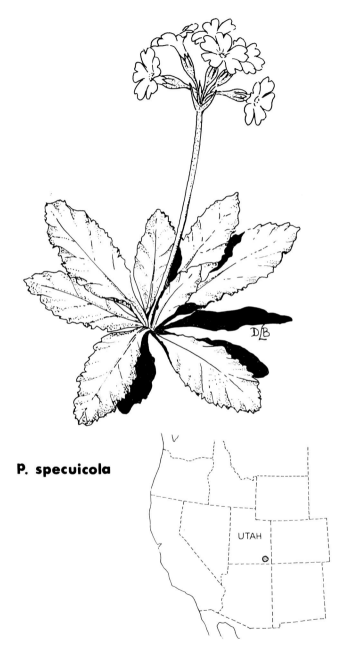

P. specuicola

UTAH

Primula specuicola Rydb. (Of caves)

A relative of *P. farinosa* L., this species is quite distinct. It has been in cultivation at the R.B.G., Edinburgh, and is currently in cultivation in Britain and the U.S.A. *P. hunnewellii* (see below) is very closely related.

DISTRIBUTION—It occurs in S.E. Utah near Bluff City. HABITAT—Pockets of soil on hot cliffs to moist sandstone walls "in dark grottoes", indeed a wide range of exposures. FORM—It can form mats 30 cm. (a foot) or more across. LEAF ROSETTE—Upright-rosulate. LEAF—Spathulate, 4–13 cm. long, 7–20 mm. wide, with rounded or obtuse tips, narrowing gradually into a short petiole; margins sinuate-dentate and crinkled; upper surface markedly, lower densely white farinose. PEDUNCLE—10–16 cm. tall, farinose, especially towards the apex. UMBEL—Of 2–10 flowers. BRACTS—Lanceolate, 4–10 mm. long, somewhat thickened at the base. PEDICELS—Farinose, 5–10 mm. long in flower, lengthening in fruit. CALYX—Farinose, campanulate, 6–9 mm. long, cut to the middle into sharply pointed lanceolate lobes. COROLLA—Exannulate, shallow funnel shaped, violet (lavender) with a yellow eye; tube yellowish, about $2 \times$ the calyx; limb 6–10 mm. in diameter, with broadly ovate to cuneate emarginate lobes which can be overlapping. CAPSULE—Shorter than the calyx.

Primula hunnewellii Fernald (Commem. Hunnewell, botanist)

This species is related to *P. farinosa* and is known only from one collection from limestone cliffs on the north rim of the Grand Canyon, Coconino County, Arizona. It is very close to *P. specuicola*, differing only in its very small calyx and exserted capsule. The botanic description is incomplete.

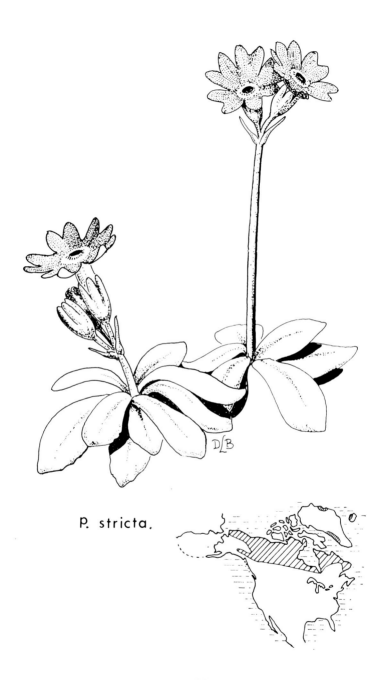

P. stricta.

Primula stricta Hornem. (Very upright)

This primula is closely related to *P. farinosa*. It is not a very attractive species, largely because of its smallish flowers, and is not often seen in cultivation.

DISTRIBUTION—Widespread in arctic and subarctic Eurasia and N. America: in Europe it occurs in the Scandinavian Mts., except the Jotunheim, in North Russia, and Iceland; in N. America it occurs in a broad band right across North Canada from Labrador, round Hudson Bay, to North Alaska. ALTITUDINAL RANGE—Up to 800 m. (2500′) in the southern parts of its range. HABITAT—Ranges from meadows and stream banks to rocky places and cliffs. FORM—An efarinose, or sparingly farinose plant with a slender RHIZOME. LEAF ROSETTE—Essentially flat. LEAF—Including the petiole, 0·5–5 cm. long, 0·2–1·5 cm. wide, narrowly elliptic, to oblanceolate, or obovate, with an obtuse or rounded tip; blade tapers to a winged petiole, which is generally shorter than blade; margins entire to wavily denticulate; midrib prominent on the lower surface, which, especially in cultivation under cover, may be quite farinose. PEDUNCLE—Varies from 2 to as much as 30 cm. in height, may be farinose, especially near the apex. UMBEL—Upright, symmetrical, 1–8 (15) flowered. BRACTS—3–8 mm., lanceolate to awl shaped, swollen at the base, often bearing tiny glandular hairs. PEDICELS—Erect, 1–3 × as long as bracts at flowering time, lengthening to 4 cm. in fruit. CALYX—Pitcher or cup shaped, 4–6 mm. long, 3–5 mm. wide, farinose between the ribs; cleaved to $\frac{1}{4}$–$\frac{1}{2}$ into lanceolate, often glandular-hairy lobes. COROLLA—Annulate, homomorphic, violet or lilac, with a strong yellow eye surrounded by a white halo; limb flat or shallow saucer shaped, 4–9 mm. in diameter, with oblong emarginate lobes; tube yellow, usually $1\frac{1}{2}$ × calyx. CAPSULE—Ovoid, a little longer than calyx.

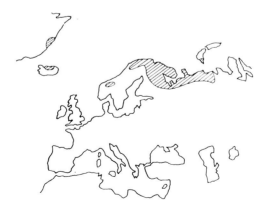

See **Plate 43**

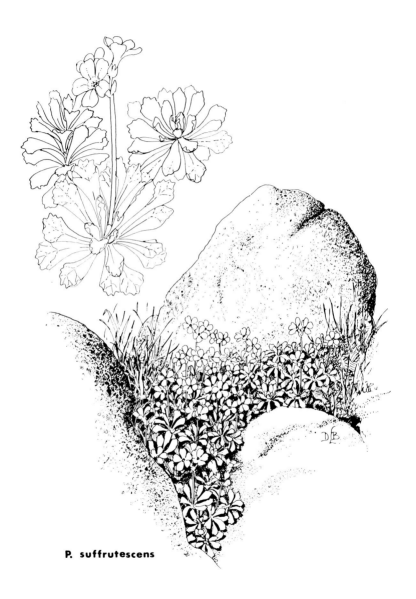

P. suffrutescens

Primula suffrutescens A. Gray (Sub-Shrubby)
(See *Curtis's Bot. Mag.*, 8990)

This very interesting and beautiful primula was introduced into cultivation in Europe in 1884 and has persisted: nice flowering specimens are sometimes seen at shows.

DISTRIBUTION—Occurs on the Sierra Nevada in California. ALTITUDINAL RANGE—3000–4000 m. (10,000–13,000′), on some of the highest peaks from Ellis Peak to Mt. Whitney. HABITAT—Rock fissures or in soil formed from the weathering of granite. FORM—A glabrous plant, glandular on all surfaces. RHIZOME–STEM—Long, branching, hard, bearing leaf rosettes at the tips of branches and persistent leaves a fair way down from the tip. LEAF ROSETTE—Open rosulate, with slightly incurving leaves. LEAF—Thick, fleshy, cuneate to spathulate, most often narrow, 1·5–3 cm. long, 0·5–1 cm. wide, broadest near the rounded apex, tapering gradually into a broad, short, winged petiole which is hardly separable from the blade; upper half of blade may be crenate-dentate or serrate, or deeply dentate with 3–8 teeth; upper surface dusky green, the lower, on which the midrib is visible, pale green to yellowish. PEDUNCLE—3–13 cm. tall. UMBEL—2–10 flowered, symmetrical to upright. BRACTS—Lanceolate to linear, 2–6 mm. long. PEDICELS—5–15 mm. long. CALYX—Campanulate, 5–7 mm. long, cut to the middle or just over into lanceolate lobes with acute tips. COROLLA—Annulate or exannulate, rose-pink to red, even to purple; limb flat to shallow funnel shaped, 14–22 mm. in diameter; tube yellow, about 2 × calyx; corolla lobes of a nice crystalline texture, broadly obovate and emarginate. CAPSULE—Globose, 4 mm. in diameter.

See **Plate 37**

P. tschuktschorum

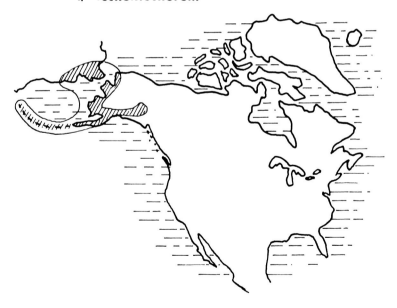

Primula tschuktschorum Kjellm.   (Of the Chukchi)

This lovely Nivalid species, very variable in both form and size, has been separated into two varieties. The specific epithet is derived from Chukchi, the name of a non-Eskimo arctic ethnic group.

DISTRIBUTION—See under varieties below. ALTITUDINAL RANGE— Mostly near sea level, but there are several very small inland populations: in the Mt. McKinley area it can climb to 2100 m. (7000'). HABITAT—Wet meadows and stream banks.

var. *tschuktschorum* Hult. is the smaller slenderer race. DISTRIBUTION— Rather limited, mainly on the Chukchi Peninsula, which is the easternmost tip of Eurasia; on St. Lawrence Island in the Bering Sea, and a few sites on the shores of that sea. RHIZOME—Short, girt with efarinose or farinose, sometimes quite large scales which surround the base of the openly rosulate LEAF ROSETTE, which is quite erect when young. LEAF—Fleshy, efarinose, lanceolate, 2–8 cm. long including the petiole, 3–10 mm. wide; tip subacute to rounded; blade tapers to a winged petiole, which may be short, to as long as the blade; margins entire or obscurely toothed; midrib prominent. PEDUNCLE—2–10 cm. tall, lengthening in fruit. UMBEL—Essentially one-sided, of 2–5 flowers. BRACTS—Lanceolate, broad-based, acute, 4–7 mm. long. PEDICELS—Often quite farinose, semi-pendent, equal to or just exceeding the bracts, lengthening to 1–2 cm. in fruit. CALYX—Campanulate, 4–6 mm. long, cut to the middle into lanceolate lobes which are usually acute. COROLLA—Violet to purple-red, with a lavender eye; tube 6–11 mm. long, just longer than the calyx to 2×; limb flat to shallow funnel shaped, 10–20 mm. in diameter, with oblong to ovate lobes which may be entire, or slightly emarginate, or even obtusely pointed; lobes tend to recurve and curl about long axis and do not overlap. CAPSULE—Cylindrical, somewhat exceeding calyx.

var. *arctica* Fernald is the much more widespread variety, being found in Alaska, all round the Bering Sea, on all its islands including the Aleutian Islands, and at the southern tip of Kamtschatka. It is the more robust variety, with broader leaves, and with umbels of mostly up to 10 flowers, sometimes even 16. The upper part of the peduncle and green parts of the inflorescence can be quite white farinose. The seed capsules are up to twice the length of the calyx.

See **Plate 40**

leaf edge × 6

P tyrolensis

Primula tyrolensis Schott   (From the Tyrol)

This primula is closely related to *P. allionii* Loiseleur, but is more difficult to flower as successfully as its popular cousin: it is not so fulsomely beautiful as *allionii*, but has a more delicate charm, which makes it a very lovely species. A particular feature is the translucent character of its petals.

DISTRIBUTION—Rather limited, in the southeastern Dolomites and the Bellunese Prealps: the northern limit runs from the area north of the Rolle Pass to Monte Civetta, some 30 km. (20 miles) to the east; the eastern limit includes the mountains around Cimolais, but here it is not clearly defined; to the south, the limit runs north of the river Piave to the Vette di Feltre, which marks the southwesternmost point, thence the western limit runs some 40 km. (25 miles) north to the Rolle; there is an isolated occurrence 30 km. (20 miles) to the S.W. in Val Caldiera, south of Borgo Valsugana. ALTITUDINAL RANGE—1000–2300 m. (3000–7500′), but it only rarely descends to below 1800 m. (6000′). HABITAT—Limestone cliffs, screes, and stony meadows, where it prefers moist shady positions; on cliffs it thrives along fissures, but does not form mats like *allionii*. RHIZOME—Becomes very long and branching. LEAF ROSETTE—Small, with mature leaves radiating outwards, giving the rosette an open look; the winter resting bud is very small and tight. LEAF—1–3 cm. long, 0·5–1·5 cm. wide, broadly obovate to almost round, with a round apex; petiole winged, mostly almost absent; blade often somewhat concave or spoon shaped when young, becoming convex in the mature stage; margins entire, but carry short stout whitish ciliate structures at regular 1·5–2·5 mm. intervals, giving it the appearance of being finely denticulate; in addition to these, the

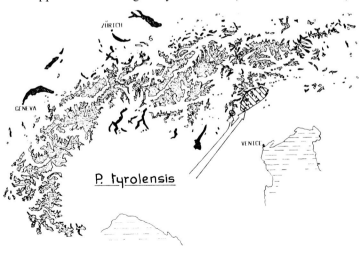

P. tyrolensis

Continued on page 149   See **Plate 23**

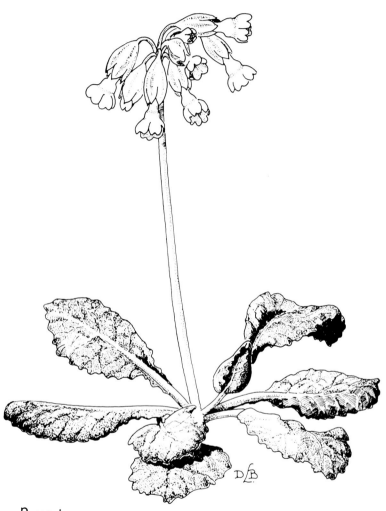

P. veris

Primula veris L. (*P. officinalis* (L.) Hill) the Cowslip (Of the Spring),

This primula vies with *P. farinosa* L. for the distinction of being the most widespread of all primulas. It was called *P. veris* long before Linnaeus, and over the centuries has accumulated a vast literature (Wright-Smith and Fletcher, *Trans. Bot. Soc. Edin.*, 1946–7, *36*, 434, quote more than 250 references!). The list of synonyms is impressive, and is given in Appendix 1.

DISTRIBUTION—It extends throughout Europe, with the exception of northern Scandinavia and northern Russia and many parts of the European Mediterranean areas. It extends eastwards through the central and southern Urals, across central and southern Siberia, to reach the upper Amur valley northeast of Mongolia; southeastwards it reaches Turkestan and northern Iran. It is absent from Turkey, except in its eastern extreme, and from the Levant and N. Africa.

Flora Europaea recognises four subspecies in Europe.
Subsp. *veris*. This is the dominant form in most of Europe, giving way to others in southern Europe. RHIZOME—Stout, bearing fleshy scales at the apex. LEAF ROSETTE—Essentially upright at flowering time, then becoming openly rosulate. LEAF—Mostly ovate to oblong-ovate, 5–20 cm. long, including the petiole, and 2–6 cm. wide at flowering time, becoming larger when mature; leaf tips round; blade narrows abruptly into the winged petiole; margins crenate to erose-crenate, sometimes entire, recurved when young; nerves and midrib impressed on the finely, sparsely hairy upper surface, prominent on the lower, which can range from nearly hairless to white tomentose; petiole winged,

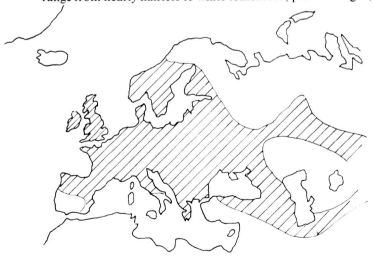

Continued overleaf　　　　　　　　　　　　　　**See Plate 60**

initially shorter than the blade, becomes more or less equal to it at maturity; sheathing at the base. PEDUNCLE—Upright, hairy, 6–30 cm. tall. UMBEL—of 2–16 flowers, which are mostly pendent, usually one-sided when few-flowered, and frequently symmetrical when many-flowered. BRACTS—Hairy, linear-lanceolate, 2–7 mm. long. PEDICELS—Hairy, 3–20 mm. long, unequal in length. CALYX—Pale green, broadly tubular-campanulate, baggy, 8–15 mm. long, hairy, especially along the five ridges; cut to $\frac{1}{4}$–$\frac{1}{3}$ into triangular to rounded lobes, which often bear one or several mucrons; the hairs on all the parts are the shortest of the trio *vulgaris, elatior, veris*, being usually $\frac{1}{4}$ mm. long. COROLLA—Exannulate, bright deep yellow with an orange mark at the base of each petal; tube as long as to a little longer than calyx; limb bowl-shaped to rarely almost flat, 9–12 mm. in diameter, with obovate, emarginate lobes. CAPSULE—Oval, 6–10 mm. long, included in the calyx.

Subsp. *canescens* (Opiz) Hayek. In this, the lower blade surface is grey tomentose, the blade narrowing gradually into the petiole; the calyx is 16–20 mm. long, the corolla 8–20 mm. in diameter, usually only slightly concave. Found in the lowlands of south-central Europe, southern France, and northern Spain.

Subsp. *columnae* (Ten.) Lüdi. This occurs in the mountains of southern Europe and in N.E. Turkey. Blade ovate, usually cordate at base, thickly whitish tomentose on lower surface; calyx 16–20 mm., widening at the mouth; corolla limb 10–22 mm. wide, almost flat; tube distinctly longer than calyx.

Subsp. *macrocalyx* (Bunge) Lüdi. Dominant in the southeast Russian and Asian regions, also occurs in E. Turkey. Leaf blade usually elliptic, narrowing gradually into a long winged petiole; undersurface more or less grey tomentose, often almost hairless; calyx somewhat conical trumpet-shaped, 15–20 mm. long, often very hairy; corolla tube longer than calyx; limb widest of any in the four subspecies, 18–28 mm.

P. villosa

Primula villosa Wulfen, in Jacq. (*P. cottia* Widmer)   (Shaggy)

A beautiful species which should be more often seen in cultivation, for it is robust, easily propagated, and flowers well.

DISTRIBUTION—It has a remarkably disjunct distribution within the Alps. In the West it occurs in a small area in the Cottian Alps west of Turin, some 350 miles W.S.W. of its main occurrence: this Cottian area centres around the Valle Germanasca near Perrero just east of the col di Sestriere. Here, *P. villosa* was given specific rank as *P. cottia* Widmer, but this is not recognised in the *Flora Europaea*. The main occurrence is in Austria on the southern flank of the Lower Tauern: here it is found in the Gurktal Alps, and eastwards to the mountains on both sides of the river Mur from Judenburg to Bruck. At its south-easternmost point at Schloss Herberstein near Weiz (375 m.) its larger form is sufficiently distinct to warrant the varietal name *commutata* (Schott) Lüdi. To the south there is an outpost on Mt. Komen (Kameni) at the eastern end of the Karawanken in Slovenia. It is interesting to note that there is a gap of some 40 miles between the easternmost point for *P. hirsuta* (Gross Glockner) and the western-most point for *P. villosa* in Austria. Finally, there is a small colony 20 miles south of Monte Rosa, in the region east of Monte Mars (1000–2000 m.). ALTITUDINAL RANGE— Mostly between 1400 m. and 1700 m., the highest occurrence at 2950 m. on Punta Cialancia in the Cottians, and one of the lowest at Schloss Herberstein at 375 m. HABITAT—Restricted to non-calcareous regions, on gneiss, schists, and volcanic rocks. It grows in stony pastures and in rock fissures, and does not make large clumps. RHIZOME—Stout, often long, with persistent withered foliage near growing tip. LEAF ROSETTE—Flat in the wild,

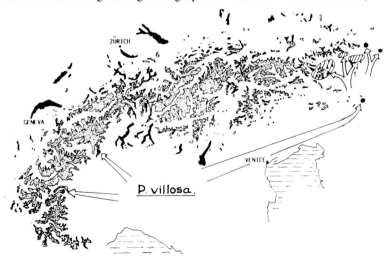

P. villosa.

Continued on page 150   See **Plate 11**

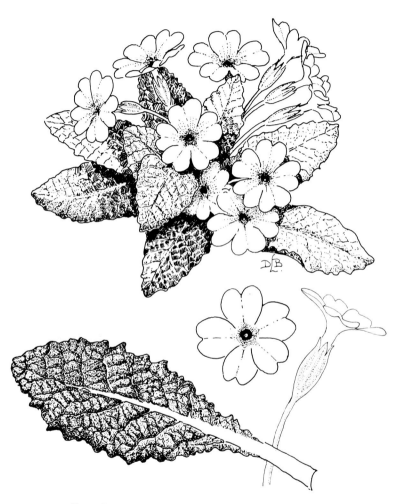

P. vulgaris.

Primula vulgaris Hudson (*P. acaulis* (L.) Hill)   (Ordinary)
(See *Curtis's Bot. Mag.*, 399, 8468, 9166)

Everyone knows the primrose and loves it—largely because of this, it has been brought back home so frequently that it has become rare in many parts of the British Isles where formerly it was common. Intensive agriculture has of course also played a big part in its decline. We can hope that with a more enlightened attitude towards nature conservation, this lovely native may again thrive everywhere in the wild. It must be said that there are still many areas well away from our industrial conurbations where one may still gaze with reverence and delight upon thousands of wild primroses in flower. It is early flowering (March/April) in the U.K. In cultivation it is strangely unpredictable, thriving and seeding itself in some gardens, reluctant, even difficult in others, even when care is taken to provide a moist shady habitat, which it so enjoys. There are, of course, many vigorous, larger than life cultivars which can give one the illusion of success.

DISTRIBUTION—It is widely, but oddly distributed in Europe, as the map shows. It is absent from most of Spain and Portugal, from most of Germany and countries to the East. Though occurring throughout Denmark and the S.W. Fjordland of Norway, it is absent from the rest of Scandinavia. Most peculiar is its absence from Sardinia when it is present thoughout Corsica, Sicily, and most of Italy. Its easternmost occurrences are round the Black Sea, throughout the Caucasus,

Continued overleaf   See **Plate 58**

and just south of the Caspian Sea in Iran. It is thinly distributed in N. Africa, from the Straits of Gibraltar to Tunisia, and at the Eastern end of the Mediterranean in S. Turkey, Syria, Lebanon, and Israel. It shows a distinct tendency to favour maritime regions In this large area of occurrence, P. vulgaris remains remarkably constant. Subsp. *vulgaris* occurs almost throughout the range of the species, and is replaced only in the extreme South-East in Europe. ALTITUDINAL RANGE—The highest locality in Britain is 675 m. (2200'), in the Alps 1500 m. (5000'), 1700 m. (5600') in Greece, and as high as 2400 m. (8000') in the Caucasus. HABITAT—Prefers open woodland and shady banks, especially by streams and ditches. Less commonly in open meadows, especially near the sea where the atmosphere is more humid. RHIZOME—Stout, short, with fleshy roots. LEAF ROSETTE— Openly rosulate. LEAF—Oblanceolate to obovate, 5–25 cm. by 2–6 cm., smaller at flowering time; round tipped, gradually tapering into petiole, which is short, winged and sheathing; margins irregularly dentate to crenate, often erose; upper surface hairless, lower hairy on midrib and veins which are prominent below and impressed above. PEDUNCLE—Absent. UMBEL—Up to 25 flowered. BRACTS—Linear, 10–15 mm. PEDICELS—6–20 cm. long, hairy, semipendent in flower, decumbent in fruit. CALYX—Tubular, 10–20 mm., prominently 5-ridged, cut to $\frac{1}{3}$–$\frac{1}{2}$ into lanceolate pointed lobes; ridges hairy. COROLLA—Pale sulphur yellow with orange markings at the base of each petal, occasionally white or pink; annulate or exannulate; odourless or fragrant; tube as long as or a little longer than calyx; limb flat to shallow funnel shaped, 20–40 mm., broadly ovate lobes. CAPSULE—Ovoid, $\frac{2}{3} \times$ calyx. SEED—2–2·5 mm., brown, sticky.

The following other subspecies are recognised:

Subsp. *balearica* (Willk.) Sm. *et* Forr. Mts. of Majorca. Petiole longer than blade, white fragrant flowers.

Subsp. *sibthorpii* (Hoffmans.) Sm. *et* Forr. Central Greece, W. Turkey, Crimea, Caucasus, Armenia, N. Iran. Leaves cuneate, corolla rose, red, crimson, lilac, purple, white, extremely rarely yellow (see *Curtis's Bot. Mag.*, 1966–8, *176*, 500). Many cultivars and hybrids (see p. 192).

Subsp. *heterochroma* (Stapf.) Sm. *et* Forr. Region bordering Caspian Sea in N. Iran. Differs from *sibthorpii* by white tomentose lower leaf surface and by flowers being rose, purple, violet, white, **and** yellow.

Subsp. *ingwerseniana* Harrison. One collection only, Mt. Olympus. White flowers. Botanical status in doubt.

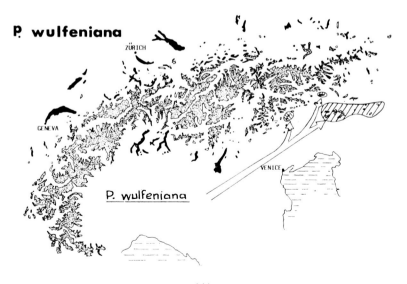

P. wulfeniana

ZÜRICH

GENEVA

VENICE

P. wulfeniana

Primula wulfeniana Schott   (Commem. Wulfen, botanist)

This species is not as often seen in gardens as *P. clusiana* Tausch. or *P. spectabilis* Tratt., probably because it is less often rewarding, being a very shy flowerer: by contrast, in the wild it can form sheets of colour because of its ability to form very large dense mats.

DISTRIBUTION—The southeastern calcareous Alps, but not as extensive as is *P. clusiana* in the corresponding northeastern area. There is also a very disjunct occurrence in the southern Carpathians, north of Bucharest in Roumania: the main Alpine occurrence encompasses the entire Karawanken from Mittagskogel in the west to Petzen in the east, as well as the Julian and Kamnicka (Sanntaler or Steiner) Alps. A separate and much smaller area is in the Venetian Prealps northeast of Belluno, around Cimolais. Finally there are two isolated patches in the Gailtal Alps, one on Spitzkegel, the other on Dobratsch (Villacher Alpe). The Carpathian occurrence is south and west of Brasov. ALTITUDINAL RANGE—Mostly 1800–2100 m. (6000–7000′), but can be found occasionally much lower down, for example in a torrent outwash fan near Cimolais. HABITAT—Found exclusively in limestone areas, mostly above the tree line in humus-rich meadow slopes; rarely it can be found in moist rock fissures. RHIZOME—Stout and branching. LEAF ROSETTE—When mature, tight rosulate to fairly upright. LEAF— Leathery, 1·5–4 (5) cm. long, 0·5–1·5 (2) cm. wide, lanceolate, to elliptic, to oblong, to oblanceolate, with a subacute, obtuse or rounded apex; blade gradually tapering into a short, broadly winged petiole; margins entire, cartilaginous, minutely glandular, though the glands are often obscured by a secretion; upper blade surfaces dark green and shiny, lower pale green, with the midrib clearly visible. PEDUNCLE— Stout, erect, 0·5–7 (8) cm. tall, lengthening to 10 cm. in fruit. UMBEL— 1–2 (3) flowered. BRACTS—3–15 mm., linear to lanceolate, acute or obtuse at the apex, frequently reach halfway up calyx. PEDICELS— Stout, erect, 2–8 mm. long. CALYX—Tubular, 6–10 (12) mm. long, often tinged reddish purple, with a sparse covering of tiny glandular hairs; cut to ⅓ into broadly ovate to roundish, rarely pointed lobes, which lie on the corolla tube; leaves, bracts, and calyx lobes have margins which tend to curl up a little, and tips which curl in. COROLLA— Exannulate, violet-pink to reddish violet, with a white eye; tube as long as calyx to 2×; limb shallow funnel shaped to flat, 2–3 (3·5) cm. in diameter, the obovate lobes notched to ⅔; the notches between the lobes often bear small white pendent outgrowths; throat glandular pubescent. CAPSULE—Rounded, 6 mm. long, about ¾ the length of the calyx.

See Plate 15

Primula cortusoides L.   (Like a Cortusa)

This Siberian species is described in Green, *Asiatic Primulas*, p. 40. It is stated by Wright-Smith and Fletcher to extend into European Russia at Ufa. The fact that it is not included in *Flora Europaea* is accounted for by the meanderings of the Russo-Siberian border, which places Ufa in Siberia, even though it is on the western flank of the southern Urals.

Primula longiscapa Ledeb. (*P. intermedia* Sims)   (Long-Stalked)

It is a tall, vigorous, efarinose species which stands close to *P. farinosa* L. It is described under its other name of *P. intermedia* by Green in *Asiatic Primulas*, p. 87. It is also described and illustrated in Sims, *Bot. Mag.*, 1809, t. 1219. It is not to be confused with the natural hybrid *P. × intermedia* Port. (*clusiana × minima*).

This species occurs in Europe in the large area east of the mid and upper Volga. The most striking aspect of this primula is the very large number (10–100) of flowers in the umbel. Its other distinction is that it has never been even mentioned in either the *Bulletin* or in the *Journal of the Scottish Rock Garden Club*.

SUBGENUS SPHONDYLIA

South of Turkey and the Caucasus, and before one reaches the treasures of the Himalaya and Tibet, is a very large partly desert partly scrubby region where there are relatively few primula species. The Sphondylia primulas have adapted to the climate this region offers, and are characteristic of it. They share it with the closely related Dionysias, and a few Nivalid and Farinosae species. A good account of the Sphondylia primulas is given by O. Schwarz in the *Bull.*, 1964, *32*, 283. The brief mention given in Roy Green's *Asiatic Primulas* includes *P. aucheri* Jaub. et Spach., which has been transferred to Dionysia and is described as *Dionysia mira* Wend. on p. 13 of Chris Grey-Wilson's A.G.S. Guide to the Genus. What used to be *P. bornmülleri* Pax is now also a Dionysia, *D. bornmülleri* (Pax) Clay, all of which underlines the close relationship of the two Genera.

The seven Sphondylia species are all yellow flowered, forming scapes normally with several verticils of flowers like the Candelabras, with the one exception of *P. davisii* W.W.Sm., which forms a single umbel. Even though O. Schwarz is optimistic about them, they are all fairly short-lived out of doors. *P. floribunda* Wall. and *P. verticillata* Forsk. are the only ones which have persisted in greenhouse cultivation. The hybrid between these two is sterile, but a special form became self-fertile and was named *P. × kewensis* Hort., and is widely grown as an indoor plant.

> *P. boveana* Dcne comes from Sinai, where it grows on the tops of the highest mountains.
>
> *P. davisii* W.W.Sm. hails from the 2000 m. region of Turkish Kurdistan. There are now several herbarium collections, and the live plant has appeared at one or two A.G.S. Shows.

P. edelbergii Schwz. grows on the mountains of eastern Afghanistan, near Kabul. Dr. O. Schwarz describes it and its cultivation in great detail in his article in the *Bulletin*, but to the best of our knowledge it has not appeared at shows yet.

P. floribunda Wall. is found below 2000 m. in the western Himalaya, from Chitral to westernmost Nepal. It is by far the most successful in cultivation (See *Curtis's Bot. Mag.*, 6712).

P. gaubeana Bornm. grows in the mountains of Luristan in Iran, again below 2000 m. It is occasionally seen in cultivation.

P. simensis Hochst. has the distinction of being the only African endemic primula. It is found in Ethiopia.

P. verticillata Forsk. grows in the mountains of the Yemen and possibly also in Somalia.

It may again be mentioned here that *P. palinuri* Petagna shows many affinities to the subgenus Sphondylia, and its geographical location is very suggestive of a close phylogenetic relation.

DESCRIPTIONS OF THE SPECIES CONTINUED

Primula algida (continued from page 13)

According to Wright-Smith and Fletcher, 3000–5000 m., but the upper limit is not reasonable (Davis in *Fl. Turk.* gives 1800–3700 m.). HABITAT—Wet alpine meadows, mossy banks, and moist rock ledges. FORM—Farinose or efarinose with a short, thick RHIZOME and forming a rosulate LEAF ROSETTE. LEAF—Oblong, obovate or oblanceolate, incl. petiole 1·5–7 cm. by 0·5–2·5 cm.; obtuse to round tipped; gradually tapering to short winged petiole, which sometimes can be ½ length of blade; margins finely denticulate, rarely entire; upper surface efarinose, lower surface white or yellowish farinose or efarinose; midrib and lateral veins impressed on upper surface and prominent below. PEDUNCLE—3–20 cm., up to 35 cm. in fruit, even longer in cultivation, farinose or efarinose. UMBEL—Symmetrical, 3–12 flowered. BRACTS—linear-lanceolate, 3–11 mm., not significantly swollen at the base, become reflexed in late flowering or in fruit. PEDICELS—Unequal in length, usually shorter than bracts and more than double their length in fruit. CALYX—Campanulate, 5–10 mm., cut to ½ or ⅓ into oblong or lanceolate lobes, often stained purple. COROLLA—Annulate, homomorphic or heteromorphic, flat, violet to lilac-pink, sometimes white; yellowish or white tube usually as long as the calyx; limb 8–15 mm. across, with deeply emarginate obovate lobes. CAPSULE—Equals calyx. SEED—Rounded or ovoid, brown, surface vesicular, 0·5 mm.

Primula allionii (continued from page 15)

quite long and very branched; branchings tight, leading to tight mats of rosettes. LEAF ROSETTE—Tight, tends to lie flat in the wild. LEAF—Variable in size and shape: length 1–5 cm., width 0·5–1·5 cm.; shape from almost round, to oblong, to spathulate; apex obtuse to rounded;

margins not cartilaginous, vary from entire to denticulate; teeth shallow and well separated to sharp and close set; blade thick and fleshy, surfaces greyish to dusky green, thickly covered with tiny (0·25 mm.) colourless, sticky glandular hairs; nervature obscure. PETIOLE—Winged and short. PEDUNCLE—Almost absent to 1 mm., maybe a little longer in cultivation. UMBEL—One to as many as seven-flowered. BRACTS—2 mm., broadly ovate, obtuse, papery. PEDICELS—1–4 mm., glandular-hairy. CALYX—4–6 mm., bell-shaped, densely glandular-hairy, cut to $\frac{1}{2}$ into obtuse or acute ovate lobes. COROLLA—Exannulate, mostly various shades of soft pure pink, sometimes with purplish shading, albinos are known; there is always a white eye; tube 10–15 mm., 2–3 × calyx; limb essentially flat, 15–30 mm., with obovate, overlapping lobes which may be shallowly to deeply notched; corolla throat can be glandular. CAPSULE—Rounded, shorter than or equal to calyx; a unique feature is that it takes as much as six months to ripen. N.B. Many cultivars fall outside the above description.

Primula glutinosa (continued from page 65)

thin textured, blue-violet with a darker ring round the throat, fading to violet; tube as long as the calyx or a little longer, of a paler colour than the limb; throat whitish with glandular hairs; limb funnel or cup shaped, 10–18 (20) mm. in diameter, with obovate, deeply notched lobes. CAPSULE—Rounded and about as long as the calyx, or a little shorter.

Primula latifolia (continued from page 87)

consolidated scree. RHIZOME—Long, stout, and branching, which permits the formation of quite large clumps. LEAF ROSETTE—Upright and loose. LEAF—Including the petiole, 3–18 cm. long, 1–5 cm. wide, broadly obovate, to oblanceolate, to elliptic; apex rounded or obtuse, even acute; upper half of the blade has deeply dentate to slightly wavy margins, rarely entire; blade fleshy, frequently somewhat flaccid, efarinose, covered with tiny colourless glandular, sticky hairs; midrib conspicuous on lower surface; blade narrows into a membraneously winged petiole which is as long as the blade and is sheathing at the base; the leaves are said to have a characteristic odour, difficult to define. PEDUNCLE—5–20 cm. tall. UMBEL—One-sided, of 1–24 (50) flowers. BRACTS—2–10 mm. long, very broadly ovate to subrotundate. PEDICELS—5–20 mm., not all of equal length. CALYX—3–6 mm. long, bell shaped, cut to $\frac{1}{3}$–$\frac{1}{2}$ into triangular, obtuse to acute lobes; all green parts of the inflorescence are covered with small glandular sticky hairs, and they are sometimes slightly farinose. COROLLA—Exannulate, scented, violet, to reddish violet or purple, the colour often being beautifully intense; tube 7–13 mm. long, 3–4 × the calyx, and frequently darker than the limb; the upper half of the tube gradually opens into the funnel shaped limb, which is 10–20 mm. in diameter with oblong to obovate, notched lobes, and is sparingly farinose round the throat. CAPSULE—More or less globose, equal to or just longer than the calyx.

Primula marginata (continued from page 97)

stem part can be quite long, giving a shrubby appearance as it trails along and down rock faces. LEAF ROSETTE—Openly rosulate. LEAF—1·5–10 cm. long, 1–4 cm. wide, obovate to oblong, obtuse or rounded at the apex, tapering to a winged petiole, which is usually short, but can be as long as the blade; blade leathery in texture, somewhat fleshy, greyish green; young leaves more or less white or yellowish farinose, whereas mature leaves are generally farinose only on the margins; leaf surfaces, though smooth, carry small sessile glands; margins regularly and deeply serrate-dentate, the appearance in this respect being very variable; midrib and lateral veins are visible on the lower surface. PEDUNCLE—Erect, 2–12 cm. tall, farinose near the apex. UMBEL—Symmetrical, of 2–20 flowers. BRACTS—2–5 mm. long, broadly ovate to lanceolate, sometimes leafy. PEDICELS—3–20 mm. long, farinose. CALYX—3–5 mm. long, bell shaped, often reddish, copiously farinose inside, much less so outside, cut to $\frac{2}{5}$–$\frac{2}{3}$ into broadly ovate or triangular obtuse lobes, which do not curve outwards. COROLLA—Shallow funnel shaped, rarely flat, exannulate; tube 3–4 times longer than calyx, of the same colour as the limb, sometimes darker; limb 1·5–3 cm. in diameter, from lilac-lavender to bluish-lavender, to sometimes violet, or even pink; a deposit of farina round the throat looks like a white eye; lobes obovate, deeply notched, sometimes overlapping; corolla faintly scented. CAPSULE—Sub-globose, equal to or longer than the calyx.

Primula pedemontana (continued from page 113)

PEDUNCLE—2·5–12 (15) cm. tall. UMBEL—Symmetrical, of 1–16 (25) flowers, usually carried well above the foliage. BRACTS—1–3 mm. long, broadly ovate and papery in texture. PEDICELS—2–15 mm. long, glandular, lengthening in fruit. CALYX—Glandular, bell to tubular-bell shaped, 3–8 mm. long, cut to $\frac{1}{3}$ into triangular acute or obtuse lobes, which are addressed to the tube in young flowers. COROLLA—Of a rich clear pink with a white eye; *Flora Europaea* goes further, giving also deep pink to purple (hybrids?); albinos occur; tube $1\frac{1}{2}$–$2\frac{1}{2}$ × calyx, white inside, pink outside, slightly glandular; limb exannulate, flat to shallow funnel shaped, 15–25 (30) mm. in diameter; lobes obovate and markedly emarginate. CAPSULE—Sub-globose, more or less equalling calyx.

Primula tyrolensis (continued from page 133)

margins are sometimes irregularly and slightly denticulate; venation, though faint, is apparent; upper surface bright green, bearing tiny sticky glandular hairs. PEDUNCLE—Ranges from obsolete to 2 cm. in length, glandular pubescent. UMBEL—1–2 flowered, rarely 3. BRACTS—Linear to oblong, leafy 3–10 mm. long, generally not of equal length. PEDICELS—Very short, rarely more than 2 mm. long. CALYX—Tubular-campanulate, 4–7 mm. long, cut to the middle or just more into oblong, round-tipped, mucronate lobes; all green parts of inflorescence covered in tiny sticky glandular hairs. COROLLA—Exannulate, rose to rose-lilac, with a white eye; tube about 2 × calyx, glandular pubescent in throat; limb shallow funnel shaped, 1·5–2·5 cm. in diameter, with deeply notched lobes, frequently with several further longitudinal splits. CAPSULE—Rounded, 3–4 mm. long, much shorter than calyx.

Primula villosa (continued from page 139)

often rosulate in cultivation. LEAF—Fleshy and sticky, broadly obovate or spathulate to oblong or oblanceolate, 2–10 (17) cm. by 1–4 cm., round tipped, usually gradually tapering to a winged petiole; margin regularly, sometimes deeply toothed, only in upper half of blade, occasionally more or less entire; both surfaces, and especially margins, densely to sparingly covered with 0·2–1·0 mm. reddish glandular hairs, which give them a russet sheen; glands often blacken with age; midrib broad and conspicuous below, lateral nerves ±prominent below; petiole usually very short, occasionally equals blade, especially at low altitude. PEDUNCLE—3–15 cm., stout, erect, covered in reddish glandular hairs. UMBEL—Borne well above the leaves, symmetrical, (1) 4–12 flowered, sometimes more. BRACTS—1–5 mm., ovate, more or less papery. PEDICELS—Densely glandular pilose, 1–7 mm. long, longer in fruit. CALYX—3–7 mm., bell shaped, glandular pilose, cut to $\frac{1}{2}$ into ovate or triangular obtuse or rounded lobes, which are parallel to the tube. COROLLA—Exannulate, magenta-rose to lilac-rose, usually pale, with a marked white eye; tube 8–12 mm., 2–3 × calyx, outer surface slightly hairy and paler than limb, inner white, throat slightly hairy; limb 15–25 (28) mm., flat to shallow funnel shaped, lobes broadly obovate and emarginate, sometimes overlapping. CAPSULE—About as long as calyx.

CHAPTER 4

IDENTIFICATION OF EUROPEAN
AND AMERICAN PRIMULAS

This chapter represents an attempt to provide a logical method of arriving at the identity of a species. We decided against the construction of a dichotomous key, for such keys are difficult to use and full of pitfalls. Our scheme is discursive and, we believe, easier to use.

The differences between so many of the species being very small, the examination of features not normally familiar to an amateur, and the use of botanical terms, are quite unavoidable, so that for the non-botanist, the use of the glossary at the end of the guide will be necessary, as will the use of a hand lens. The initial separation into main groups depends very much on a correct decision between the following pairs of terms, the exact meaning of which must be gleaned from the glossary: annulate, exannulate; revolute, involute; farinose, efarinose; heteromorphic, homomorphic; entire, dentate, denticulate. Having reached a preliminary conclusion by the use of this chapter, you should then check it against the description of the individual species. Please remember that there is always the possibility of your particular specimen showing a variation which takes it outside the range given in the description—Nature is built that way. In difficult cases, judgement and experience are very important. Also remember that quite often juvenile leaf features are different from adult features. When examining a primula in the wild, it is useful to bear in mind geographical distributions: thus a yellow flowered primula in northern Britain is extremely unlikely to be *P. elatior* and totally unlikely to be *P. auricula*. In the Alps, where the situation is complex, the Reader will find the list of occurrences on the inside cover useful. Last, but not least, identification in the field is bedevilled by the possible presence of hybrids . . . this must always be borne in mind. A knowledge of which pairs of parents hybridise frequently, and which don't, does help. We can only refer you to Chapter 5.

The scheme is as follows:

EUROPEAN SPECIES.   All corolla colours except yellow

1 | Farinose, annulate, and revolute |

farinosa, halleri, scandinavica, scotica, stricta, frondosa.
Caucasus: *algida, bayernii, darialica, dealbata, glacialis, longipes.*

2 | Farinose, exannulate, and revolute |

glacialis, dealbata.

3 | Efarinose, annulate, and revolute |

151

nutans (sibirica), longiscapa, egaliksensis.

4 | Efarinose, exannulate, and revolute |

amoena, juliae, megaseaefolia, renifolia.

5 | Efarinose, exannulate, and involute |

A–leaves entire or dentate
allionii, apennina, carniolica, kitaibeliana, pedemontana,
villosa.*
B–leaves always entire
*clusiana, deorum, glaucescens, integrifolia**, spectabilis,
wulfeniana.*
C–leaves always dentate
daonensis, glutinosa, hirsuta, tyrolensis, latifolia***, minima.

6 | Farinose, exannulate, and involute |

marginata.

  * corolla throat farinose
 ** very rarely faintly toothed
*** very rarely entire, inflorescence rarely slightly farinose

GROUP 1   FARINOSE, ANNULATE, AND REVOLUTE

In this group of fourteen species, three immediately stand out by
the length of the corolla tube, which is 2 to 3 times longer than the
calyx: the very familiar *P. halleri* (=*P. longiflora*) and the less familiar
P. glacialis and *P. dealbata* (=*P. auriculata*) from the Caucasus. They
are clearly differentiated in Table 1.

TABLE 1

	halleri	*glacialis*	*dealbata*
Stamens and style	homomorphic	heteromorphic	
Leaves	usually farinose	usually efarinose	farinose
Leaf margin	entire	sharply denticulate	
Corolla colour	lilac-violet	lilac	white with lilac tips

Note that *P. glacialis* and *P. dealbata* may also exist in an exannulate form, and *P. halleri* can be heteromorphic in Bulgaria.

A further easily recognised pair are the Nivalids, *P. longipes* and
P. bayernii; the former is large and vigorous and has opulent umbels
of lavender-blue to reddish-mauve semi-pendent flowers, and the
latter is very closely related, but somewhat smaller and white flowered.

152

The remaining eight are much less easy to separate, and one is obliged to scrutinise "botanical" features very carefully.

The main division is into:

Heteromorphic: *farinosa*

Hetero- or homomorphic: *algida, darialica, ossetica, frondosa*

Homomorphic: *scandinavica, scotica, stricta*

The separation of *farinosa* and the heteromorphic forms of the second group is defined in Table 2.

TABLE 2

	farinosa	*frondosa*	*darialica*	*algida*
Leaves	usually farinose		usually efarinose	usually farinose
Leaf margins	entire to finely denticulate	finely denticulate when juvenile, crenate when mature	always finely denticulate	finely denticulate, rarely entire
Bract base	swollen	not swollen		
Bract attitude	always erect (lie close to pedicels)		become reflexed	
Pedicels	about as long as bracts to twice as long	always much longer than bracts	usually longer than bracts	usually shorter than bracts
Calyx lobes	obtuse, rarely acute	always acute	usually acute	acute or obtuse
Seed capsule	little longer to 2×calyx	equal, to a little longer than calyx	2×calyx	about as long as calyx
Corolla tube	equal, to slightly longer than calyx	as long as, to 2×calyx	1½ to 2× calyx	as long as calyx

It may be noted that *P. algida* has caused many headaches in the past, not only in relation to *P. farinosa*, but also to *P. auriculata* (*P. glacialis*). In addition it is useful to note that the corolla colour of *P. darialica* is given as rose to carmine-red, whereas the corolla of *P. frondosa* has much more blue in its make-up, being rose-lilac to reddish-purple.

P. ossetica is a rarity which has been collected only once, so we don't need to consider it here.

The separation of the species in the homomorphic group and the homomorphic forms of the second group is again not easy, and one begins by studying Table 3.

TABLE 3

	scotica	scandinavica	stricta	frondosa	algida
Leaves	farinose		efarinose to sparingly farinose	usually farinose	
Leaf margins	entire or faintly crenulate to denticulate	usually denticulate sometimes entire	entire to wavily denticulate	denticulate when juvenile to crenate when mature	denticulate, rarely entire
Bract base	somewhat swollen	swollen		not swollen	
Bract attitude	erect (lie close to pedicels)				become reflexed
Pedicels	as long as the bracts	as long as to twice the length of bracts	as long as to three times the length of bracts, very erect	very much longer than bracts, often semi-pendent	usually shorter than bracts
Calyx teeth	rounded to obtuse		obtuse to acute	always acute	acute to obtuse
Corolla tube	1½ times as long as calyx			as long as to twice as long as calyx	as long as calyx
Seed capsule	1 to 1½ times as long as calyx	slightly longer than calyx		more or less as long as calyx	
Corolla colour	bright dark purple	purplish violet	lilac to violet	rose-lilac to reddish purple	lilac-pink to violet
Corolla diameter	5–8 mm.	9–12 (15) mm.	4–9 mm.	10–15 mm.	8–15 mm.
Peduncle at flowering	0·5–6 (10) cm.	4–10 (18) cm.	2–20 (30) cm.	4–12 cm.	3–20 cm.

Additional notes are: *P. scotica* is a lovely, squat, and brightly coloured species, once seen never to be forgotten; it is on average the lowest growing of the group. *P. scandinavica* is close to it, but larger in all its parts and nowhere near as brightly or intensely coloured. *P. stricta* is the most variable in height; with its very upright habit (stricta means upright) and its flowers small in relation to the length of the peduncle, it is quite different in general appearance from all the

154

others. *P. frondosa* has the laxest umbel in this group, and *P. algida* the tightest.

GROUP 2   FARINOSE, EXANNULATE, AND REVOLUTE
To be differentiated as indicated in Table 1.

GROUP 3   EFARINOSE, ANNULATE, AND REVOLUTE
P. nutans (*P. sibirica*) has petioles which are longer than the leaf blade and umbels with 1–10 flowers, whereas *P. longiscapa* (*P. intermedia*) has petioles which are shorter than the leaf blade and umbels with 10–100 flowers. The third species in this group, *P. egaliksensis*, occurs at only one locality in Iceland: since its main distribution is over wide tracts of Northern Canada, it is better dealt with under American Primulas.

GROUP 4   EFARINOSE, EXANNULATE, AND REVOLUTE
I—One, two, or more single flowers on simple pedicels (no peduncle):
Medium to small, roundish, rugose, hairless leaf on very long hairless petiole; very long hairless pedicels: *juliae*.
II—One, two, or more flowers in an umbel on a peduncle:
  (a) medium to small, roundish to kidney shaped, rugose leaf with white woolly undersurface, and hairy petiole, peduncle, and pedicel: *renifolia*.
  (b) large, leathery, dark green leaf on a conspicuously hairy petiole: *megaseaefolia*.
  (c) medium to large leaves of various shapes, but never round, with a very rugose blade, sometimes white woolly undersurface; a purplish oxlip (has been called *P. elatior* subsp. *meyeri*): *amoena*.

GROUP 5   EFARINOSE, EXANNULATE, AND INVOLUTE
SUBGROUPS A AND B, PLANTS WITH ENTIRE LEAVES
I—One to several single flowers on simple very short pedicels (no peduncle): *allionii*.
II—One, two, or more flowers in an umbel borne on a peduncle:
  (a) leaf surfaces and margins hairless: *carniolica, glaucescens, spectabilis, wulfeniana*.
  (b) leaf surfaces hairless, margin ciliate: *clusiana*.
  (c) leaf surfaces glandular hairy: *apennina, integrifolia, kitaibeliana, pedemontana, villosa*.

Distinction of species in IIa
carniolica is best separated from the other three by its broad bracts which are much shorter than the pedicels: the other three have narrow bracts which are from half as long to even longer than the pedicels. In addition, *carniolica* has a delicate corolla with a wide tube of the same colour as the petals, and has a white farinaceous ring round the throat (the only farina on the plant).

spectabilis is the only one in this group to have a pitted upper leaf surface, a quite easily seen characteristic, especially in slanting light. Other *spectabilis* features are largish, untidy looking leaves, and juvenile leaves which tend to overlap to form a sort of cylindrical bunch.

glaucescens and *wulfeniana* have much more regular, tidy looking leaves: those of *glaucescens* are plain green and the cartilagenous margin is minutely crenulate, a feature clearly seen with a hand lens, whereas those of *wulfeniana* are darker green, and have an entire, if rough edged, cartilaginous margin. Further differences are that *glaucescens* has 2–6 flowered umbels, and the corolla is reddish pink to lilac, whereas *wulfeniana* has 1–2, sometimes 3 flowered umbels and the corolla is violet pink to reddish violet, a range of colour which contains much more blue than the other two, and, incidentally, than *clusiana*.

Distinction of species in IIc

The main division is into *integrifolia* and *kitaibeliana* with colourless glandular hairs on the one hand, and *apennina*, *pedemontana* and *villosa* with yellow to orange-brown glandular hairs on the other. In *integrifolia* the leaf hairs are mainly on the margin, with very few, sometimes none on the surfaces, whereas in *kitaibeliana* the surfaces are densely covered in small glandular hairs, even if the marginal ones are longer. The other big difference lies in the corollas, which in *integrifolia* does not have a white eye, but is glandular hairy at the throat, which sometimes gives the impression of a whitish eye; in *kitaibeliana* however, there is a clear white eye. Of the two, *kitaibeliana* is the larger species.

For the separation of *apennina*, *pedemontana* and *villosa* see below.

SUBGROUPS A, B AND C, PLANTS WITH TOOTHED LEAVES

I—One, two, or more single flowers on simple pedicels (no peduncle):
   (a) small, greyish green, fleshy leaf covered in minute sticky glandular hairs, pedicels very short to obsolete: *allionii*.
   (b) small, oblong, bright green hairless leathery leaf with a truncate, deeply toothed apex, pedicels very short: *minima*.

II—one, two, or more flowers in an umbel on a peduncle:
   (a) largish, oblong to elliptic hairless leaf, faintly denticulate near the tip: *carniolica*.
   (b) small, upright elliptic hairless glandular, sharply denticulate leaf: *glutinosa*.
   (c) small, roundish bright green thin textured leaf with tiny sticky glandular hairs: *tyrolensis*.
   (d) medium to largish leaves of various shapes, beset with small to very small glandular hairs:
        hairs colourless: *kitaibeliana*, *latifolia* (sometimes *hirsuta*).

P. palinuri (p. 109) Plate 1   *Photo: G. F. Smith*

P. auricula (p. 23) Plate 2   *Photo: H. Taylor*

P. auricula (p. 23) Plate 3
Photo: H. & W. Bevington

P. marginata (p. 97) Plate 4
Photo: G. F. Smith

P. marginata (p. 97) Plate 5
Photo: G. F. Smith

P. latifolia (p. 87) Plate 6
Photo: G. F. Smith

P. carniolica (p. 33) Plate 7
Photo: D. B. Lowe

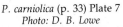

P. hirsuta (p. 73) Plate 8
Photo: H. & W. Bevington

P. daonensis (p. 43) Plate 9
Photo: G. F. Smith

P. pedemontana (p. 113) Plate 10
Photo: C. Banham

P. villosa (p. 139) Plate 11   *Photo: G. F. Smith*

P. spectabilis (p. 123) Plate 12
Photo: C. Greenfield

P. spectabilis (p. 123) Plate 13
Photo: C. Greenfield

P. glaucescens
(p. 63) Plate 14
Photo: H. Taylor

P. wulfeniana
(p. 145) Plate 15
Photo: G. F. Smith

P. clusiana
(p. 35) Plate 16
Photo: H. Taylor

P. allionii (p. 15) Plate 17   *Photo: G. F. Smith*

P. allionii (p. 15) Plate 18   *Photo: G. F. Smith*

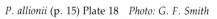

P. allionii (p. 15) Plate 19   Photo: G. F. Smith

P. allionii (p. 15) Plate 20   Photo: J. Jermyn

P. integrifolia (p. 79) Plate 21   Photo: *G. F. Smith*

P. integrifolia (p. 79) Plate 22   Photo: H. & W. Bevington

P. tyrolensis (p. 133) Plate 23   Photo: G. F. Smith

P. kitaibeliana (p. 85) Plate 24
Photo: G. F. Smith

P. minima (p. 101) Plate 25   *Photo: G. F. Smith*

P. glutinosa (p. 65) Plate 26
Photo: G. F. Smith

P. deorum (p. 47) Plate 27
Photo: G. F. Smith

P. deorum (pp. 47, 58) Plate 28   *Photo: G. F. Smith*

P. angustifolia (p. 19) Plate 29   *Photo: M. Collins*

P. angustifolia (p. 19) Plate 30   *Photo: M. Collins*

P. parryi (p. 111) Plate 31   Photo: B. A. Mech

P. parryi (p. 111) Plate 32   Photo: B. A. Mech

P. cusickiana (p. 39) Plate 33   *Photo: R. J. Poff*

P. cusickiana (p. 39) Plate 34   *Photo: J. Lunn*

P. rusbyi (p. 117) Plate 35
Photo: G. F. Smith

P. ellisiae (p. 55) Plate 36   *Photo: G. F. Smith*

P. suffrutescens (p. 129) Plate 37   Photo: *G. F. Smith*

P. cuneifolia subsp. *saxifragifolia* (p. 37) Plate 38
Photo: R. Redfield

P. cuneifolia subsp. *saxifragifolia* (p. 37) Plate 39
Photo: R. Redfield

P. tschuktschorum (p. 131) Plate 40   *Photo: S. Walker*

P. nutans (=*sibirica*) (p. 107) Plate 41   *Photo: H. Taylor*

P. borealis (p. 31) Plate 42
Photo: R. Redfield

P. stricta (p. 127) Plate 43
Photo: B. Burrow

P. mistassinica (p. 105) Plate 44   Photo: M. Collins

P. magellanica (=*decipiens*) (p. 95) Plate 45
Photo: T. V. Callaghan

P. magellanica (=*decipiens*) (p. 95) Plate 46
Photo: B. Burrow

P. incana (p. 77) Plate 47
Photo: *B. Burrow*

P. halleri (p. 69) Plate 48
Photo: *G. F. Smith*

P. farinosa (p. 57) Plate 49   Photo: *B. Burrow*

P. algida (p. 13) Plate 50   *Photo: B. Burbidge*

P. auriculata (p. 27) Plate 51   *Photo: B. Burrow*

P. scotica
(p. 121) Plate 52
Photo: G. Wheeler

P. scotica
(p. 121) Plate 53
Photo: A. J. Clement

P. luteola
(p. 93) Plate 54
Photo: B. Walker

P. juliae
(p. 83) Plate 55
Photo: B. Burrow

P. amoena
(p. 17) Plate 56
Photo: G. Barrett

P. renifolia
(p. 115) Plate 57
Photo: J. Dixon

P. vulgaris (p. 141) Plate 58
Photo: G. Wheeler

P. elatior (p. 51) Plate 59   *Photo: H. & W. Bevington*

P. veris (p. 135) Plate 60   Photo: G. Wheeler

P. allionii and *P.* × *miniera* (top right) (pp. 15, 170) Plate 61
Photo: G. F. Smith

P. wulfeniana (right) and *P.* × *vochinensis* × *P. wulfeniana* (left)
(pp. 172, 174) Plate 62   *Photo: G. F. Smith*

P. × juribella (p. 169) Plate 63
Photo: G. F. Smith

P. × miniera (p. 170) Plate 64
Photo: G. F. Smith

P. × bowlesii (p. 166) Plate 65
Photo: G. F. Smith

P. × muretiana (p. 170) Plate 66
Photo: H. Taylor

Unknown, probably
a hybrid. Plate 67
Photo: H. Taylor

P. × *floerkeana*
(p. 168) Plate 68
Photo: G. F. Smith

P. × *crucis*
(p. 167) Plate 69
Photo: S. Mayr

P. *allionii* 'Anna Griffith'
(p. 179) Plate 70   *Photo: B. Burrow*

P. 'Fairy Rose' (p. 182) Plate 71
Photo: B. Burrow

P. 'Margaret' (p. 182) Plate 72
Photo: D. B. Lowe

P. 'Joan Hughes' (p. 182) Plate 73
Photo: J. E. G. Good

P. 'Old Red Dusty Mil
(p. 185) Plate 74
Photo: B. Burrow

P. vulgaris Double Whi
(p. 195) Plate 75
Photo: K. Haywood

P. × *pubescens* 'Rufus'
(p. 185) Plate 76
Photo: A. Evans

hairs yellow, through orange to red: *apennina*,
daonensis, hirsuta, pedemontana, villosa (the Erythrodrosum group).

Distinction of species in IId

kitaibeliana has elongated leaves on short petioles, and faintly
denticulate margins; *latifolia* has broadish leaves (hence specific
epithet) on long petioles, mostly in quite an upright stance, the
margins are usually clearly toothed. The two species are very
different: see detailed descriptions of each.

An individual of *hirsuta* with colourless hairs is distinguished by
its short peduncle; out of flower it is distinguished from *kitaibeliana*
by its roundish always clearly toothed leaves, and from *latifolia* by the
openly rosulate character of the leaf rosette as against the characteristic upright stance of the leaves of *latifolia*.

The Erythrodrosum group is made up of five quite closely related
species which frequently are very difficult to tell apart. There is overlap
in form between all of them, and this is particularly true of *daonensis*
and *hirsuta*. Even in the case of the "clearly different" *villosa* and
pedemontana, there is a report (A. Kress, *Ber. Bayer. Bot. Ges.*, 1973,
44, 187) of the existence of fairly homogeneous populations which
are morphologically intermediate between the two species . . . Even
140 years ago Duby proposed that there should just be *P. hirsuta*, and
Koch separated *P. pedemontana*, but lumped the other four. More
recently, P. H. Davis in a note dated 1952 in the R.B.G. Edinburgh
Herbarium sheets for *P. apennina* writes that the taxonomic status of
apennina is not beyond question, and that all the primulas in the
Erythrodrosum group could be held to be subspecies of *P. hirsuta*.

Table 4 will help in separating them (see overleaf).

TABLE 4

	pedemontana	apennina	hirsuta	daonensis	villosa
Hirsuteness of leaves	more or less glabrous on both surfaces; hairs on margins only	hairy on both surfaces and on margins			
Size and colour of hairs	0·15 to rarely 0·25 mm.; dark red glands	0·05–0·15 mm.; yellowish to orange glands	0·15–0·30 mm. rarely to 0·5 mm.; small yellowish glands	0·15–0·30 mm.; largish reddish glands	0·25–0·50 mm. sometimes to 1 mm.; small dark red glands
Leaf margins	entire to shallowly toothed	shallowly toothed or entire	clearly toothed	clearly toothed	mostly toothed, sometimes entire
Peduncle	nearly always exceeding leaves	equalling or exceeding leaves	generally shorter than leaves	equalling or exceeding leaves	
Ratio of length of mature seed capsule to calyx	0·9–1·1	0·7–0·9	0·5–0·8	1·0–1·2	1·0–1·3

Pedemontana is usually easily separated from the others by darker green leaves and a marked red glandular leaf margin especially in younger leaves, and by carrying its flowers well above the leaves.

Villosa is the most obviously hairy; the longer flower scape and the longer seed capsules distinguish it from *hirsuta*. The longer hairs and more vigorous appearance of *villosa*, as well as the differences in average leaf shapes tell it apart from the slenderer *daonensis*, which, in turn, by having longer seed capsules and by often having characteristic wedge-shaped leaves, is differentiated from the stouter *hirsuta*, with its roundish leaves, short peduncle, and short seed capsules.

Apennina very seldom has well defined marginal teeth: this separates it from *hirsuta* and *daonensis*, which always have toothed leaves. The very short hairs separate *apennina* from the obviously hairy *villosa*. *Apennina* is closest in appearance to *pedemontana*, but differs from it in having yellowish to orangy hairs over the whole leaf surface; *pedemontana* has red hairs localised almost entirely on the margins.

Hirsuta has very variable leaf shapes and sizes, is always toothed, and because of the usually short peduncle, carries its flowers among or just above the leaves.

GROUP 6 FARINOSE, EXANNULATE, AND INVOLUTE

The constantly densely farinose and dentate leaf margin of *marginata*, and the conspicuous stem (aerial part of the rhizome) make it well-nigh impossible not to recognise this very familiar species.

EUROPEAN SPECIES.   Yellow flowered

1 PLANTS WITH RUGOSE LEAVES, REVOLUTE
    (a) No peduncle, long pedicels: *vulgaris*.
    (b) One-sided umbel on tall peduncle; pale yellow corolla with a flat to funnel shaped limb; corolla tube fits tightly in the calyx: *elatior*.
    (c) Umbel, not always one-sided, on tall peduncle; rich golden yellow corolla with a bowl-shaped limb, very rarely flat; corolla tube generally much narrower than calyx: *veris*.

2 PLANT WITH RUGULOSE (FAINTLY RUGOSE) LEAVES, REVOLUTE
A large plant with ovate leaves and a 30–60 cm. (1 to 2′) peduncle bearing an Allium-like many-flowered umbel; the small tubular corollas not obviously like those of a primula: *grandis*.

3 PLANTS WITH NON-RUGOSE LEAVES
    (a) Hairless, efarinose, elongated leaves which are bright dark green on both surfaces and not fleshy, revolute: *luteola*.
    (b) Quite variable in form and size, mostly with broadish leaves which are greyish green and fleshy, are more or less glandular hairy and frequently farinose, involute: *auricula*.
    (c) Roundish, pale, greyish to dull green fleshy leaves which are always efarinose; two very distinctive features are the thick hard stem (aerial rhizome) and the large leafy bracts, involute: *palinuri*.

AMERICAN SPECIES

1
Farinose leaves and inflorescence, annulate, revolute

    A–Heteromorphic
        intercedens, mistassinica, (borealis).
    B–Hetero or homomorphic
        laurentiana.
    C–Homomorphic
        incana, magellanica, comberi.

2
Farinose leaves and inflorescence, exannulate, revolute

    specuicola.

3 | Efarinose, annulate |

    A–Heteromorphic and revolute
      borealis.
    B–Homomorphic and revolute
      egaliksensis.
    C–Heteromorphic and involute
      cuneifolia, suffrutescens (see 5)
    D–Homomorphic and involute
      cuneifolia subsp. *saxifragifolia.*

4 | Efarinose leaves, farinose inflorescence |

    A–Exannulate, heteromorphic, and involute
      cusickiana, maguirei, nevadensis.
    B–Exannulate or annulate, heteromorphic, and involute
      ellisiae, rusbyi.
    C–Not known if annulate or exannulate; homo or hetero-
    morphic, revolute
      tschuktschorum.

5 | Efarinose, exannulate, heteromorphic, involute |

    angustifolia, capillaris, parryi, suffrutescens (see 3).

GROUP 1   FARINOSE LEAVES AND INFLORESCENCE,
            ANNULATE, REVOLUTE.

The separation of the species in this group is difficult to achieve
with certainty, as there is considerable overlap: all have swellings at
the base of the bracts, have similar seed capsule to calyx ratios, similar
corolla tube to calyx ratios, and all have dentate or denticulate leaves.
Floral structure allows a separation into two subgroups 1A+1B and
1B+1C.

    HETEROMORPHIC SUBGROUP: otherwise very close to *mistas-
    sinica, intercedens* stands out because of its yellow farina;
    mistassinica is easily recognised by its unique ability to form
    leaf buds on its main roots, so that young plants develop round
    the parent. Apart from this, *mistassinica* can be separated from
    laurentiana as follows: *mistassinica* is the slenderer species with
    the smaller maximal leaf size of 7 by 1·6 cm.; *laurentiana* is the
    more robust and vigorous species, which quickly forms a
    clump with several rosettes and inflorescences, and has the
    much larger maximal leaf size of 13 by 3 cm. *Borealis* is a very
    variable species, and it is difficult to pinpoint differences: the
    probability of meeting it in this group is extremely low (see
    group 3), for not only is it rarely farinose, but is also very rare
    indeed in cultivation.

HOMOMORPHIC SUBGROUP: *incana*, *magellanica*, and *comberi* all have tight umbels with pedicels shorter than to equal to the bracts, and they all have white or yellowish farina; *laurentiana* on the other hand, though it may sometimes have short pedicels, normally has relatively long ones, and its farina is always white; flower colour can help too, for a white flowered plant is most likely to be *magellanica* (this species can sometimes have efarinose leaves); a yellow eye suggests *incana*, whereas an orange-yellow eye fits *magellanica*, *comberi*, and *laurentiana* best; a long corolla tube about twice the length of the calyx denotes *comberi*, the other three have tubes which are about equal to the calyx; finally *magellanica* has the largest flowers, 10–20 mm., *incana* the smallest, 6–10 mm., with *laurentiana* in between, 8–13 mm.

GROUP 2   FARINOSE LEAVES AND INFLORESCENCE, EXANNULATE, AND REVOLUTE.

The only species in this group, *specuicola*, is rare in the wild, and practically non existent in cultivation.

GROUP 3   EFARINOSE AND ANNULATE

The four species in this group are very readily separated.

In addition to being heteromorphic and revolute, *borealis* has flowers which are frequently large for the size of plant, whereas the homomorphic and revolute *egaliksensis* has usually quite small flowers; *borealis* may at times be slightly farinose (see Group 1). The above pair with revolute leaves are easily separated from *cuneifolia* and *suffrutescens*, which have involute leaves: *cuneifolia* has a short stout rhizome, smooth surfaces to all green parts, which are often tinged with maroon or purple, and the corolla tube is always only a little longer than the calyx; *suffrutescens* has long branching hard rhizomes above ground (=stems, hence the specific epithet) and tends to form mats, has glandular surfaces to all green parts, and the corolla tube can be up to twice the calyx length.

GROUP 4   EFARINOSE LEAVES, FARINOSE INFLORESCENCE

Cusickiana, *maguirei*, and *nevadensis* are closely related: the first is rare, the other two extremely rare in cultivation. Compared with *ellisiae* and *rusbyi*, they are the smaller plants, with shorter peduncles in the 3–10 cm. range, with usually 1–4 flowered umbels, and corolla colours with much more blue in them (violet to deep violet with a marked yellow eye). *Ellisiae* and *rusbyi* are likewise closely related; the former is common, the latter much less so in cultivation, and many plants which are labelled *rusbyi* are in fact *ellisiae*; compared with *cusickiana*, they are the larger plants, with longer peduncles in the range 6–20 cm., with usually 4–12 flowered umbels, and with corolla colours which are redder (rose-violet, rose-red, rose-magenta, magenta, deep purple); these two species are difficult to separate clearly—*ellisiae* is the more fulsome of the two, with several inflorescences in the mature plant, and a corolla tube which is $1–1\frac{1}{2}$ times the length of the calyx; *rusbyi* has a corolla tube which is 2–3 times longer than the calyx, and flowers which can take on a much more intense colouring than those of *ellisiae*; finally, *ellisiae* flowers in the early summer and *rusbyi* in the late summer. *Tschuktschorum* is the only species in this group to have revolute leaves; an additional distinction is that it has a seed capsule which is longer than the calyx.

GROUP 5   EFARINOSE, EXANNULATE, HETEROMORPHIC, AND INVOLUTE

Suffrutescens is the only one in the group to have an aerial branching stem; in addition, it has small leaves, broadest near the tip, which is strongly toothed; *parryi* has quite large, long leaves, with margins which are finely denticulate to entire, the plant emits a strong, sometimes offensive odour; *angustifolia* is a smallish species, with relatively long, narrow leaves, hence its specific epithet, which are usually entire; in contrast to the other two species, the flowers are borne not much above the leaves, in the wild often among the leaves; *capillaris* is an extremely rare species, which can be looked upon as a small *angustifolia*.

CHAPTER 5

THE NATURAL HYBRIDS

General Introduction

When species A is crossed with species B, the resulting hybrid plants are a collection of individuals most of which have a form about mid-way between those of the parents, but many of which have forms which are clearly closer to the one or to the other parent. Among those which are more or less midway, some organ may be closer to the one parent, and another organ may be closer to the other parent, thus some may have an inflorescence closer to A and leaves closer to B, and in others these affinities may be the other way round: the combination of variations is thus quite large, and such a collection of individuals is often referred to as a hybrid swarm. Very many experiments have further shown that the average distribution of forms is the same, regardless of which of the two parents is the seed parent.

If the hybrids are sterile, then most of the forms will show clear characteristics of both parents; a completely different situation arises, however, when the hybrids are fertile, for then they can cross with one another and with either of the parents and generate a virtually complete and continuous series which merges at both ends with the parent species. In such a situation it becomes difficult at times to decide which is hybrid and which is species. After several back crossings with one of the parent species, the characteristics of the other parent may virtually disappear: this occurs in the wild, and can create exciting and bewildering situations (see for example C. C. Mountfort, *Bull.* 1942, *10*, 61). On reading some articles about hybrids, it is easy to gain the quite wrong impression that morphologically largely homogeneous hybrid populations are the norm: thus in *Trans. Roy. Soc. Edin.*, 1947–8, $\frac{3}{4}$*1*, 668, Wright-Smith and Fletcher write, "*P.* × *biflora* (*glutinosa* × *minima*) found on the Monzoni Thal approaches *P. minima* in the short glossy wedge-shaped leaves notched at the ends and arranged in compact rosettes; the large rose-purple flowers are always carried in twos on 2–3 inch stems."

We would like to emphasise most strongly that wherever two species hybridise, the hybrid population normally is composed of a wide range of forms; only on the special occasions when one of the parent species has been locally virtually swallowed up by hybridisation, can one see a population of hybrids which is mostly close to the dominant species, and even then there is a range of forms—remember that this special situation can only develop with fertile hybrids. The stabilisation of a particular form like *biflora* (see p. 168) within a wild population, even when one of the parents is very dominant, must remain a most improbable phenomenon.

The horticulturist, by repeated selection of a particular form over many generations, may stabilise the genetic make-up of that strain

163

to the point where it largely breeds true: this is a long and very artificial process.

The ability to form hybrids varies greatly within the Genus Primula. First of all, the formation of hybrids may only occur between parents which belong to the same Section, thus no hybrid is known between a species in the Section Primula (Vernales) and one from the Section Auriculastrum. The artificial hybrid between *juliae* and *megaseaefolia*, two species which until recently were in the Vernales, is now an exception, for both parents have been placed in Sections of their own. Even within a Section, the ability to form hybrids varies enormously, thus the Section Aleuritia (Farinosae) in Europe and America stands apart in that hybrid Farinosae are virtually unknown (one possible exception is *egaliksensis × incana*), by contrast most species in the Auriculastrum Section hybridise with one another so freely, that one begins to wonder how they speciated in the first place.

Nomenclature.

The nomenclature of hybrids is greatly confused by the very many different names applied to the same cross either by different Authors, or even by one Author (see Appendix IV). The greatest culprit here is a certain Gusmus: Farrer, in *The English Rock Garden*, provides the slight note of irritation which sums up the situation when he writes, "*P. ×ventricosa* is a superfluous name of Gusmus for nobody knows what."!

The situation badly needs simplification, and we would like to support a scheme which was used by E. Widmer in her book *Die Europäische Arten der Gattung Primula* published in 1891: in this scheme, *one* name only covers *all* forms of the hybrid derived from one particular pair of parents. No less than eight different names were given to the hybrids from *P. hirsuta* and *P. minima* (see Appendix III, p. 243): Widmer selected *P. × steinii* Obrist. as having precedence over the others; a few years ago, research by Fritz Kummert showed that *P. ×forsteri* Stein has precedence, indeed, Mr. Kummert investigated the 23 naturally occurring Auriculastrum hybrids, and produced the following list, to which we have added *P. × miniera*, an unofficial name given to an undoubted hybrid found near the Col di Tenda by C. C. Mountfort in 1927, and still in cultivation and by others since. We are indebted to Mr. Kummert for his permission to publish his work.

The Naturally-Occurring Hybrids

The numbers are a cross reference to the diagram opposite, which is based on a similar diagram by Mr. Kummert, and which summarises at a glance the overall pircture with regard to the natural Auriculastrum hybrids.

A. AURICULASTRUM SECTION

P. × berninae Kerner	*latifolia × hirsuta*	1
bowlesii Farrer	*pedemontana × latifolia*	2

164

carueli Porta	*glaucescens × spectabilis*	3
crucis Bowles	*marginata × latifolia*	4
discolor Leyb.	*auricula × daonensis*	5
escheri Brügg.	*auricula × integrifolia*	6
facchinii Schott	*minima × spectabilis*	7
floerkeana Schrad.	*glutinosa × minima*	8
forsteri Stein	*hirsuta × minima*	9
heerii Brügg.	*hirsuta × integrifolia*	10
intermedia Porta	*clusiana × minima*	11
juribella Sünd.	*minima × tyrolensis*	12
kolbiana Widm.	*latifolia × daonensis*	13
lempergii F. Buxb.	*auricula × clusiana*	14
miniera Anon.	*allionii × marginata*	15
muretiana Monitzi	*integrifolia × latifolia*	16
obovata Huter	*auricula × tyrolensis*	17
pubescens Jacq.	*auricula × hirsuta*	18
pumila Kerner	*minima × daonensis*	19
seriana Widm.	*daonensis × hirsuta*	20
truncata Lehm.	*minima × villosa*	21
venzoides Huter	*wulfeniana × tyrolensis*	22
venusta Host.	*auricula × carniolica*	23
vochinensis Gusmus	*minima × wulfeniana*	24

YES = exists in the wild.
• = should exist but does not.
· = could just about exist but does not.
? = should exist and there are doubtful claims.
?? = should *not* exist and there are doubtful claims.
BLANK = cannot exist in the wild.

165

There are 210 theoretically possible natural Auriculastrum hybrids. 24 of these (28 if doubtful claims are confirmed) are found in the wild; 28 others are geographically possible but have not been found (32 if the doubtful claims are not confirmed). 154 are not possible by reason of geographical separation.

The naturally-occurring Primula (Vernales) Section hybrids are named as follows:

P. × digenea Kerner	*elatior × vulgaris*
media Peterm.	*elatior × veris*
variabilis Goupil	*veris × vulgaris*

An indication of the form of the hybrid can be given by a third descriptor as a *forma* name: these will be found, where they appear to be necessary, in the description of the individual hybrids.

Of particular interest and importance are those simple hybrids which are now in commerce, and have a reasonably constant form: *P. × forsteri* and *P. × bileckii* are good examples. Such names will continue to be used, but where confusion could arise, a more formal description would be *P. × forsteri* Stein forma hort. *forsteri* and *P. × forsteri* Stein forma hort. *bileckii*; a straightforward wild collected specimen would not have the "hort.", thus for example *P. × forsteri* Stein forma *kellereri* (see p. 169). Another case is *P. × biflora*: the Nurseryman's plant would be *P. × floerkeana* Schrad. forma hort. *biflora*.

It is particularly noteworthy that, apart from a possible *egaliksensis × incana*, there is no report of natural hybrids in North America. This may well be the consequence of the fact that there is only a thin scatter of primulas, and very little overlap between the species in each Section. The only significant overlap occurs between *P. parryi* and *P. angustifolia*, but even these are ecologically well separated (See map on p. 10).

1. P. × berninae Kerner (*latifolia × hirsuta*)

Well known in cultivation, this cross occurs over a wide area in the Engadine, the Bernina, and the Bergamasque Alps. It is a fertile hybrid, yielding a complete range of forms, many of which are strikingly beautiful and floriferous, like the popular commercial 'Windrush Variety' with its large reddish purple flowers. The combinations of *hirsuta* (with its quite open bright pink to mauve flowers with a white eye, held in a symmetrical umbel on a short peduncle), and of *latifolia* (with its often intense violet to reddish violet funnel shaped corolla with a long tube, no eye, and a sprinkling of farina at the throat, a one sided umbel on a long peduncle) are obviously full of potential for the production of beautiful hybrids. *P. × berninae* deserves much more attention than it seems to get.

2. P. × bowlesii Farrer (*pedemontana × latifolia*)   **Plate 65**

The parent species meet in the Graian Alps from the Gran Paradiso to the Petit Mont Cenis. The cross occurs in abundance in the latter area: the peak of its flowering probably occurs at a slightly different time from that of its seed parent, *P. pedemontana*, for on two occasions in our experience, the hybrid was difficult to find among the flowering *pedemontana*, and on a third it was the other way round, with a dominance of mostly quite unattractive hybrid flowers, and here and there a beauty. One specimen which we have grown has leaves closer to *pedemontana* and an inflorescence with a tallish peduncle, with a symmetrical umbel of evenly soft pink open funnel shaped flowers with no white eye. Our experience contrasts with Wright-Smith and Fletcher, who speak of "the sparse and rare hybrid". Our guess is that the hybrid is fertile, though we have no proof other than the abundance and wide range of forms in the wild: we can find no statement in the literature on this point.

3. **P. × carueli** Porta (*glaucescens × spectabilis*)

This cross is found in a limited region north of Brescia where the parents meet. With parents so closely related, it must be quite difficult to recognise the cross when one sees it! Furthermore, the cross is fertile, leading to a full range of intermediates, which adds to the confusion. The hybrid is said to have no garden merit beyond that of the parents.

4. **P. × crucis** Bowles (*marginata × latifolia*)   **Plate 69**

This rare and fertile hybrid is found in the central Cottian Alps just north of Monte Viso, where *marginata* just meets the southern edge of the Graian region of occurrence of *latifolia* (the type specimen was collected on the Col de la Croix, hence the epithet); *P. × crucis* also occurs west of the Col di Tenda, in the Mont Clapier region, which corresponds to the southernmost occurrence of *latifolia*.

Farrer enthuses over this cross, and mentions a superlative form which was named 'Blue Bowl', alas now lost to cultivation. We have not seen a live specimen of this hybrid, but the photograph (Plate 69) taken by Siegfried Mayr of plants, which he and Mr. F. Kummert found in the Clapier region, illustrates the very high potential of this cross. One reason for the rarity of this cross will be that the flowering periods of the parents don't normally overlap, *marginata* being an early flowerer.

5. **P. × discolor** Leyb. (*auricula × daonensis*)

This fertile cross is of quite limited occurrence in nature, since *auricula* favours limestone and *daonensis* does not: it is found in the southern Adamello region around Val Daone. It is said to be a very variable cross, with purplish to yellowish-white flowers: *auricula*-like hybrids can often be recognised by the reddish glandular hairs of *daonensis*, and *daonensis*-like forms can be spotted by almost entire leaves or by the presence of farina. Some forms resemble the garden plant, Old Red Dusty Miller. There is a good photograph in Farrer's *The English Rock Garden*.

6. **P. × escheri** Brügger (*auricula × integrifolia*)

This is another rare hybrid, found in the mountains around the headwaters of the Rhine, that is in Glarus, the Davos area, and the northern flanks of the Adula and Albula. Whether or nor this cross is fertile has not been noted. Widmer reports a murky red corolla, a many-flowered umbel, and entire to remotely denticulate elliptic to oblong leaves.

7. **P. × facchinii** Schott (*minima × spectabilis*)

The parents meet in the Valli Giudicarie and the Brenta region, where the cross is said to be fairly frequently found; Alpe Magiassone is quoted as a good spot to find it in. Whether or not the cross is fertile is not noted. The usual full range of forms is to be seen: Widmer suggests forma *dumoulinii* for those close to *minima*, and forma *magiassonica* for those close to *spectabilis*. All forms are said by Widmer to have only one- to two-flowered umbels, which seems strange.

8. **P. × floerkeana** Schrad. (*glutinosa × minima*)　　　**Plate 68**

This cross is quite common wherever the parents meet, which is over most of the main chain of the eastern half of the Alps. The cross is fertile, so that often in the wild the majority of a population is composed of an astonishing variety of hybrid forms and it is difficult to find the pure species. This cross is the most abundant in the Alps, and with such contrasting parents yields a very wide range of forms: the full exploration of the horticultural potential of *P. × floerkeana* would be a really worthwhile project. It is interesting to note that Widmer devotes no less than seven pages to it, as against four pages to *P. × pubescens*, the only other hybrid of comparable importance. Contrary to what has been said here and there in the literature, many of these hybrid forms are of surpassing beauty, with rich purples and glowing dusky pinks.

Making use of existing epithets, we suggest the following:

P. × floerkeana Schrad. forma *biflora* for specimens close to *minima*;
　　　,,　　　　　　,,　　,,　*salisburgensis* for specimens of inter-
　　　　　　　　　　　　　　　　　　mediate form;
　　　,,　　　　　　,,　　,,　*huteri* for specimens close to *glutinosa*.
　　　　　　　　　　　　　　　(see also p. 190)

9. **P. × forsteri** Stein (*hirsuta × minima*)

This usually sterile cross, as *P. × bilekii* and as *P. × forsteri* of commerce, is one of the most widely grown simple hybrids. In the wild it occurs somewhat sparsely in the mountains of the region south of Innsbruck, around the Brenner Pass. At the western end of the distribution of *P. minima* in the main chain of the Alps, *P. hirsuta* has already become rare, even though it continues to occur in most of the High

Tauern well to the east of the Brenner Pass. In the wild, and among artificially generated swarms (Fritz Kummert) there is a full range of forms: following Widmer, we would like to propose:

P. ×*forsteri* Stein forma *kellereri* for plants close to *hirsuta*;
,,   ,,   ,,   *steinii* for plants of intermediate form;
,,   ,,   ,,   *bilekii* for plants close to *minima*. (This name
                                    is often written *bileckii*).

See also p. 190. The difference between *P. minima* and, say, *P.×forsteri* forma *bilekii* of commerce is marginal: the latter has brighter flowers with more red in them and broader petals, up to three flowers in the umbel, but usually two, quite a spattering of glandular hairs on the leaves, which tend to be broader at the wedge top, with more teeth which have shorter cartilaginous tips. Forma *kellereri* can differ from *hirsuta* only by having cartilaginous tips to the leaf-teeth, longer bracts, and shorter glandular hairs.

10. P. × heerii Brügg (*hirsuta* × *integrifolia*)

A not very commonly occurring sterile hybrid, but of excellent repute, as indicated by the attentions paid to it by the horticulturists Sündermann and Gusmus (see synonyms list on p. 243). It is to be found on the Bernina, in the upper Engadine, and all round the head-waters of the Rhine. It has also been found where the parents meet in the Pyrenees. It can usually be distinguished from *hirsuta* by the absence of a white eye to the corolla, and from *integrifolia* very often by the presence of teeth on the leaf margins.

11. P. × intermedia Porta (*clusiana* × *minima*)

The parents meet over most of the area of distribution of *clusiana*. At its best, it can produce very large soft rose flowers quite freely: Will Ingwersen (*Bull.*, 1935, *3*, 180) rated it as one of the best of the hybrids. Alas, we have not seen a specimen. With *clusiana* as the seed parent, the hybrid is said to be sterile; Farrer claims to have found the reverse cross, that is with *minima* as the seed parent, and reports it to be fertile. It is a pity that it is so very rarely seen in cultivation (see R. Ginns, *Bull.*, 1960, *28*, 89). H. Taylor, quoted by M. and P. Stone in the *Bull.*, 1981, *49*, 255, believes *P. clusiana* 'Murray-Lyon' to be a form of this hybrid.

12. P. × juribella Sünd. (*minima* × *tyrolensis*)   Plate 63

This relatively rare cross has not often been described. One account describes a form close to *minima*, with an inward curling of the leaf, characteristic of *tyrolensis*, as also purple shadings of the corolla. We found a specimen, likewise close to *minima*, in Val Venegia near the Rolle Pass in the S.E. Dolomites. The rarity of this hybrid is probably due to the infrequent co-occurrence of the parents, which normally inhabit quite different habitats. Whether or not the cross is fertile is not known.

13. **P. × kolbiana** Widmer (*latifolia × daonensis*)

The two parents just overlap at the eastern end of the Bergamasque (Orobic) Alps and west of the Tonale Pass. The cross has only been collected once, and, according to Wright-Smith and Fletcher, doubt attaches to its existence. We have seen plants south of the Tonale Pass, growing among *P. daonensis*, which have *latifolia* floral characteristics, that is funnel shaped and of a purply colour with no white eye, but in spite of diligent searching, we failed to find *P. latifolia*.

14. **P. × lempergii** F. Buxb. (*auricula × clusiana*)

The claim for the existence of this cross in nature rests on three collections by Gusmus at the western end of the Eisenerzer Alpen: this plant was efarinose and differed from *clusiana* only by having teeth on the upper half of the leaves. Widmer reports that repeated searches for this cross failed in spite of the fact that the two species grow together over a very wide area in the wild, but agrees that Gusmus' plants are of hybrid origin, declares that the second parent could be either *auricula* or *minima*, and includes other names in this ill-defined class (see Appendix III, p. 243). (—See Buxb. *Öst Bot. Zeits.*, 1937, *86*, 296).

15. **P. × miniera** (*allionii × marginata*)   **Plates 61, 64**

This hybrid has probably been found three times in the wild: the first time by C. C. Mountfort in August 1927 in the vallon de la Minière near St. Dalmas de Tende (*Bull.*, 1940, *8*, 311; 1949, *17*, 340; 1979, *47*, 348); the second time by J. Burgess in 1966 in the Roya valley; the third time by one of us (G.F.S.) on the Cime de Durasque at 1250 m. In all three instances the hybrid was growing among *P. allionii*, and on the Cime de Durasque the second parent was seen some 300 m. away. The photograph of Mountfort's find (*Bull.*, 1979, *47*, 342) shows clearly a strong relationship with *P. marginata* in the foliage, and an affinity with *P. allionii* in the flowers: the second find is similar, but in the third find, the affinities are the other way round. Mountfort's plant was given an Award of Merit by the R.H.S. in 1979.

This hybrid has been generated several times artificially (see p. 181).

P. marginata 'Beatrice Lascario' collected near the Col di Tenda was originally described as an *allionii × marginata* hybrid (*J. Roy. Hort. Soc.*, 1936, *61*, Proceedings p. 96), but considerable doubt attaches to this claim. A different spelling, 'Beatrice Lascaris', is widely used.

16. **P. × muretiana** Moritzi (*integrifolia × latifolia*)   **Plate 66**

This reputedly sterile cross occurs not infrequently all round the Upper Engadine, including the Bernina Group. As one might expect from the marked difference in the appearance of the parents, this hybrid takes a wide range of forms: at its best, its flowers are more brilliant than either parent's. Plants closer in form to *latifolia* could be called forma *dinyana* (*P.* × *dinyana* Lagger was the name given to such forms); plants closer to *integrifolia* could be described as forma *muretiana*.

17. P. × obovata Huter (*auricula* × *tyrolensis*)

Wright-Smith and Fletcher express much doubt about the existence of this cross. However, Mr. R. Würdig found it in Val Venegia (R. Travignolo) just N.E. of the Rolle Pass, and gave us a specimen. This has now flowered. The leaves are obovate, 22 mm. long and 11 mm. wide, with entire margins, having the colourless glandular hairs of *auricula*, the greener and thinner texture of *tyrolensis*, and most leaves have the short stout whitish ciliate structures on the upper margins, quite typical of *tyrolensis*. The flowers are close to *tyrolensis* in appearance and pink. We have looked hard for it, and though we found the two species growing close together, we saw no hybrid plants: it would seem to be rare. *P. auricula* can be found over the entire area of occurrence of *P. tyrolensis*.

18. P. × pubescens Jacq. (*auricula* × *hirsuta*)

The natural cross is not to be confused with the Nurseryman's Pubescens hybrids, which are of long horticultural standing and are the products of a long process of artificial selection (see p. 184). In the wild, this cross may be found quite frequently wherever the parents meet. Since *P. auricula* occurs almost exclusively on limestone, and *P. hirsuta* avoids it, these two species do not come together very frequently, and then only at some limestone-silicate boundary. This occurs in the Tyrol, Vorarlberg, Graubünden, Sankt Gallen, Glarus, Uri, Obwalden, the Bernese Oberland, Valais, and Vaud. It is a fertile hybrid, and consequently there is a full range of forms and flower colour: quoting W. Lüdi in Hegi, "Where the hybrid occurs, it often outnumbers the parents, and such a slope offers a strange and bewildering scene, when at flowering time nearly every plant is different from the next." Corolla colours range from white, yellow, pink, red, purple, to terra-cotta and even brownish; most of the colours have a faded look, and the really attractive ones are in a minority. The hybrid status of plants close to *hirsuta* is often revealed by entire leaves, or the presence of farina, down to just a little on the calyx.

19. P. × pumila Kerner (*minima* × *daonensis*)

This sterile cross has been found around the head of Val di Breguzzo, south of the Adamello, and probably occurs elsewhere in the region; it also occurs on the Alpi Magiassone in Valli Giudicarie. It has been collected several times, and varies in form over a wide range.

20. P. × seriana Widmer (*daonensis* × *hirsuta*)

This has probably been collected only once, by Kellerer at the eastern end of the Bergamasque (Orobic) Alps. Widmer says that it is difficult to recognise, since the parents are so closely similar.

21. P. × truncata Lehm. (*minima* × *villosa*)

Since the Austrian occurrences of *villosa* are entirely within the large area of occurrence of *minima*, this sterile cross may be found wherever there is *villosa*. It is however rare, both in the wild and in cultivation. Forms reported from intermediate to close to *minima*.

22. P. × venusta Host. (*auricula* × *carniolica*)

We have not seen this important hybrid, nor do we know of anyone who has, yet at the turn of the century it was listed in many Nurserymen's catalogues. Many of its forms are reputed to have been really beautiful, and this has been the cause of its downfall in the wild: it became the victim of commercial depredations and virtually disappeared from the wild, a very sad story. It was fairly common on Mount Jelenek, and of course elsewhere in the Idria region. It is a fertile hybrid, and is the parent of the now still very widespread and popular artificial hybrid with *P. marginata*, *P. × marven* (see p. 189).

Mountfort (*Bull.*, 1940, *8*, 306) describes one form of *P. × venusta* as being rose coloured round the edges of the petals, changing to pale yellow at the centre, and Farrer talks of rosy, crimson, purple, or brownish colours. Interestingly Mountfort says that Sündermann used to send out plants as × *venusta* with efarinose leaves and no apparent characters of *carniolica* . . . dear oh dear! . .

23. P. × venzoides Huter (*wulfeniana* × *tyrolensis*)

Quite a rare hybrid, it is to be found between Val di Torno and Cimolais, at the easternmost occurrence of *tyrolensis*, where it just meets the westernmost *wulfeniana*. It is not mentioned in Smith and Fletcher, but is described by C. C. Mountfort in the *Bull.*, 1940, *8*, 312, where he says that it is shy flowering in cultivation. Widmer has seen specimens close to *wulfeniana* and others close to *tyrolensis*. Whether or not the cross is fertile is not reported.

24. P. × vochinensis Gusmus (*minima* × *wulfeniana*)   Plate 62

Quite common wherever the species meet, which is the easternmost Dolomites around Cimolais, the western half of the Karawanken, and its easternmost mountain, Petzen. It occurs in a wide range of forms, all small plants, mostly single or twin flowered, with a brilliance of colour contributed by *wulfeniana*. Although there is no report on the question, this cross is very likely to be fertile, judging from our observations in the wild.

DOUBTFUL HYBRIDS.

There are five in this category.

P. × lebliana Gusmus (*auricula × wulfeniana*) on which there is no information.

P. × weldeniana Reichb. (*auricula × spectabilis*) which E. Widmer discounts totally.

P. glaucescens × P. hirsuta—one very incomplete specimen was identified by Widmer as *hirsuta*: several botanists have searched in vain for a hybrid among thousands of the two species growing together near Sondrio, in the Bergamasque Alps.

P. × hugueninii Brügg (*integrifolia × glutinosa*) is based on one doubtful specimen found on the Parpaner Rothorn above Arosa, where the westernmost outlier of *P. glutinosa* finds itself among *P. integrifolia*.

P. pedemontana × P. marginata is suggested for one specimen found in the same region (exact locality not given) which yielded *P. × bowlesii* (*latifolia × marginata*) and is mentioned by C. C. Mountfort in the *Bull.*, 1940, *8*, 308. This would necessitate a *P. pedemontana* occurrence well south of its normal distribution, which is possible; since *P. hirsuta* and *P. marginata* co-occur in the Cottians, it is just possible that what was taken to be *pedemontana* is *hirsuta*; another possible candidate is *P. villosa*. Any of these combinations would be new.

B. VERNALES SECTION

P. × digenea Kerner (*elatior × vulgaris*)
This cross occurs fairly frequently and is fertile, so gives rise to a complete range of forms. Those approaching *elatior* can be named forma *falkneriana*, and those close to *vulgaris* would be forma *caulescens*.

The remarkable situation of *P. elatior* in England, where it occurs in only a few well defined areas, mostly in Cambridgeshire, must be mentioned: these areas are surrounded by *P. vulgaris*, which however does not enter them, hybrids thus only occur round the margins. The reason for this exclusion of *vulgaris* is not established; one clue might be that the *elatior* areas correspond to calcareous soil. Analogous situations in the rest of Europe, where *elatior* and *vulgaris* are abundant, are unknown (see C. Miller, *J. Ecology*, 1922, vol. *10* for a possible explanation).

P. × media Peterm. (*elatior × veris*)
In spite of the relatively frequent co-occurence of the parents, this cross is quite rare. An exception is again found in Cambridgeshire: whereas no hybrids are found over most of the meadows and woodland where *veris* and *elatior* mingle, they are numerous in marshy ground!

P. × variabilis Goupil (*veris × vulgaris*)
This cross is quite common, as the large number of synonyms testifies (see p. 243). It is fertile, and hence there is a complete range

of forms: in the list of synonyms, those marked 1 are close to *veris*, those marked 2 are intermediate, and those marked 3 are close to *vulgaris*. Horticultural variants and cultivars of this cross form the very important group of garden plants, the Polyanthus primulas (see p. 177).

The identification of natural hybrids.

Species are usually fairly clearly defined, and each of them has relatively narrow ranges of variation, most of which do not overlap significantly with those of other species. It is therefore easy to give a description of a species. With the natural hybrids, however, the situation is very much more complicated: a hybrid can take on any of a wide range of forms between those of the two parents, and a description covering all the possibilities would be very cumbersome. We will not attempt to do this, and believe that the best way to visualise the possible appearances of a hybrid is to have in mind, or to have in print before one, the descriptions of the two parents, and then mentally to construct the range of intermediate forms for each of the parts in turn, the leaf, the calyx, the corolla, etc. as well as for the plant as a whole. For our purposes, the main function of a description is to assist in identification: with hybrids, the process involves assuming a particular parentage, and examining the specimen to see whether or not all its anatomical features are compatible with the particular assumption; if not, one tries a different combination until a reasonable match emerges. Deciding between similar species as one parent is extremely difficult, often impossible: it is immediately obvious that if we can in any way exclude a number of species as possible parents, the task will be that much less difficult. To begin with, we can exclude the formation of hybrids between species of different Sections, then it is important to remember that hybridisation within the European and American Aleuritia (Farinosae) Section is virtually non-existent.

The simplest situation obtains in the wild, or with a specimen collected from a known location in the wild. We have to find out which species are known to occur in that location (see the distribution maps and, for the Alps, the table of occurrences on p. 164), and establish which Sections they belong to: in most cases this yields two species as possible parents, and examination of the specimen will usually reveal features which can be ascribed to one or the other parent, and none which is incompatible with either. The problem takes on another dimension if there are three or four possible parents. Three parents can give rise to three different hybrids, four parents can give rise to six. Here we have to assume that one of the species is unlikely to meet and cross with the hybrid of two other species, although this remains a possibility: none has to our knowledge been reported from the wild. *P.* × *marven*, the well known artificial hybrid, is a good example of such a hybrid, for it is a cross between *P.*

174

marginata and *P.* × *venusta*, itself the hybrid between *P. auricula* and *P. carniolica*.

Let us take a couple of actual cases. In the Brenner and High Tauern Alps one can have *PP. glutinosa, hirsuta,* and *minima* growing together: consultation of the diagram on p. 165 reveals that only two of the three possible hybrids have been found, they are *P.* × *forsteri* (*hirsuta* × *minima*) and *P.* × *floerkeana* (*glutinosa* × *minima*). Confusion can arise in the case of hybrids morphologically close to *P. minima,* and one has to pay attention to secondary characteristics: in this case, the presence of glandular hairs on the *minima*-like leaves points clearly to × *forsteri* (the hairs come from *P. hirsuta*); a total absence of glandular hairs, and the presence of minute sticky glands strongly suggests × *floerkeana,* and if, in addition, the corolla colour is not a pure reddish or magenta-pink, but a purply or maroony pink, then one is certainly dealing with × *floerkeana.* If one is *very* lucky, the specimen could have dusky purple flowers on a tall peduncle, with ovate denticulate leaves with glandular hairs round the margins—one would then, for the first time, have discovered *P. glutinosa* × *hirsuta* in the wild!

Another case might be of a specimen found in the Upper Engadine, where *PP. hirsuta, latifolia,* and *integrifolia* might meet: here we would have the three possibilities, *P.* × *heerii* (*hirsuta* × *integrifolia*), *P.* × *muretiana* (*latifolia* × *integrifolia*), and *P.* × *berninae* (*hirsuta* × *latifolia*). Now the plant we have found has broadish toothed leaves on longish petioles, a peduncle which carries the multiflowered umbel of dark purplish pink flowers just clear of the leaves, and the leaves are covered with a mixture of colourless and yellowish glandular hairs—the latter point to *hirsuta,* for *latifolia* and *integrifolia* have exclusively colourless glandular hairs; the tallish peduncle and the dark purplish pink flowers point to *latifolia*—hence the plant is likely to be *P.* × *berninae.*

Finally, let's take the case of a hybrid between two closely related species, such as *P.* × *carueli* (*glaucescens* × *spectabilis*): here the problem is recognising it as a hybrid in the first place (see p. 174). In a favourable case, the hybrid might have the long 30 mm. bracts of *P. glaucescens* and the pitted, untidy leaf of *P. spectabilis,* but in most cases, only a specialist who has studied the situation in the field for several seasons might be in a position to pontificate . . .

A point to be emphasised is that there is a wide range in the ability of various pairs of parents to form hybrids: thus, wherever *glutinosa* and *minima,* or *latifolia* and *pedemontana,* or *auricula* and *hirsuta* meet, one can be sure of finding plenty of hybrids, whereas where *marginata* and *latifolia,* or even *minima* and *hirsuta* meet, there will be only a few hybrids.

So far we have been considering the identification of hybrids in the wild, and we have seen that this is not too difficult in most instances.

175

A very much more difficult, sometimes quite impossible, problem airses when someone, say at a show, comes up to you with a plant originating from a nursery, or raised from garden seed and asks, "What is it?". As indicated above, the section Aleuritia (Farinosae) is fairly safe, and one can assume that the unknown is almost certain to be a species—But with Sections Primula (Vernales) and Auriculastrum anything can happen in a garden or nursery . . . The problem is well illustrated by the very popular plant 'Linda Pope', which is probably a hybrid whose origin and parentage are, and are likely to remain, unknown. In such cases one can only make an educated guess.

CHAPTER 6
ARTIFICIAL HYBRIDS
AND GARDEN VARIETIES

Introduction

This topic is a large and complicated one and obviously cannot be covered in great detail in a book of this size. There are very many artificially produced hybrids, forms and varieties. The naturally occurring hybrids are covered in Chapter 5, but in theory, all of these crosses can be reproduced artificially.

Some of the most common garden plants are artificial primula hybrids. Every gardener is familiar with the large flowered Polyanthus and Primrose hybrids. There are many strains of these and they are produced commercially in large numbers for use in spring bedding, as pot plants or in mixed borders. Grown *en masse* they produce a wonderful display in the spring. We have only included those Primroses and Polyanthus hybrids which are more compact and more suited to use by alpine gardeners. We have also excluded the very specialised Show Auriculas and Alpine Auriculas which we felt were outside the scope of this work. Hybridisation is very frequent in both Auriculastrum and Vernales sections but very rare in other sections. Most of the hybrids produced are fertile and so can be subsequently used for further crossing. This has led to a very complicated situation. Some of the facts and descriptions are difficult to substantiate; documentation, in both the past and present, is rather sparse. Sometimes several plants are being sold under the same clonal name or one plant is being sold under several names. One of the most common reasons for confusion is where seedlings from a clone are given the same name as the parent. A clone is a certain form which can only be reproduced by vegetative means (cuttings or division). Seedlings *SHOULD NOT* be given the same name as the parent unless the parent is of 100 per cent. true breeding and has been self pollinated in isolation. Many of the named varieties within a species (or hybrid group) are often very similar, not being distinct from the general run of seedlings, and showing no particular merit. It is a pity that these have been given names as it only tends to add to the confusion. Any variety that is to be given a clonal name should be distinct and be easily recognisable from other clones.

SECTION: AURICULASTRUM

There are a large number of hybrids and varieties in the group. Most are fertile. All the *artificial* (garden) interspecific hybrids we know of are listed in the table overleaf. The reader is referred to

Chapter 5 for information on the naturally occurring hybrids. Where a naturally occurring hybrid has been produced artificially, it will be mentioned here.

	AURICULA	PALINURI	CARNIOLICA	MARGINATA	LATIFOLIA	APENNINA	DAONENSIS	HIRSUTA	PEDEMONTANA	VILLOSA	CLUSIANA	GLAUCESCENS	SPECTABILIS	WULFENIANA	ALLIONII	INTEGRIFOLIA	KITAIBELIANA	TYROLENSIS	DEORUM	GLUTINOSA
PALINURI																				
CARNIOLICA																				
MARGINATA	YES																			
LATIFOLIA	YES		YES																	
APENNINA																				
DAONENSIS																				
HIRSUTA	YES			YES																
PEDEMONTANA	YES		YES	YES	YES			YES												
VILLOSA	YES			YES	YES			YES												
CLUSIANA																				
GLAUCESCENS																				
SPECTABILIS									YES											
WULFENIANA																				
ALLIONII	YES		YES	YES				YES	YES	YES										
INTEGRIFOLIA																				
KITAIBELIANA	YES																			
TYROLENSIS																				
DEORUM																				
GLUTINOSA																				
MINIMA								YES				YES	YES		YES		YES			

Occurrence of artificial hybrids in the Auriculastrum Section.

We have not tried to make a comprehensive list of all the known named varieties. We have listed most of those currently available and briefly described those which we consider to be the most distinct and popular. Quite a number are not commercially available at the present time. We have dealt with the species in alphabetical order covering the hybrids and varieties of each. As far as we know there are no artificial interspecific hybrids with *PP. apennina*, *clusiana*, *daonensis*, *deorum*, *glutinosa*, *integrifolia*, *palinuri*, *tyrolensis* and *wulfeniana* as one of the parents. (At the time of writing).

A few varieties do not fall clearly under one species or hybrid so we have put these together under a miscellaneous heading.

P. allionii: varieties and hybrids

(a) Varietal clones of *P. allionii*

P. allionii is a variable species, especially with regard to flower size and colour. A large number of clones are in cultivation, some of which were originally collected in the wild. Because of the wide range of forms in cultivation it is pointless and irresponsible to collect any more material from the wild. The flower colour varies from white, through various shades of pink to reddish-purple. A large proportion of the varieties are lilac-pink in colour and many are very similar in appearance. We have only described a small number of clones due to shortage of space. Those described are the ones which we feel are the most popular and distinct. We would like to pay tribute to the late Mr. F. Barker, and to Mrs. H. M. Earle and Mr. K. R. Wooster who have in the past worked hard to produce new and better *P. allionii* clones.

P. allionii alba
Covers the white forms of *P. allionii*. One clone received a Certificate of Merit in 1931. See also 'Avalanche' and 'Snowflake'.

P. allionii 'Anna Griffith'   Plate 70
Collected in the wild by the late Mr. H. Hammer. It was rescued by Mrs. K. N. Dryden from the collection of the late Anna Griffith and named after her. It is a compact form with toothed leaves of quite a bright green. The flowers are a delicate shade of very pale pink, the petals having several notches. A lovely distinct variety. Thrum-eyed. A.M. 1983.

P. allionii 'Apple Blossom'
Has large delicate rose pink flowers shading to white. The petals have wavy edges. Received an A.M. in 1945. Raised by the late Mr. F. Barker. The leaves are mid green, crenate and quite broad. Thrum-eyed. It may be a hybrid.

P. allionii 'Avalanche' (*P.a. alba* 'Avalanche')
Large flowered albino form. Beautifully rounded flowers. Leaves crenate. Raised by Mr. Joe Elliott. A.M. 1974. Pin-eyed.

P. allionii 'Celia'
Is a fine form with up to 7 or 8 perfectly formed overlapping petals. The leaves are quite a rich green. Raised by Mrs. H. M. Earle in 1947. The flower colour is a rich deep lilac-pink. Thrum-eyed.

P. allionii 'Crowsley Variety'
Very popular and well known. The flowers are of a deep, rich crimson with a white eye. The leaves are small greyish green and very slightly toothed. Received a Certificate of Merit in 1934. Collected by Dr. R. Bevan when not in flower. Pin-eyed.

P. allionii 'Margaret Earle'
Raised in 1946 by Mrs. H. M. Earle from *P. allionii* 'Superba'. The flower is 3 cm. in diameter with wavy petals and is similar to the seed parent except in being thrum-eyed instead of pin-eyed. Received a Preliminary Commendation in 1978.

P. allionii 'Mary Berry'
Makes a prostrate mat instead of the usual mound. The leaves are light green and slightly crenate. The flowers are up to 3 cm. in diameter and of a dark reddish purple. A.M. 1952. Raised by the late Mr. Gerard Parker. Thrum-eyed.

P. allionii 'Pinkie'
Raised in 1951 by Mr. K. R. Wooster. Very dwarf and forms a tight cushion. Its colour is a clear pink as opposed to the usual lilac-pink. Early flowering (February). A.M. 1978. Thrum-eyed.

P. allionii 'Praecox'
A very early variety. It often starts to flower in November. It has lilac-pink flowers. Raised by the late Mr. F. Barker. Thrum-eyed.

P. allionii 'Snowflake' (*P.a. alba* 'Snowflake')
Raised by Mr. K. R. Wooster in 1956. Has white crystalline flowers which are often faintly flushed with pink, and up to 3 cm. in diameter. The petals are overlapping with notched tips and a wavy outline. A.M. 1967. Thrum-eyed.

P. allionii 'Superba'
Parent of *P.a.* 'Margaret Earle' which is similar. Has broad over-lapping petals. The large flowers are rose coloured with a white eye. Pin-eyed.

P. allionii 'Viscountess Byng'
Leaves greyish green and almost devoid of teeth. The colour of the flower is purplish-pink with a white eye. The petals are broad and wavy. A.M. 1937. Thrum-eyed. Rare in cultivation.

P. allionii 'William Earle'
Raised in 1949 by Mrs. H. M. Earle from *P.a.* 'Viscountess Byng'. Has large flowers (up to 3 cm. diameter) which are lilac-pink with a good white eye. The petals are quite wavy at the margins and very broad so that the five petals form an almost complete disc. Thrum-eyed. A.M. 1978.

Other varieties include: 'Austen', 'Elizabeth Earle', 'Marjorie Wooster', 'Nymph', 'Pennine Pink', 'Tranquillity'.

(b) *P. allionii* hybrids

P. allionii is known to cross with at least seven other species. Only one natural hybrid has been found. In cultivation *P. allionii* has been successfully crossed with *P.P. auricula, carniolica, hirsuta, marginata, minima, pedemontana* and *villosa*. Other crosses should occur but we have not heard of them. Seed has been produced from crosses with *P.P. clusiana, glaucescens* and *palinuri* but so far no germination of these has occurred. *P. allionii* will also cross with a range of hybrids such as *P. allionii* hybrids, *P. marginata* hybrids and *P.* × *pubescens* Hort. Most *P. allionii* hybrids are fertile.

1. **P. allionii × P. auricula** (*P. × loiseleuri*)

As both parents are variable, so are the offspring. If a farinose *P. auricula* is used, then the hybrids will show traces of farina. Most of the hybrids are compact plants but very variable as far as size of flowers and length of peduncles are concerned. When a white *P. allionii* is crossed with *P. auricula* the flowers tend to be pale yellow. One such cross (raised by Mrs. J. A. Burrow) received a P.C. in 1982 and has since been named *P. × loiseleuri* 'Lismore Yellow'.

2. **P. allionii × P. carniolica**

The plants resulting from this cross are intermediate with some being closer to one or other of the parents. Mrs. Ivanel Agee in the U.S.A. produced a very good batch (36) of plants from this cross, some being very attractive. One of these has been tentatively named *P.* 'Ivanel'.

3. **P. allionii × P. hirsuta**

The offspring are intermediate between the parents and are compact. The peduncle is usually absent or very short. The leaves are glandular hairy. The best known of this cross is *P.* 'Ethel Barker' in which the leaves are long petioled and downy, the flowers borne freely, three to five together. The peduncle is extremely short and the colour is a bright carmine with a white eye. It was raised by Mr. F. Barker and received an A.M. (A.G.S.) in 1937.

4. **P. allionii × P. marginata** (*P. × miniera*)

At least three wild collected clones are in cultivation (see p. 170 for description). There are also several produced from artificial crosses. The plants are usually compact with leaves that are farinose on the margins and slightly farinose on the surfaces. The peduncle is short and few flowered. The flower size and colour are variable. *P. × miniera* 'Violet Chambers' is a named clone which was produced by Mrs. Ivanel Agee in the U.S.A. while *P. × miniera* 'Sunrise' was produced by Jack Drake in Scotland.

5. **P. allionii × P. minima**

A clone from this cross was in cultivation in the early 1970's. We do not know if it still exists. We have made this cross and produced seed several times but so far have not managed to germinate any.

6. **P. allionii × P. pedemontana**

This cross usually produces very compact slow growing plants. In the plants we have seen, the leaves are closer to *P. pedemontana* whereas the flowers are closer to *P. allionii*. The peduncle is usually absent or very short. Most are very attractive with large lilac pink (or white) flowers with a white eye.

7. **P. allionii × P. villosa**

The plants are compact and intermediate between the parents. Mrs. Ivanel Agee in the U.S.A. crossed *P. allionii* with *P. villosa* ssp. *commutata*.

8. **P. allionii × hybrids of P. marginata**

The hybrids from this cross are usually very compact and floriferous. The most popular cross has been between *P. allionii* and *P.*

'Linda Pope', producing some lovely and well known plants. *P.* 'Beatrice Wooster' (*P. allionii* × *P.* 'Linda Pope') has leaves similar to *P. allionii* but larger and less sticky. Flowers on farinose scapes held just above the leaves, clear pink with a large white eye. Thrum-eyed. Raised 1947 by Mr. K. R. Wooster. P.C. 1952. A.M. 1969. F.C.C. 1983. *P.* 'Fairy Rose' (*P. allionii* × *P.* 'Linda Pope') **(Plate 71)** has very jagged saw-edged leaves and bears large rose pink flowers on a short peduncle.

The flowers have a very small white centre and have a strong tendency to produce extra petals. Raised by Mr. K. R. Wooster in 1947. Thrum-eyed. A.M. 1951.

P. 'Joan Hughes' **(Plate 73)** (*P. allionii* × *P.* 'Linda Pope') has very compact cushions of soft *marginata*-like leaves which are regularly toothed. Flowers borne in umbels of up to 20 on very short, slightly sticky peduncles. Colour is a deep magenta pink which is noticeably darker on the edges of the petals. Flowers approximately 1·5 cm. diameter with rounded overlapping petals which have notched tips. In the centre is a conspicuous band of white from which radiates fine white lines. Very slow to multiply vegetatively. Raised by Jack Drake. A.M. 1967.

P. 'Purple Emperor' ('Fairy Rose G') (*P. allionii* × *P.* 'Linda Pope') is a very slow, low-growing plant with only scalloped leaves. The extremely large flowers are produced on the shortest peduncles, usually about three to four to the scape. Flowers a rich bluish-purple with a very small white eye. Raised by Mr. K. R. Wooster.

9. P. allionii × P. pubescens Hort.

This cross produces a very wide range of offspring. There are obviously a very large number of possibilities. *P.* 'Margaret' (*P. allionii* × *P. pubescens* Hort.) **(Plate 72)** has compact rosettes of greyish-green, faintly notched, pointed, ovate or broadly lanceolate leaves with finely ciliated margins. The flower scapes are about 2 cm. long and bear an umbel of up to 20 flowers which have a diameter of nearly 2·5 cm. and are lilac-pink with a white eye. The petals open quite flat and are well overlapped and notched at the apex. A.M. 1961.

P. 'Gladaline' (*P. allionii* × *P. pubescens* Hort.) forms a rosette of light green, shining, toothed, slightly farinose leaves up to 5 cm. in length. The 5 cm. scape bears a head of about 9 cherry pink flowers with a yellow eye. Raised by Mr. G. B. Jones. P.C. 1952.

P. auricula: varieties and hybrids

P. auricula is a variable species and most of the naturally occurring forms are in cultivation.

(a) *P. auricula* varieties

The wild forms are described on p. 24. There are also a number of plants which are treated as varieties of *P. auricula* but which may be sports or hybrids of that species, these include the following:

P. auricula 'Blairside Yellow'
Small neat plant of 5–10 cm. Efarinose. Flowers small, yellow (up to 1·5 cm. diameter). Leaves up to 5 cm. long by 2 cm. wide with shallow regular teeth. P.C. in 1958. Very popular.

P. auricula 'Broadwell Gold'
A vigorous plant. The leathery leaves are heavily dusted with golden farina. The heads of flowers are carried on 10 cm. stems and are a deep gold. The petals are frilled and the flowers have fine mealy eyes.

P. auricula 'Queen Alexandra'
Old Irish variety. Vigorous plant with entire or slightly toothed leaves. Produces large fragrant, frilled, primrose yellow flowers in many flowered umbels.

(b) *P. auricula* hybrids

Artificial hybrids with *PP. allionii, hirsuta, kitaibeliana, latifolia, marginata, pedemontana* and *villosa* are known. Crossing *P. auricula* with the white forms of the various species should give a range of plants which are compact with yellow, pale yellow or white flowers. Only a few of these crosses have so far been produced. More effort would increase the number of yellow flowered plants, a colour which is not common in the Auriculastrum Section. In addition, there are two well known and popular aggregates of artificial hybrids, *P. × pubescens* Hort. and the Garden (or Border) Auriculas.

1. **P. auricula × P. allionii** (*P. × loiseleuri*)
This is described under *P. allionii* hybrids on p. 181.

2. **P. auricula × P. hirsuta** (*P. × pubescens*)
This cross is described under *P. × pubescens* in the chapter on natural hybrids. See also under *P. × pubescens* Hort. on p. 184.

3. **P. auricula × kitaibeliana**
This cross is very rare and is not generally available. Mr. F. Kummert has produced plants from this cross.

4. **P. auricula × P. latifolia**
This hybrid has been produced but we do not know the raiser. The most interesting result would propably be obtained by crossing a compact *P. auricula* with a good form of *P. latifolia alba*.

5. **P. auricula × P. marginata**
Several people have produced this cross (including Mr. and Mrs. H. Taylor and ourselves). The resulting plants are intermediate although some may be quite close to one of the parents. One form which is close to *P. marginata* is *P.* 'Rhenaniana' (*P.* 'Rheiniana'). This was produced by Mr. G. Arends in 1903 by crossing *P. auricula* with *P. marginata*. Flowers violet blue with white centre, 5–10 on each peduncle. Leaves elliptical, often obtuse (about 8 cm. long by 3 cm. broad) with large teeth. Farina yellowish.

6. **P. auricula × P. pedemontana** (*P. × sendtneri*)
This cross produces compact plants but some of the colours may be unattractive. Mr. and Mrs. H. Taylor have made this cross. *P. pedemontana alba* is probably the best form to use.

7. P. auricula × P. villosa

The resulting plants are intermediate between the parents. We do not know the raiser.

8. P. × pubescens Hort. Aggregate

P. auricula has been extensively used to produce the group of hybrids called *P. × pubescens* Hort.

P. × pubescens is the naturally occuring cross between *P. auricula* and *P. hirsuta*. Plants from this cross were in cultivation as early as the 17th century. These hybrids were fertile and they and their progeny were crossed and re-crossed to produce the group called *P. × pubescens* Hort. Later some of these were crossed with certain other species (such as *P. villosa*) to produce an even more diverse aggregate. Most are floriferous and vigorous. Some of the named varieties (such as 'Mrs. J. H. Wilson') have been in existence for a long time. Some of the most distinctive are as follows.

P. × pubescens alba. A group name which covers any white forms of *P. × pubescens*. The most common is an attractive compact plant with globular heads of white flowers (up to 15 in each head).

P. × pubescens 'Bewerley White' is a vigorous variety which covers itself with heads of creamy white flowers.

P. × pubescens 'Boothman's Variety' is of neat habit and has proved to be fast growing and floriferous. Flowers bright crimson with a clear white eye. The petals are well overlapped and notched.

P. × pubescens 'Christine' makes a compact rosette of yellowish green nearly sessile, shallowly crenate leaves. The peduncles are 7–10 cm. long and each carry 2–8 flowers of a deep old rose shade with a white eye. Raised by Mr. J. Drake. A.M. 1960.

P. × pubescens 'Faldonside' is an old variety. The flowers are a dusky reddish pink with a white eye. A neat plant, the peduncles being 7–10 cm. high.

P. × pubescens 'Freedom' is a vigorous variety which has heads of deep lilac flowers. The leaves are dark green and toothed. The stems may become rather elongated as the plant matures.

P. × pubescens 'Harlow Car' is a vigorous plant with heads of large creamy white flowers. The foliage is mid green and shallowly toothed with regular teeth. Peduncles 7–10 cm.

P. × pubescens 'Mary Curle' has rosettes of pale green broadly lanceolate, toothed leaves. Bears umbels of up to 18 reddish purple flowers carried on 5–7 cm. peduncles with farinose pedicels. The corolla is trumpet shaped with a long narrow tube and a white farinose eye. The calyx is farinose. A.M. 1964.

P. × pubescens 'Mrs. J. H. Wilson' is one of the oldest varieties. Very popular and well known. The plant makes a compact rosette of greyish-green, rather thick lanceolate to obovate leaves. The young leaves are sharply serrated at the tip but this disappears with age and the mature foliage is only slightly toothed. The peduncle is about 7 cm. long and carries a many flowered umbel of fragrant purple, white centred flowers. The flowers are approximately 2·5 cm. diameter and have overlapping petals which are notched at the tip. A.M. 1960.

P. × *pubescens* 'Ruby' has wine-red flowers, rather smaller than most but very nicely set off by a white centre.

P. × *pubescens* 'Rufus' makes a rosette of pale green, shallowly toothed leaves measuring up to 7 cm. long by 5 cm. across and carries showy heads of up to 16 flowers on peduncles about 9 cm. long. The individual flowers are about 3 cm. diameter with well overlapped notched petals whose colour is an unusual shade of red with a golden eye (almost brick red) (see **Plate 76**).

P. × *pubescens* 'The General' is a vigorous variety with rosettes of pale green shallowly toothed lanceolate leaves. The flowers are a rich velvety red with yellow eyes carried in a few flowered umbel on peduncles which are 7–10 cm. high.

Other *P.* × *pubescens* varieties include: 'Balfouriana'; 'Blue Wave'; 'Cedric'; 'C. J. Porter'; 'Commodore'; 'Crighton Red'; 'Glasnevin'; 'Gnome'; 'Helvetica'; 'Henry Hall'; 'Ilene'; 'Jean Walker'; 'Kingscote'; 'Ladybird'; 'Linnet'; 'Marlene'; 'Moonlight'; 'Mrs. Freeman'; 'Mrs. G. F. Wilson'; 'Purple Spark'; 'Red Indian'; 'Roberton Hall'; 'Ruby'; 'The Cardinal'; 'Violetta'; 'White Pearl'; 'Zuleika Dobson' (this has been lost).

9. Border Auricula Aggregate (Garden Auriculas)

These are hardy hybrids of *P. auricula* which are close to that species, and most retain the powdery white eye. The following are often grown by alpine gardeners:
P. 'Blue Velvet'—deep violet-blue, white eyed flowers.
P. 'Old Irish Blue'—rich velvety blue flowers.
P. 'Old Red Dusty Miller'—large scarlet flowers with a large farinose white eye on a yellow background (see **Plate 74**).
P. 'Old Yellow Dusty Miller'—yellow flowers with a farinose white eye.

Other varieties include: *P.* 'Blue Dusty Miller'; *P.* 'Clare'; *P.* 'Joan Elliott'; *P.* 'Lennon's White'.

P. carniolica hybrids

Artificial hybrids with *PP. allionii* and *pedemontana* are known. The hybrid with *P. allionii* has been discussed on page 181. Mr. and Mrs. H. Taylor crossed *P. carniolica* with *P. pedemontana* and produced a group of plants which have yet to flower. The leaves resemble *P. carniolica* at the moment. It would be interesting to make other *P. carniolica* crosses as it is a very desirable species. An artificial *P.* × *venusta* (*P. carniolica* × *P. auricula*) would be worth producing as the wild *P.* × *venusta* appears to have virtually disappeared from cultivation and from the wild.

P. clusiana: varieties and hybrids

P. clusiana 'Murray-Lyon'.
This is a large flowered form which may contain some 'blood' from another species (*P. minima* possibly). The flowers are up to 4 cm. in diameter.

P. daonensis hybrids

We know of no artificial hybrids of *P. daonensis* although Mr. and Mrs. H. Taylor have produced seed by crossing it with *PP. marginata* and *minima*. This seed has not yet germinated.

P. glaucescens hybrids

The artificial hybrid with *P. minima* has been produced by Mr. F. Kummert in Austria.

P. hirsuta: varieties and hybrids

(a) *P. hirsuta varieties*
P. hirsuta var. exscapa
The scape on this variety is extremely short or absent. One clone of this has been established in cultivation for many years.
P. hirsuta alba
Includes all white flowered forms. One clone has been in cultivation for a long time under the name *P. hirsuta* var. *nivea*. Several other clones are in cultivation.
(b) *P. hirsuta* hybrids
Artificial hybrids with *PP. allionii, auricula, latifolia, pedemontana* and *villosa* are known.

The hybrid with *P. allionii* has been discussed on p. 181. *P. hirsuta* has been used extensively to produce the group of hybrids called *P. × pubescens* Hort. (*hirsuta × auricula aggregate*). These are described under *P. auricula* hybrids on p. 184. Mr. and Mrs. H. Taylor have produced a hybrid between *P. hirsuta alba* and *P. latifolia alba*. Mr. F. Kummert in Austria has produced hybrids between *P. hirsuta* and *P. minima*. Mr. and Mrs. Taylor have also produced a hybrid between *P. hirsuta* and *P. pedemontana*. The hybrid with *P. villosa* has been produced by Mr. F. Kummert. There is one named form of *P. × berninae* (*P. hirsuta × P. latifolia*) known as *P. × berninae* 'Windrush Variety' which is compact and slow growing with crenate leaves. The flowers are of a good size, freely produced and of a delicate shade of reddish pink tinted with mauve. They have white eyes.

P. kitaibeliana hybrids

No wild hybrids of *P. kitaibeliana* are known. In cultivation *P. kitaibeliana* has been crossed with *P. auricula* and *P. minima* (produced by Mr. F. Kummert in Austria).

P. latifolia hybrids

Artificial hybrids with *PP. auricula, hirsuta, pedemontana* and *villosa* are known. The hybrids with *P. auricula* (see p. 183) and *P. hirsuta* (see p. 183) have already been dealt with. Several people have crossed *P. latifolia* with *P. pedemontana* (including Mr. and Mrs. H. Taylor). When *P. latifolia* is crossed with *P. pedemontana alba* the colour of *P. latifolia* should be retained. This is a very desirable cross. Plants of *P. latifolia* × *P. villosa* have been produced but we do not know the raiser.

A named variety of *P.* × *crucis* (*P. latifolia* × *P. marginata*) was described by Reginald Farrer in *The English Rock Garden* (*P.* × *crucis* 'Blue Bowl'). Beautiful specimens of *P.* × *crucis* were found in the wild more recently by S. Mayr and F. Kummert. It would be well worth while reproducing this cross artificially using good forms of each species. As far as we know *P.* × *crucis* 'Blue Bowl' has been lost to cultivation.

P. marginata: varieties and hybrids

(a) Varietal clones of *P. marginata*

P. marginata is a variable species and quite a large number of named clones exist. The following are some of the most popular and distinct forms.

P. marginata alba. This covers all the white forms of the species. As far as we know there is no really good white form in cultivation as yet. The most common one in cultivation has small flowers which are pinkish at first fading to white as they age.

P. marginata 'Barbara Clough'. Flowers pinkish lilac, nicely rounded with a white eye. Leaves broadly lanceolate with medium sized teeth (up to 9 cm. long by 3 cm. wide). Farina yellowish.

P. marginata 'Beamish Variety'. Flowers blue with a white farinose eye. Leaves broadly lanceolate with medium sized teeth (about 7 cm. long by 2 cm. wide). Farina whitish. There is some confusion about this variety as two forms are sometimes labelled as this.

P. marginata 'Beatrice Lascaris'. This is a compact slow growing form. Flowers medium size of a good clear blue with a white farinose eye. Leaves broadly spathulate (about 3 cm. long by 1·5 cm. wide) with very small regular teeth. Farina yellowish. It may possibly be a hybrid. (Sometimes produces glandular hairs on the young side shoots.) Corolla flat. Wright-Smith and Fletcher list this as a primary hybrid between *P. marginata* and *P. allionii*, but we do not agree with them. It appears to contain much more than 50 per cent. of *P. marginata* 'blood'. This is borne out by the fact that it passes on characteristics which are typical of *P. marginata* when used for hybridising.

P. marginata 'Caerulea'. Flowers a good clear blue, corolla funnel shaped. Leaves spathulate (about 6 cm. long by 1·5 cm. wide) with medium sized narrow teeth. Farina whitish, the leaves are heavily coated. This is similar to *P. marginata* 'Holden's Variety' in some aspects. A.M. 1980.

P. marginata 'Clear's Variety'. Flowers small, lilac with white eyes. Leaves spathulate (about 6 cm. long by 2 cm. wide), deeply toothed. Farina yellowish. The peduncles and pedicels are short.

P. marginata 'Correvon's Variety'. Vigorous variety. Flowers large, lavender. Leaves deeply cut (about 5 cm. long by 3 cm. wide) with medium sized teeth. Farina yellowish.

P. marginata 'Drake's Form'. Larger than the type. Flowers pale lilac lavender. The foliage is particularly attractive and it resembles *P. marginata* 'Pritchard's Variety' in a number of aspects. Raised by Mr. J. Drake. A.M. 1951.

P. marginata 'Elizabeth Fry' Old variety. Flowers large, silvery-lavender borne four to five on each peduncle. Leaves spathulate (about 5 cm. long by 2 cm. wide) with small to medium sized teeth. Farina yellow. The flowers are held on small peduncles.

P. marginata 'Highland Twilight'. Neat habit. Flowers rich purple-blue. Leaves broad (about 4·5 cm. long by 3 cm. wide) with small shallow teeth.

P. marginata 'Holden's Variety' (*P.m.* 'Holden Clough'). Compact form. Flowers small, blue. Leaves narrow (about 5 cm. long by 1·5 cm. wide), regularly serrated, heavily powdered. Farina whitish. Corolla funnel shaped.

P. marginata 'Inschriach Form'. Flowers blue. Leaves spathulate (about 5 cm. long by 2·5 cm. wide) with narrow teeth of medium size. Farina yellowish.

P. marginata 'Ivy Agee' (*P.m.* 'Agee'). This was produced by Mrs. Ivanel Agee in the U.S.A. Flowers large lilac-blue with a pronounced cream eye. Leaves heavily farinose.

P. marginata 'Kesselring's Variety'. This is similar to *P.m.* 'Pritchard's Variety' but the plants and flowers are smaller. It also flowers two to three weeks later. Flowers deep lavender. Farina whitish. There is some confusion over this variety.

P. marginata 'Pritchard's Variety'. Flowers lilac-purple with a white farinose eye, carried in an umbel of up to 8 on 5 cm. to 8 cm. peduncles. Leaves broadly spathulate (up to 9 cm. long by 4 cm. wide), greyish green, with jagged toothed margins. Farina white, found chiefly on the edges of the leaves. The leaf blades and flower scapes are only slightly farinose. A.M. 1964.

P. marginata 'Rosea'. Flowers lilac-pink. Leaves narrowly elliptical (up to 5 cm. long by 1·5 cm. wide) with small teeth and the blade narrows into a small petiole.

P. marginata 'Rubra'. Flowers deep rosy-lilac, Leaves broadly ovate-lanceolate (about 7 cm. long by 2·5 cm. wide) with medium sized teeth. Farina very pale yellow.

P. marginata 'Waithman's Variety'. Flowers light blue. Leaves spathulate (about 5 cm. long by 2 cm. wide) with large teeth. Farina white.

Other varieties which are available include: 'Baldock's Purple'; 'Crenata'; 'E. L. Bolton'; 'Highland Fraser'; Jenkin's Variety'; 'Lilac'; 'Superba'.

(b) *P. marginata* hybrids

Artificial hybrids with *PP. allionii, latifolia, auricula, pedemontana* and *villosa* are known. The hybrid with *P. allionii* is discussed under *P. allionii* (see p. 181) The hybrid with *P. latifolia* is also discussed under *P. latifolia* hybrids (see p. 187). The hybrid with *P. auricula* has been dealt with under *P. auricula* hybrids (see p. 183). The hybrids with *P. pedemontana* and with *P. villosa* are intermediate between the parents.

P. marginata also crosses with a range of hybrids. The best known are as follows:

P. 'Hurstwood Susan' (*P. marginata* × *P.* 'Decora') which has obovate leaves (up to 8 cm. long) with small amounts of farina. The peduncles are up to 10 cm. high with umbels of scented violet-purple flowers with a white eye. The flowers are about 2 cm. diameter with up to eight flowers carried in each umbel. A.M. 1970. Raised by Mr. J. G. Strangman. We have no information on *P.* 'Decora'.

P. 'Hyacinthia' is a robust plant raised by Mr. G. H. Berry in 1943. It was produced from *P. marginata* 'Beamish Variety' (by line breeding). The leaves are serrated and show some farina on the edges but are smooth green on the whole. The large flowers (up to 3 cm. diameter) are hyacinth blue with six uniform, overlapping petals. A.M. 1945. A very good variety.

P. 'Lilac Domino' is a seedling of 'Linda Pope'. The flowers are similar to *P.* 'Linda Pope' but smaller. The leaves are shorter with less farina.

P. 'Linda Pope' (*P. marginata* × ?) is the best known of all the *P. marginata* hybrids and an outstanding variety. It was raised by a Mr. Pope of Birmingham and called after his daughter. The pollen parent is still in doubt. It has large rounded flowers of an attractive mauve-blue held on an erect scape. The large toothed leaves are heavily powdered with whitish farina. The flowers have a white farinose eye. A.M. 1920, F.C.C. in 1967.

P. 'Marven' (*P. marginata* × *P.* × *venusta*) makes a rosette of shortly stalked light green leaves which are powdered with farina, particularly on the margins. The stout farinose peduncles bear umbels of up to 15 flowers carried on short farinose pedicels. The flowers are a deep violet-blue with overlapping petals. The flower has a very dark eye in the centre which is conspicuously ringed with white farina. The farinose calyx is a dark greenish black. Certificate of Merit in 1964.

P. 'White Linda Pope' (P. 'White Lady') seedling of 'Linda Pope' having large obovate, dentate leaves. The peduncles are about 10 cm.

high bearing an umbel of up to 10 flowers. The flowers (each about 2·5 cm. across) open a pale green and fade to white as the flowers mature. They have a pale greenish yellow eye.

Other *P. marginata* hybrids include: 'Coningsby Blue'; 'Janet'; 'Pamela'; 'Ringdove'.

P. minima hybrids

Artificial hybrids with *PP. allionii, glaucescens, hirsuta, kitaibeliana* and *spectabilis* are known. The hybrids with *PP. allionii* (see p. 181), *glaucescens* (see p.186), *hirsuta* (see p. 186) and *kitaibeliana* (see p.186) have already been dealt with. The hybrid with *spectabilis* has been produced by Mr. and Mrs. H. Taylor. They crossed *P. minima alba* with *P. spectabilis* and produced one plant. It has leaves which are very frilled and about half the size of *P. spectabilis*. It has not yet flowered. They have also produced seed by crossing *P. minima* with *PP. daonensis* and *pedemontana* but they have not yet germinated.

Some clones of the *P. minima × hirsuta* aggregate are well known garden plants. (They were probably collected in the wild originally.). They all have white eyes to the flowers, e.g.

P. × forsteri forma hort *bileckii*. This clone is close to *P. minima* and forms a mat or low cushion. The leaves are similar to *P. minima* but broader, darker green and in 2 cm. wide rosettes. The flowers are a deep reddish pink and almost sessile. The petals are broader than in *P. minima*.

P. × forsteri forma hort *forsteri*. This clone is close to *P. minima* but has glandular leaves which are rounded at the tip. The peduncle is short and carries one to three flowers. The flower is pink about 2·5 cm. diameter and the throat has many long villous hairs.

P. × forsteri forma hort *kellereri*. This clone is quite close to *P. hirsuta* but differs in the short glands and in the small leaves being armed with horny pointed teeth. It also has longer bracts. The peduncle bears three to six crimson flowers (2–2·5 cm. diameter). This is rare in cultivation.

P. × forsteri forma hort *steinii*. A vigorous clone with spoon shaped leaves which are glandular with seven to ten horny-pointed teeth. The peduncle is up to 6 cm. long bearing two to seven large flowers. The flower is crimson, about 2 cm. diameter with a villous throat.

One clone of the *P. minima × glutinosa* aggregate is a well known garden plant:

P. × floerkeana forma hort *biflora*. Quite close to *P. minima* from which it differs mainly in having two flowers on a short peduncle. These are large and of a bright pink (see also p. 168).

P. pedemontana hybrids

Artificial hybrids with *PP. allionii, auricula, carniolica, hirsuta, latifolia, marginata* and *spectabilis* are known. The hybrids with *PP. allionii* (see p. 181), *auricula* (see p. 183), *carniolica* (see p.185), *hirsuta* (see p. 186), *latifolia* (see p. 187) and *marginata* (see p. 189) have already been dealt with. Mr. and Mrs. H. Taylor have produced one plant of the hybrid between *P. pedemontana* and *P. spectabilis*. This is about mid-way between the parents. *P. pedemontana* has also been crossed with *P. ×pubescens alba* (produced by Mrs. Ivanel Agee in U.S.A.).

P. spectabilis hybrids

Artificial hybrids with *PP. minima* and *pedemontana* are known. The hybrid with *P. minima* is discussed opposite, that with *P. pedemontana* above.

P. villosa hybrids

Artificial hybrids with *PP. allionii* (see p. 181), *auricula* (see p. 183), *hirsuta* (see p. 186), *latifolia* (see p. 187) and *marginata* (see p. 189) are known. These have already been dealt with under the hybrids of these species.

Miscellaneous hybrids of the Auriculastrum Section

Include the following:

P. 'Barbara Barker' (*P.* 'Linda Pope'×*P.* ×*pubescens* 'Zuleika Dobson') has large lavender-blue flowers 2 cm. across with white eyes, borne several to a peduncle. The plain green leaves have very distinct, white notched margins. Raised by Clarence Elliot.

P. 'Bellamy Pride' (*P. auricula* × ?) has trusses of white flowers shading to very pale pink, held just above the foliage. They are scented. The foliage is slightly toothed at the margins and covered with fairly dense white farina. Raised by Mr. F. Walker.

P. 'Belluensis'. We do not know the origin or the exact appearance of this. All the plants we have seen under this name have been the same as *P. ×pubescens* 'Freedom'.

P. 'Broxbourne' (?) is a compact plant whose overall height does not exceed 8 cm. It is very free flowering, with soft pink flowers of up to 3 cm. diameter. A.M. 1979.

P. 'Crimson Velvet' (*P. latifolia* hybrid?) is a compact plant with toothed leaves. The flowers are deep crimson held on erect stems.

P. 'Dianne' (*P. ×forsteri* × ?) bears a distinct resemblance to *P. × forsteri* (seed parent) but has larger rosettes. The leaves are broadly spathulate with the apex cut into six or seven sharp conspicuous teeth. The flower scapes are 2·5–4 cm. long and carry 1–3 flowers. The corolla is a pleasing shade of deep magenta-crimson. Raised by Mr. J. Drake. P.C. in 1960.

P. 'Rachel Reid' (?) has large flowers which are deep purple with white eyes. The large leaves are ovobate with toothed margins and slightly farinose.

P. 'Zenobia' (?) has leaves up to 7 cm. long by 2·5 cm. wide with regularly toothed margins. The leaves are covered in whitish farina. The flowers are purple with a white eye.

SECTION: VERNALES

There are a large number of hybrids and varieties in this group. Most are fertile. A number of commercial firms sell strains of Primrose and Polyanthus rather than named clones. The most notable of these is Barnhaven (originally from Oregon but now based in the N.W. of England.) There are also many named clones in circulation. Members of the American Primrose Society in particular have been busy producing many new cultivars in the last few years. We have only covered the main groups of hybrids and, even then, somewhat superficially due to restriction of space.

One primary hybrid from this section which is well worth growing is the one between *P. juliae* and *P. elatior* (there is a picture of this in *Curtis's Bot. Mag.*, 1956–57, *171*, 302). This has been produced by Professor D. H. Valentine and others.

The following are the main aggregates of hybrids in this section:

Primula × pruhoniciana (syn. P. × juliana)

This is a name which covers the many hybrids between *P. juliae* and other members of the Vernales Section. *P. juliae* was discovered in the Caucasus in 1900 and was introduced into cultivation shortly afterwards. Mr. F. Zeeman from Pruhonitz crossed *P. juliae* with a blue *P. vulgaris* variety and he labelled the resulting plants *P. pruhonitziana.* At about the same time (1913 onwards) Mr. G. Arends in Germany crossed *P. juliae* with several coloured forms of *P. vulgaris*. These hybrids he called *P. × helenae*. After further selection he began to name and release varieties. (These included 'Betty Green', 'Jewel' and 'Wanda'.)

Since then a large number of growers have used *P. juliae* to produce new *P. × pruhoniciana* varieties. The list of varieties is now a very long one and because of this we have only included some of the established ones (including those commercially available). As well as named varieties there are also a number of strains in circulation (such as the Barnhaven New Juliana Strain). The most easily available varieties are marked with a star. The others are very rare and some may be possibly lost.

(a) Varieties of Primrose habit (or semi-Polyanthus habit.)

> **Afterglow**—rich rust-orange colour with distinct eye.
> **Apple Blossom**—apple blossom pink.
> **Avalon**—violet-blue, prefers shade.
> **Belles des Jardins**—clear rosy red, old variety.
> **Belvedere**—lilac, large flowers, old variety.

*Betty Green—crimson with a clear yellow eye.
*Blue Cushion—blue, vigorous.
*Blue Horizon—bright grey-blue with yellow eye. Sport of Wanda. Vigorous, free flowering. P.C. 1950.
*Blue Riband—deep blue with red shading at centre. Vigorous.
Blue Velvet—deep purple-blue of velvet texture.
Bridget—rich mauve-pink with a large yellow eye.
Buckland Belle—deep violet-blue flushed with crimson, and with a large pale yellow eye. Vigorous.
*Bunty—purple-blue with yellow eye. Free flowering.

Camilla—purple-cerise. Free flowering.
Cecily Mordaunt—violet-blue flowers shaded with crimson at the centre.
*Cherry—cherry red.
Cottage Maid—lilac-pink with a stripe down each petal.
*Craddock White—white with yellow eye.
*Crimson Cushion—blood-red flowers.
Crimson Glory—large crimson-red flowers.
*Crimson Queen—large red flowers.
*Crispii—mauve-pink.

David Green—dark red with almost no eye.
*Dinah—velvet burgundy-red flowers with an olive green eye.
Dorothy—sulphur-yellow flowers with frilled petals, rare.
*E. R. Janes—salmon-pink flushed orange. Very good. Popular.
F. Ashby—deep crimson flowers, bronze foliage, compact.
Flene—velvet-crimson flowers of unique shape.
Flower Cushion—salmon-red.
Frühlingzauber—royal-purple, vigorous, free flowering.
Gem of Roses—large rose pink flowers, large yellow eye surrounded by white.
*Gloria—scarlet with white markings on the inside edge of the petals, yellow eye.
*Groeneken's Glory—bright mauve-pink with green eye.
Harbinger—large white yellow-eyed flowers, rare.
Henleigh Beauty—reddish-pink with yellow eye.
*Icombe Hybrid—large rosy-mauve flowers with white eye. Vigorous.
*Iris Mainwaring—pale blue flushed pink, compact.
*Jewel—reddish-purple, compact.
*Jill—mauve-purple with greenish-white eye, compact.
Joan Schofield—red flushed with vermillion and having a large yellow star-shaped eye, early.
John Ashworth—mahogany-red, compact.
John Hammond—large cherry-red flowers with large orange eye. Rare.
Julius Caesar—large red flowers, dark bronze leaves.
Kathleen—large dark blue flowers flushed with red and mauve.
Keith—pale yellow, frilly petals, dwarf, rare.
Kingfisher—blue with a yellow and red eye. Compact.
Lilac Bunty—rosy-lilac.
*Lilac Time—pale rosy lilac, flowers on short Polyanthus stems.
*Lingwood Beauty—red flowers with deep orange eye.
Lizzie Green—brick-red starry flowers.
Lucinda Green—deep mauve with candy stripes down each petal, early.
Madge—pink, of very dwarf Polyanthus habit.
Martin Argles—deep reddish-purple with orange and red eye.
Maureen Genders—deep red edged white with a large pale yellow star like eye.
Mauve Queen—mauve, very early.
Miranda—rich purple-red, early.
Miss Massey—deep crimson, very dwarf, rare.
*Morton Hybrid—red with large yellow eye, very dwarf.

*Mrs. Frank Neave—small red flowers, long flowering.
*Mrs. Macgillavry—rich violet-mauve, popular.
Mrs. Pirrie—rich mauve.
*Pam—reddish-purple, small flowers, long flowering.
Pauline—orange shaded with yellow, large flowers.
*Perle Von Bottrop—vivid red-purple.
Primavera—orange-red with large orange eye.
Purple Beauty—rich crimson flushed with mauve.
*Purple Cushion—similar to 'Wanda' but with reddish leaves.
*Purple Splendour—large red-purple flowers with pale yellow eye.
*Queen of the Whites—large clear white flowers.

Red Carpet—vivid scarlet, masses of very small flowers.
Red Star—large red flowers with yellow eye.
Reine des Violettes—violet with yellow eye, semi-Polyanthus habit.
Riverslea—dark mauve, very dwarf.
*Romeo—very large violet flowers, vigorous and prolific.
Rosy Morn—purple-pink with large yellow eye.
Rubin—small pinkish-red flowers with orange eye, reddish leaves.

Schneekissen (Snow Cushion)
Sir Bedivere—dark reddish star shaped flowers, eyeless.
*Snow Cushion—small flowers of pure white. A.M. 1937.
*Snow White—white flowers, vigorous.
Sunset Glow—orange-scarlet, compact, better in shade.
Sweet Lavender—lavender flushed with pink, old variety.

The Pilgrim—crimson with orange and scarlet eye.
The Sultan—rich brown.
Tiny Tim—similar to 'Pam' with orange red flowers.
Trizone—has three zones on the petals; blue, purple and red.
Veronica—steel blue with deep orange eye.
*Wanda—purple-red flowers. The most popular variety.
Wanda's Rival—rich rosy-mauve, same habit as 'Wanda'.
*Wendy—pale pink flushed mauve, frilled petals.
*Wisley Crimson—large purple-red flowers, bronze green foliage.

(b) Varieties of Polyanthus habit.

Anita—deep blue suffused with red, long flowering.
Barrowby Gem—yellow shaded with green, early and long flowering.
Bartimeus—dark velvety-crimson with no eye, old variety.
*Beamish Foam—pink splashed with pale yellow.
Beltany Red—reddish-tangerine with green eye and edged with gold.
Blue Cocade—violet-blue with yellow eye.
Charles Bloom—velvet red-purple with orange eye.
Czar—plum colour, large flowers.
Emperor—red-purple with large white centre and a white spot on the edge of each petal.
Fair Maid—orange-scarlet with a double centre of gold.
Felicity—rich purple-pink with green eye, frilled petals, late.
Hunter's Moon—apricot with yellow centre.
*Ideal—purple with a yellow eye.
*Kinlough Beauty—salmon-pink with cream stripe down each petal.
*Lady Greer—pale yellow, small flowers.
*McWatt's Cream—small cream coloured flowers.
Miss Osborne—small mauve flowers.
Pink Foam—small pale pink starry flowers.
Prince Albert—reddish purple with a blue stripe down the edge of each petal.
Raspberries and Cream—red edged with cream.
Red Ensign—velvet-red with golden eye.

Serenity—red striped with yellow, small flowers.
Spring Darling—cherry-red, vigorous.
*****Tawny Port**—port wine coloured flowers, reddish leaves, dwarf Polyanthus habit, long flowering.
The Bishop—large deep purple flowers.
*****The Bride**—pure white.
Topsy—wine-red with bronze centre.
William Genders—violet-pink striped with white.

Double Primroses

(including those of Polyanthus and semi-Polyanthus habit)

The early double Primroses were sports of *P. vulgaris* (or other Primrose species). When *P. juliae* was introduced in 1900 several people used it in plant breeding experiments to produce more doubles. Since then many breeders have tried their hand at producing new double varieties.

The following is a list of established varieties. Many are rare in cultivation. There are also many newer named varieties and strains in existence. Those marked with an asterisk are the ones which are most common.

*****Alba Plena** (=Double White)   (Plate 75)
Alexandra Bowhill—large violet flowers with frilled petals. Vigorous.
Amaranthina Plena—crimson-red on short Polyanthus stems may be the old variety 'Brilliant'.
Arthur De Smit—rich purple edged with yellow.
*****Arthur du Moulin**—produced towards the end of the 19th century; very deep violet flowers on short Polyanthus stems. Vigorous. One of the few doubles to produce pollen in quantity.
Bon Accords—this was a group of a dozen double Primroses raised at Cocker Brothers Nurseries near Aberdeen early this century. Still very vigorous. Some of the flowers produced form short Polyanthus stems whilst others on the same plant are borne the same as the native Primrose. Bon accord is the motto of the City of Aberdeen. Bon Accord Salmon and Bon Accord Yellow are thought to be lost to cultivation. Some are perfumed.
Bon Accord Beauty—large purple-blue flowers, the petals being edged with white and spotted white near the edges.
Bon Accord Blue—rich blue.
Bon Accord Brightness—said to be lost but the variety 'Crathes Crimson' may be this.
Bon Accord Cerise—cerise-pink.
Bon Accord Elegans—pink, edged and flecked with white.
*****Bon Accord Gem**—rosy-red shaded with mauve. Vigorous.
Bon Accord Jewel—purple shaded with red on the reverse.
Bon Accord Lavender—lavender with yellow centre.
*****Bon Accord Lilac**—lilac and the petals are marked with yellow at the base.
Bon Accord Purity—large creamy-white flowers tinged with green, frilled petals.
*****Bon Accord Purple**—burgundy-purple flushed crimson on the reverse. Large flowers, Polyanthus habit.
Bon Accord Rose—rose flowers. Vigorous.
Burgundy—large burgundy-red flowers flecked with white.
Buxtons Blue—turquoise-blue. Vigorous.
Carnea Plena—a sport of 'Double White', tinged pale pink.

195

Castlederg—deep yellow splashed with pink and brown.
*****Chevithorne Pink**—pink flowers on short Polyanthus stems.
*****Chevithorne Purple**—deep purple-blue edged with white.
*****Cloth of Gold**—yellow with large pale green leaves.
Crathes Crimson—purple-crimson, perfumed, vigorous.
Crimson Emperor—crimson. Vigorous.
*****Crimson King**—large deep ruby-red flowers on short Polyanthus stems.
Crimson Paddy—ruby-red, also known as 'Paddy'.
Crimson Velvet—(='Madame Pompadour').
Crousseii Plena—(='Marie Crousse').
Curiosity—deep yellow flecked with pink and bronze, dwarf Polyanthus habit.
Delmonden Mauve—purple-blue. Vigorous.
Derncleugh—bronze-red, the petals with yellow margins, Polyanthus stems.
Dingy—(='French Grey')
Double Cream—Cream, vigorous.
Double Green—green flowers.
*****Double Sulphur**—sulphur-yellow.
*****Double White**—white vigorous, Primrose habit.
Double Yellow—yellow, base of petals shaded orange.
Downshill Ensign—violet-blue, late, vigorous, short Polyanthus stems.
French Grey—off white flowers.
Golden Ball—yellow, heavily shaded with pink.
Golden Pheasant—('Curiosity').
Keilour Dawn—apricot-yellow.
Ladies' Delight—(='Quaker's Bonnet')
*****Lady Isobel**—deep yellow on Polyanthus stems.
Lilacina Plena—(='Quaker's Bonnet').
Madame Pompadour—velvet red flowers.
Margot—(='Salmonea').
*****Marie Crousse**—violet, splashed and edged with white.
Marine Blue—deep blue with red markings at base of each petal.
*****Mrs. A. M. Wilson**—large red flowers, vigorous, Polyanthus habit.
Nigra Plena—very deep reddish-maroon.
Old Rose—(='Bon Accord Rose').
Old Scotch Red—(='Crimson King').
*****Our Pat**—sapphire blue flowers, leaves crimson-bronze veined, vigorous, late.
Paddy—(='Crimson Paddy').
Pauline Hawkes—reddish brown flowers.
Pompadour (='Madame Pompadour').
Prince Silverwings—reddish-lilac flecked with white and edged with silver.
Purple Paddy—deep purple, petals edged with silver.
*****Quaker's Bonnet**—pinkish-lilac, vigorous.
*****Red Paddy**—small red flowers, flushed pink and edged with silver.
Rex Theodore—very dark red, edged with silver, Polyanthus habit.
Ronald—very small semi-double flowers of lilac blue.
Rosea Plena—rose-pink.
Rose du Barri—pink flushed orange.
Rubra Plena—(='Red Paddy').
Salmonea—salmon-pink.
Sanguinea Plena—(='Red Paddy').
Tortoiseshell—(='Derncleugh').
Tyrean Purple—pink flushed with red, vigorous.

Jack-in-the-Greens (Primroses and Polyanthus types.)

The blooms are normally single but behind the petals is a ruff like arrangement composed of small 'leaves'. There may also be a rosette of leaves on the top of the peduncle. These were very popular in the 16th century. The leafy ruffs persist after the petals die. They are sometimes called Jack-in-the-Pulpits.

Donegal Danny—dusky pink flowers, Polyanthus habit.
Eldorado—yellow flowers, Polyanthus habit.
Maid Marion—large golden-yellow flowers with darker centre.Primrose form.
Robin Hood—red edged with white, Polyanthus habit.
Salamander—very large flowers, 5 cm. diameter, velvet-red flowers each petal having a white spot towards the edge. Primrose habit.
Tipperary Purple—mauve-purple flowers, Primrose habit.

Hose in Hose (Primroses and Polyanthus types.)

In these the flowers have two rows of petals giving the appearance of two flowers, the tube of the upper 'flower' originating from the centre of the lower. They are also known as Duplex, Double-decker or Cup and Saucer Primroses. They are usually scented. Some are of Polyanthus habit.

(P) denotes those of Polyanthus form.

Aberdeen Yellow—old variety, small clear yellow flowers.
Ashfort (P)—tall brownish-red flowers.
Brimstone (P)—semi-Polyanthus habit, sulphur-yellow flowers.
Canary Bird—early and free flowering canary-yellow flowers.
Castle Howard—primrose-yellow.
Erin's Gem—cream flowers, the lower having an attractive green stripe.
Flora's Garland—deep pink flowers.
Goldilocks (P)—deep yellow flo v rs
Irish Molly—mauve-pink, also known as Lady Molly.
Irish Sparkler (P)—red flowers.
Lady Dora (P)—deep yellow.
Lady Lettuce—apricot-yellow tinged with pink.
Old Spotted Hose (P)—crimson-red, each petal spotted near the edge.
Old Vivid (P)—scarlet with very striking orange-yellow centre.
Oranges and Lemons—deep yellow splashed with orange.
Pam Hose—h se in hose form of *juliae* hybrid 'Pam', red.
Ruddigore—crimson-red.
The Clown —magenta-red splashed with white.
Wanda Ho e—hose form of 'Wanda', purple red flowers.
Windlest aw (P)—pale primrose-yellow.
Sparkle – crimson.

Garryard Polyanthus (frequently spelled Garryarde)

The Garryard Polyanthus was known in Ireland before *P. juliae* or *P. vulgaris* ssp. *sibthorpii* were introduced in 1900. According to Mr. Cecil Monson there was only one original Garryard variety. This was 'Garryard Appleblossom', produced before the end of the last century by Mr. Whiteside Dane who came from Garryard in the County of Kildare, Eire. Mr. Monson grew Garryards for much of his life and he traced their history back to its original source. His grandmother received 'Garryard Appleblossom' from Mr. Whiteside Dane and she later passed plants of it on to him. 'Garryard Appleblossom' is thought to have been lost during the last war. Mr. Monson, writing in an article published by the American Primrose Society (Vol. 35, No. 4, Fall issue. Pages 3–5), states that a typical Garryard should have strong bronze Primrose (*P. vulgaris*) type leaves and stout red stems with heads of large flowers. Over the past fortyfive years many Polyanthus and Primrose varieties with bronze leaves have been included under the Garryard label. Many of these have been produced using *P. juliae* or *P. vulgaris* ssp. *sibthorpii*. Of the established varieties only 'Garryard Canterbury' and 'Garryard Enchantress' are close to the original 'Garryard Appleblossom' in appearance. These were raised by Mr. Champernowne at Buckland.

The following are old established varieties which are usually included under the Garryard label. Some of these may have 'Garryard Appleblossom' in their parentage. The ones marked with a star (*) are the most common.

> **Buckland Variety**—rich velvety-red.
> **Canterbury**—rich cream shaded with apricot pink.
> **Enchantress**—cream, veined and flushed with pink.
> **Enid**—deep pink, otherwise similar to 'Guinevere'.
> ***Guinevere**—large pink flowers.
> **Hillhouse Pink**—pale pink with a distinct orange eye.
> **Hillhouse Red**—deep crimson.
> **In Memoriam**—purple flushed with crimson and with an orange star shaped centre.
> **Sir Galahad**—white frilled petals.
> ***The Grail**—brick-red with large yellow eye.
> ***Victory**—purple.
> **Wisley Red**—deep red.

Cowichan Polyanthus

This is a strain of Polyanthus developed originally by Florence Bellis (Barnhaven, U.S.A.) from a clone of the same name. The original clone was a chance garden hybrid which was found in the Cowichan district of British Columbia (Canada). It was a dark glowing garnet red in colour with no eye. The original plant was weak and self sterile but it was used as the pollen parent in many breeding programmes. Barnhaven produced the Cowichan strain of Polyanthus which showed many of the characteristics of the original plant, but in a range of colours. Other breeders have also worked to improve the Cowichan Polyanthus. Today the colours range through deep garnet, ruby and strawberry reds, through dark blues to deep pink. All Cowichans should have a satiny sheen to the petals, be of a deep clear colour, have no eye and have reddish bronze foliage.

Gold and Silver-laced Polyanthus

These are a specialised form of Polyanthus which have been in cultivation for more than 150 years. They have very dark red (mahogony or black) flowers, each petal neatly edged with a narrow 'gold' or 'silver' line giving the appearance of ten petals. They also have a large round golden eye. Barnhaven have maintained a good strain of these.

Other Sections

Hybrids are very rare in the sections other than Auriculastrum and Vernales. There is a record of a hybrid produced by crossing *P. megaseaefolia* (Section: Megaseaefolia) and *P. juliae* (Section: Vernales) but we have not seen it. Mr. L. E. Wigley has crossed *P. megaseaefolia* with a pink primrose (Section: Vernales). The resulting plants are vigorous, floriferous, and have retained the early-flowering habit of *P. megaseaefolia*.

CHAPTER 7

CULTIVATION

Introduction

In general, the European and American primulas can be considered relatively easy to grow when compared to many of their Asiatic cousins. They will survive in quite a wide range of climates and soil types (below). They usually grow best in an area with a relatively high summer rainfall, a well drained soil and plenty of light (e.g. Scotland and N.W. England). A large number of factors affect the way in which the plants grow. Because of this it is sometimes difficult to give blanket recommendations for all situations. We have relied to a great extent on personal experience and on the advice of a small number of successful growers in formulating our recommendations.

CULTIVATION IN THE OPEN GARDEN

Soils

Most primulas will do moderately well in a range of soils. They are relatively deep rooted and require a good root run which always contains a ready supply of moisture. The roots require air (oxygen) for healthy growth and because of this the soil should be well drained. Absence of excess moisture particularly during the winter months is important to their survival and general health. The soil should never become waterlogged as this causes a lack of air which quickly damages the roots. Damaged roots allow the entry of root rot fungi which spread quickly in wet conditions. In nature some species live in very wet conditions but the water is not usually stagnant and it contains plenty of oxygen which the plant roots can utilise. Primulas require an adequate supply of nutrients to keep them healthy. Nitrogen, phosphorus and potassium are the most important. Many soils already contain a reasonable level of nutrients and the addition of a fertiliser is not essential although it may be beneficial (see Application of Fertilisers; opposite).

In general terms the best soil is probably a rich medium loam to which some well rotted organic matter has been added. Organic matter has a high water and nutrient retaining capacity. Heavy clay soil can be improved by the addition of organic matter and coarse sand (only practical on a small scale). An acid clay also benefits from the addition of ground chalk or ground limestone. An alternative to adding organic matter and sand is to make a raised bed, containing a well drained compost, above the clay. Here the roots can grow down to extract water from the clay, but still be in well drained conditions where there is plenty of air. A clay soil is a rich soil as far as nutrients are concerned but it is very liable to waterlogging. A sandy soil is usually very free draining and it retains only small amounts of water and nutrients. Because of this it has a tendency to dry out. The addition of well rotted organic matter greatly improves its water and nutrient holding capacity. A sandy soil will also benefit from the application of a general fertiliser containing nitrogen, phosphorus and potassium (see p. 000).

pH

A soil is said to be acid if the pH is below 7, neutral if at 7 and alkaline if above 7. European and American primulas grow well at pH levels between 5 and 7 (optimum is probably 6–6·5 in general terms = slightly acid). Quite a number of European primulas are tolerant of pH levels above 7 (= alkaline). In fact, certain species usually grow in alkaline conditions in the wild. There is no evidence to suggest that these species must have alkaline conditions in cultivation (they grow very well in acid conditions too.) Certain species are restricted to acid conditions in nature and some of these resent pH levels above 7 in the garden (see under individual species in cultivation chapter). The addition of organic matter to a soil generally makes it more acid and the addition of lime, ground limestone or chalk makes it more alkaline.

Organic matter

The following are often used to increase the organic matter content of the soil:
  (a) Sphagnum moss peat
  (b) Sedge peat
  (c) Well rotted farmyard or stable manure
  (d) Well rotted leaf mould (often Oak or Beech)
  (e) Well rotted spent hops.

Amount of light

The amount of light given to a primula should be related closely to the amount of moisture available at the roots. Where the natural moisture levels are high, such as Scotland and North West England, most species will stand as much sun as they can get. In the drier South East of England a number of species will require at least light shade (or shade during the hottest part of the day.) Growers in countries with hot dry summers will need to grow them in more shady conditions to keep them healthy. An alternative to more shade is frequent irrigation to keep plenty of moisture at their roots, as the main objective of shade is to prevent a dry root run.

Application of fertilisers

Most species growing in a rich medium loam (or a clay soil) will not require the addition of extra fertilisers. There should already be plenty of nutrients present for strong healthy growth. If extra nitrogen is added, leaf growth may be produced at the expense of flowers. However, with 'slow' species an application of a weak liquid feed after flowering (or two applications separated by 2–3 months) may be beneficial to obtain increased vegetative growth, (e.g. Phostrogen 10:10:10 at a dilution of 5 ml. in 10 litres—(1 teaspoonful in 2 gallons) —or Chempak liquid fertiliser 20:20:20 at 5 ml. in 10 litres, applied at a rate of 0·25–0·5 litres per plant—(approximately $\frac{1}{2}$–1 pint per plant).

If the soil is sandy the amount of available nutrients will be low. In this case the application of a fertiliser should be beneficial. One application of a granular fertiliser (slow release) such as Growmore ($7\% $ N: 7% P_2O_5:9% K_2O) at a rate of 40–75 grams per square metre (1–2 oz. sq. yd.) in spring and/or two applications of a liquid feed (Phostrogen 10:10:10 see above) one in spring and one in summer can be used.

Members of the Vernales Section will benefit from the addition of fertilisers, especially if no extra organic matter is added. This is dealt with in the general cultivation of the Vernales Section on p. 227.

CULTIVATION IN POTS

Nearly all the species mentioned in the text have, at some time, been successfully grown in pots.

Siting

They are usually kept in the alpine house or frame or stood outisde in a convenient site. In warmer areas plants which spend much of their time in the alpine house are better moved outside in the summer. This is to keep the plants cooler and to reduce the incidence and build up of red spider mite which multiplies rapidly in hot dry conditions. They should be moved outside to a site which is shady or partially shaded. In other areas the plants may be kept in the alpine house though this should be shaded for the summer months. In a frame the glass can be removed in the summer and the plants lightly shaded.

Ventilation

Maximum ventilation should be given at all times when the plants are being grown in the alpine house.

Regular care

Remove any dead or dying leaves to reduce the incidence of botrytis (Grey Mould). Check for aphid and Red-Spider mite attack and spray if necessary. (Spray if any of these are found, before their numbers build up. See Pests and Diseases section for directions.)

Pots

Both clay and plastic pots are commonly used for growing the plants. Clay pots are usually plunged to the rim in moist sand or some other convenient medium to reduce drying out. Plastic pots can be free standing as they do not dry out as quickly.

Watering

Watering is overhead, or around the inside rim of the pot, or by partial immersion. Where the clay pots are plunged, the sand is also kept moist. Regular watering is important in summer, although the compost can be allowed to dry out to some extent between waterings. The plants need much less water in the winter months and care must be taken not to keep the compost too wet. Too much water at this time of year increases greatly the chance of fungal infections and damage to the plants. The plants should not be allowed, at any time of year, to get so dry that the leaves start to wilt. This may cause flower abortion or reduce the vegetative growth.

Composts

A range of composts are used for European and American primulas. Most common are ones based upon John Innes potting composts (7 parts sterilised loam:3 parts peat:2 parts sand+chalk+fertilisers), e.g. John Innes No. 2 (60%)+peat (20%)+sand or gravel (20%) or   John Innes No. 2 (50%)+peat (25%)+sand or gravel (25%) or   John Innes No. 2 (50%)+gravel (50%) etc.

The main problem with John Innes composts is their variability. Some John Innes composts which are sold have too much clay in them or too much sand, so it is important to buy it from a reliable source. Because of this some growers prefer using loamless composts (peat+sand+ferilisers+chalk) which are much more uniform. (e.g. Levington commercial or Arthur Bowers). Others prefer making up their own composts from the following materials; sterilised loam, peat, sand, leaf mould, gravel, fertilisers and ground chalk. e.g. 40% loam+30% leaf mould+30% gravel plus 2 Kg./cu. m. (1oz./5 cu. ft.) of John Innes base fertiliser (or equivalent). From this it can be seen that a number of composts can be used successfully providing they are of an open nature (free draining), contain enough fertilisers and retain sufficient moisture.

Top dressing

Between 0·5 and 1 cm. of gravel (alpine grit) is normally used as a top dressing to keep down moss and weeds, to reduce drying out and to keep the crown of the plant and the base of the leaves relatively dry. If the base of the leaves gets too wet in winter this usually leads to the spread of botrytis (Grey Mould) or other fungal diseases.

Potting-on

The plants are normally re-potted when the roots start to grow round the inside of the pot at the base and before they become pot bound. They should be potted-on into slightly larger (next size up) pots at any time between the end of flowering and early winter. After being potted-on they should be well watered and shaded for a few days.

Feeding

It is not essential to give primulas any extra nutrients other than those provided by potting-on. Some growers give their plants one or more weak liquid feeds in the summer months and this may increase the growth of their plants. (e.g. Phostrogen 10:10:10 at 5 ml./10 litres (1 teaspoonful in 2 gallons). This would be particularly beneficial with slow growing species. If the potassium level is higher this may encourage better flower production for the following spring: e.g. Phostrogen 10:10:27 at 5 ml./10 litres.

PESTS AND DISEASES

Introduction

Primulas, particularly those of the Auriculastrum Section, are relatively free from attacks by pests and diseases. Aphids, Red Spider mites, Vine Weevils and slugs are the major pests and botrytis (Grey Mould), root rots and viruses the major diseases. Weeds may act as hosts for pests and diseases so it is important to keep the garden as weed free as possible (a difficult task in larger gardens). All the chemicals mentioned in this section are readily available at garden centres and shops. Only the chemical names have been given, they may be sold under various brand names. Always follow the instructions on the container (especially safety precautions and recommended doses).

Pests

1. **Aphids** (Greenfly etc.)

Aphids are a serious pest of many plants including primulas. They damage the plants by sucking the sap. This feeding reduces the vigour of the plant and may cause distortion of growth. They may also transmit virus diseases from plant to plant. Several species feed on the foliage and flower buds of primulas, e.g. Peach Potato Aphid (*Myzus persicae*) and Potato Aphid (*Macrosiphon euphorbiae*). Both of these species are vectors of virus diseases. A few species may attack the roots of primulas. The most important species is the Auricula Root Aphid *Pemphigus auriculatae*). This feeds on the roots (or junction of roots and stem) and produces a white powdery wax which makes an infestation easy to see. Root Aphids are often associatied with ants and are carried by them from plant to plant in exchange for the honey dew they excete. Plants attacked by Root Aphids may also go yellow and start to wilt as well as losing vigour. Root damage caused by aphids may allow the entry of other pests and diseases such as nematodes, fungi and bacteria. Aphids are controlled to some extent by their natural enemies. Ladybirds and the larvae of Lacewings, Hoverflies and some parasitic Wasps all feed on them.

Control

(i) against foliage infestation
Pirimicarb aerosol spray is recommended if practical because it does not harm Ladybirds or Lacewings. It is also quick acting. Where

infestations are heavy or widespread Pirimicarb, Malathion, HCH or Dimethoate sprays may be used. A fumigant smoke containing HCH (gamma HCH) can also be used in the alpine house (windows and doors closed).

(ii) against Root Aphids

A drench is necessary if the chemical is non-systemic (e.g. Malathion). Systemic insecticides such as Dimethoate may be applied as a spray or as a drench. Some grasses are alternative hosts for Root Aphids so primula beds should be kept clear of grass weeds. Any new plants obtained should be checked thoroughly for infection before planting, Keeping your garden as ant free as possible will reduce any spread. Root aphids may also be introduced in unsterilised leaf mould.

2. **Red Spider Mites** (see below).

Red Spider mites are closely related to the spiders. They have four pairs of legs and their colour varies from yellowish green to brownish red. They are just visible to the naked eye and feed on the foliage of plants by sucking the sap (particularly on the underside of the leaves). They should not be confused with the small spider which is easily visible, bright red in colour, and which runs around at quite a high speed. This spider is harmless to plants. The most common species of Red Spider on primulas is probably the Glasshouse Red-Spider Mite (*Tetranychus urticae* Koch). The symptoms of feeding start as a fine whitish speckling which may change as feeding increases to the whole

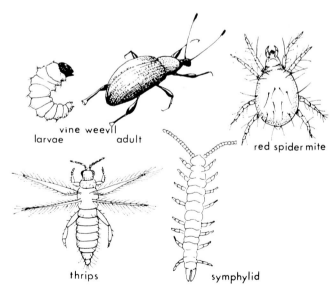

vine weevil
larvae   adult

red spider mite

thrips   symphylid

leaf turning a sickly yellow. Fine webbing may also be present if the infestation is heavy. Serious attacks of Red Spider mites are more common in the drier areas of the U.K. particularly in the S.E. of England. They thrive in warm dry conditions, multiplying very rapidly. Because of this any primulas in the alpine house in the summer are particularly liable to attack. Red Spider mites seem to be most attracted to members of the Vernales Section, but heavy infestations have also been seen on plants from other groups. Mites reproduce by eggs after mating. During the summer up to seven generations may occur. After mating in the autumn, females search for winter quarters where they will hibernate till spring. Hibernation may occur just below the surface of the soil, in cracks in poles and canes or in any convenient place in the alpine house or frame.

Several natural predators such as anthocorid bugs and typhlodromid mites help to keep the numbers of Red Spider mites down. Chemical control may be achieved by spraying with Dimethoate, Malathion or Diazinon during the summer months. More than one spraying may be required to control the mites effectively as these chemicals do not kill the eggs. It is advisable to use different chemicals on each occasion as resistance to a single chemical may build up if it is used repeatedly. Both Dimethoate and Diazinon are systemic. Spraying the plants regularly with water also helps to keep the numbers down as they do not multiply so rapidly in cool wet conditions.

3. **Weevils** (see illustration on p. 205).

The Vine Weevil (*Otiorhynchus sulcatus*) is the most common but several other species also attack primulas. The Vine Weevil can be a destructive pests of primulas. The adult is wingless and crawls among the plants. They are parthenogenetic, producing eggs asexually. The males of this species are unknown. Adults are usually to be found during the summer months. It is the larvae that do most of the damage. The larvae are white, about 1–1·5 cm. long with a large brown head and gradually tapering to a point at the end of the body. When disturbed they assume a comma shape. They may be present o the plants between July and spring. They feed on the roots and the bas of the stems. The symptoms visible on the plants above ground are usua'ly flagging growth, leaf yellowing or wilting. The adults may also feed on the plants by taking a semi-circular piece out of the margin of a leaf or petal. They feed at night and hide by day.

Control

The larvae may be controlled by drenching the plants thoroughly with a solution of HCH (gamma BHC). Holes may be carefully made in the soil by pushing a pencil or sharpened stick obliquely under the crown to ensure that the liquid reaches the area where the larvae are feeding. The adults are resistant to most chemicals though HCH may be effective (often it is not). Traps may be set in the form of rolled corrugated cardboard or upturned plant pots full of straw. The weevils tend to hide in these and can then be destroyed when the traps are examined daily. Any plants attacked by Vine Weevil larvae can be lifted and divided (at which time any larvae present can be destroyed). The divided pieces can then be treated as cuttings until they recover.

4. Slugs and snails

These may feed on the leaves and shoots and cause serious damage to the plants. Slug bait containing Metaldehyde or Methiocarb or a Metaldehyde spray can be used to control them.

5. Symphylids (*Scutigerella* spp., *Sympylella* spp.) (see illus., p. 205).

Symphylids may feed on the root hairs and roots of primulas. They are slender creatures which resemble centipedes. The adults are white or pale brown in colour, about 8 mm. in length and possess long slender antennae. Attacked plants may wilt during hot weather if the damage is great. In less severe cases a loss of vigour may be the only symptom. Symphylids can be controlled by drenching the plants with HCH solution (gamma BHC).

6. Sciarid flies (Fungus Gnats) (e.g. *Bradysia paupera*).

The larvae of these are pests of seedlings, rooted cuttings and established plants in pots in the alpine house. They feed on both decaying organic matter and plant roots. The larvae grow to about 5 mm. in length and have white translucent bodies with black shiny heads. The adults are small black flies which resemble midges and are about 3 mm. long. They are particularly attracted by damp peaty compost or heaps of decaying vegetation and manure. Control is by drenching the plants with Malathion. Two or three applications at fourteen day intervals may be required.

7. Thrips (*Thrips* spp. and *Taeniothrips* spp.) (see illus., p. 205).

These are very small dark coloured insects with slender bodies (about 1 mm. long). Both adults and young feed on leaves, young shoots and flowers. In severe attacks the young leaves or flowers may become distorted. They feed by scraping the surface tissue and sucking up the exuded sap. Control is achieved by spraying with Pirimicarb, Malathion or Dimethoate. HCH dust (gamma BHC) can also be used as an alternative to spraying.

8. Moth and butterfly caterpillars (several sp.)

Several species may feed on the leaves of primulas. They are most common during July, August and September. Control is by spraying with liquid Derris or by dusting with Derris powder.

9. Birds

Sparrows and other birds may damage primulas by pecking the buds and flowers. In some gardens this is a serious problem. Fine bird netting or black cotton suspended over the plants or a few strands of floristry wire (approx. 25 cm. long) sticking up around the plants are possible remedies.

Other pests which may sometimes attack primulas are; Springtails, nematodes (Eelworms), Woodlice, Root Flies, Glasshouse Leaf Hoppers and Bryobia Mites.

Diseases

Root rots and virus diseases are the most important.

1. Root rots
Species from several genera may attack the roots of primulas.

  (i) Foot rots   —*Phytopthora* spp. (*P. primulae* and *P. verrucosa*). *Corticium solani, Fusarium* spp.

 (ii) Root rots   —*Pythium* spp.

(iii) Violet root rot —*Helicobasidium purpureum.*

(iv) Black root rot —*Thielaviopsis basicola.*

Some of these may be serious as the initial rot quickly spreads to the older roots and the base of the stem. In severe cases the plant may be killed. A plant with root rot may be rescued by taking stem cuttings from above the rotting area. Check that the centre of the stem when cut is clean and undamaged. Most of these rots are difficult to control chemically. Drenching with 'Benlate' or 'Cheshunt Compound' may prevent the disease spreading to nearby healthy plants.

2. Virus diseases
These are microscopic plant pathogens which can only reproduce within living cells. Certain virus diseases may show no visible symptoms other than loss of vigour. More obvious symptoms may include distortion of flowers and leaves and yellow mottling. Several virus diseases may attack primulas, but the most common is probably Cucumber Mosaic Virus. This has been confirmed on several *Primula* species and is probably very common. It is thought to be common in several weed species and may be carried by many garden plants such as Dahlia, Penstemon, Lupin, Delphinium, Buddleia and Privet. In some of these and possibly also in primulas Cucumber Mosaic Virus may show no obvious symptoms. In most primulas this virus affects the growth of the plants and the appearance of the flowers. If any primula shows distorted growth of either leaves or flowers for more than one season it is quite likely that a virus disease may be the cause. Any primulas which are thought to have a virus disease should be destroyed by burning. There is no practical cure for this as far as the amateur is concerned. Virus diseases are spread in several ways. Aphids and leaf hoppers transmit viruses when they feed on a healthy plant after an infected one. They can also be spread by propagation equipment when taking cuttings. Dipping the knife or razor blade in methylated spirits and then flaming it, between each batch of cuttings, is a worthwhile precaution. Little is known about the possibility of seed transmission. It appears unlikely that a plant grown from seed will be affected by virus unless it has already been contaminated by a visiting insect.

3. Leaf Spots
May be caused by several different types of fungi:

  (i) *Aschochyta primulae*

(ii) *Cercosporella primulae* Allesch.
(iii) *Phyllosticta primulicola* Desm.
(iv) *Ramularia primulae* Thrum.
 (v) *Pseudomonas* spp.
(vi) *Heterosporium auriculae*.

Black, brown or yellow spots usually appear on the leaves. These may be common in some areas, particularly on members of the Vernales Section, but are rarely serious. If present, the infected leaves should be removed and the plants sprayed with Bordeaux mixture, or Benlate or Thiophanate-Methyl (Fungus Fighter).

4. **Botrytis** (Grey Mould)

It usually only attacks the old and dying leaves. A grey haze of sporing bodies may be seen on the infected parts. If it becomes serious on the older leaves it may spread to the younger ones and the plant may be killed. Botrytis thrives only in damp conditions. It is quickly controlled by reducing the humidity (by increasing ventilation) and spraying with 'Benlate' or Thiophanate-Methyl ('Fungus Fighter') or dusting with 'Captan'. If the infected leaves are removed by hand first this will improve the control.

5. **Other diseases which occasionally attack primulas are:**
 (i) Downy Mildew —(*Peronospera oerteliana*)
 (ii) Primula Rust —(*Puccinia primulae*)
(iii) Dying off Disease —(*Rhizoctonia* spp.).

Propagation

Seed

Most of the species mentioned in the text can be propagated quite easily from seed. For some species, such as those of the Farinosae group, seed is the usual method of propagation. Plants of species produced from seed usually have good vigour although they often vary slightly from their parents (e.g. with regard to flower colour and size and size of plant, etc.). This variation often gives rise to good new clones. Unless the seed bearing parent has been isolated and hand pollinated with pollen from the same species, hybrids may occur in the offspring. This occurrence is most common in pin-eyed plants where several closely related species are grown side by side, and is especially common in the Auriculastrum and Vernales groups. Most hybrids are fertile but they do not breed true. Much has been written about the germination of primula seed. Many statements are contradictory and the subject appears to be quite complicated. It is difficult to lay down any hard and fast rules with regard to germination. Because of this we have relied chiefly on personal experience and discussion with other growers. The following statements appear to be reliable for most species:

(a) Fresh seed gives more reliable germination but is not essential.
(b) It is probably better to sow as soon as possible.
(c) Light increases the germination percentage in many cases, so leave

the seed uncovered or use a light covering of gravel. (Light can penetrate a thin gravel layer and the gravel prevents the seed being washed away by the rain if the pot is standing outside). The gravel also reduces the growth of mosses and liverworts on the surface.

(d) Better germination may be obtained after chilling (being subjected to a cold period) particularly if the seed is not fresh. The seed must be moist when the chilling occurs. The seeds are chilled by first mixing with moist sand in a small container and then placing in a temperature of 1–5°C for 4–10 weeks. A domestic refrigerator (@ 5°C) is suitable for this. An alternative is to sow before mid-February and allow the pots to be subject to the winter weather. With seed of the Farinosae, Vernales, and Parryi Sections reasonable germination often occurs without chilling (if the seed is quite fresh).

(e) Even with fresh seed some species are very slow or erratic in their germination so keep the pots at least three years.

(f) Primulas germinate best at temperatures below 21°C. Between 5°C and 15°C is probably the optimum range.

Sowing Methods

Either loam or loamless compost can be used to germinate primula seed. If loam is used it should be sterilised first to kill off any weed seeds or pests and diseases. John Innes seed compost (2 parts loam, 1 part peat, 1 part sand plus small amounts of ground chalk and superphosphate) can be used or any one of several available loamless composts (peat and sand mixture plus some chalk and fertilisers). As primula seed is not usually available in large quantities, either a $12\frac{1}{2}$ cm. pan (5″) or a $7\frac{1}{2}$ cm. pot (3″) can be used as a container. Plastic pots or clay pots are used (or possibly old yogurt containers etc.) Plastic pots can be left free standing when sown, whereas clay pots are better plunged in moist sand. The seed should be sown thinly except where the germination is known to be poor. When sown, the seed is lightly covered with a sprinkling of small gravel chippings (or left uncovered). The pots should be carefully labelled. If plastic pots are used a code number can be written on the side of the pot in pencil. (This is best done before the pot is filled.) This will usually last for 2–3 years and does away with the need for a separate plastic label which is too easily removed.

Watering is done by standing the pots in water which is about 2 cm. deep. They are removed when the gravel becomes damp. The pots are then placed in a shady, sheltered spot open to all weathers (*P. allionii* is better kept under cover). Some growers prefer standing them in a shady frame or a shady part of the alpine house, where they are afforded more protection against the elements. The pots should not be allowed to dry out.

Pricking out

Some growers prick out the seedlings as soon as they are large enough to handle (into trays, pots or pans). Others allow the seedlings to develop into small plants before transferring to individual pots. The second method may be quite difficult if germination has been very good and the roots of the small plants have become entwined.

Division

All the species can be propagated by division. In fact many benefit from regular division every two to three years. Division should be carried out carefully, causing as little damage as possible. The plant should be lifted and any excess soil removed. The crowns are then separated by hand. If they do not pull apart easily, a sharp knife should be used to cut the piece of stem which joins the crowns together. The possibility of fungal infection is reduced by dusting any cut or damaged stems with a fungicide such as 'Captan'. Before being re-planted or potted any dead, dying or damaged leaves should be removed. The plants are normally divided between the time they finish flowering and early autumn. The divisions need time to establish and produce new growth before winter comes. They will be genetically identical to the parent plant.

Cuttings

Quite a number of species, particularly those of the Auriculastrum group can be propagated by cuttings. Cuttings should only be taken from vigorous healthy plants. The size of cutting varies between $1\frac{1}{2}$ cm. and 10 cm. depending upon the type of plant. The cutting should be removed from the plant using a sharp knife. The cut should be at right angles to the stem. The lower, older leaves are removed to expose a length of bare stem at the base of the cutting. The cutting is then inserted firmly in the compost, making sure that no leaves are buried. Any leaves which are buried or partially so will tend to rot. Some growers dip the base of the cutting in hormone rooting powder before insertion. This is thought to speed up rooting but is not essential. The compost used for cuttings is a mixture of peat and sharp sand (usually 50/50). Cuttings can be taken at any time between March and October. If taken in spring, non flowering shoots should be used. The cuttings will root more quickly if taken in the middle of summer when the light and temperature levels are high. Seed trays, pots or pans can be used as containers. The cuttings should be labelled and then watered using e can with a fine rose. After watering they are placed in a shady frame or shady part of the alpine house and kept moist. The cuttings can ba given more light if a propagation hood (perspex) is used. This keeps a high humidity round the cuttings which prevents their drying out due to the higher light levels. There are normally adjustable vents on the top to keep the humidity at the correct level and to reduce condensation. The higher light levels mean that rooting is quicker and better. A propagator with basal heat is an advantage in spring and autumn. Commercially a mist unit may be used. The cuttings take quite a time to root fully. Those taken in the middle of summer take 6 weeks or more. Those taken in the autumn may not be rooted fully until the following spring.

Cultivation of individual species

Section: AURICULASTRUM

Sub-section Euauricula

Contains two species *P. auricula* and *P. palinuri.*

P. auricula

This species was introduced into Britain before 1600. It is very variable both in the wild and in cultivation. Collected plants are quite common in gardens. Nurserymen usually sell plants originating from the wild under one of the several varietal names, e.g. *P. auricula albocincta; P. auricula ciliata.* The true species is usually easy in cultivation although some forms are much more vigorous than others. They will grow well in all types of soil providing there is plenty of water and air present. *Primula auricula* does not appear to resent either sun or shade, although the best position is probably a sunny well drained site with plenty of available moisture. In areas where the soil is liable to dry out, partial shade is recommended. It does best in a fairly rich mixture, so well rotted organic matter incorporated into the soil is beneficial, especially on light soils.

All forms usually flower well and set seed freely. Beware of stray pollen from other species and hybrids, as *P. auricula* hybridises freely with most other species in the Auriculastrum section. Germination is usually good but may be staggered over several years. Vegetative propagation is easy by division or cuttings. The plants benefit from division every two to three years.

Garden forms and hybrids are very common and bewilderingly variable. Crosses with *P. hirsuta* and with the subsequent hybrids have given rise to a large number of cultivars which are grouped under the name *P.* ×*pubescens* Hort. Plants which are close to *P. auricula* and retain the powdery eye are usually listed as *P. auricula* cultivars, or as Border Auriculas.

P. palinuri

This is a vigorous species originating from southern Italy near sea level. In spite of this *P. palinuri* is perfectly hardy outside in Britain. In the very cold winter of 1981–82 it withstood temperatures of minus 20°C, devoid of snow cover, without any ill effects. It is a long lived plant and specimens of over thirty years are known. It is easy to grow, the ideal situation being a sunny sheltered position with good drainage. A collar of gravel around the base of the stem and under the leaves reduces the possibility of rotting during the wet winter months. A piece of glass overhead during the winter will give further protection but is not usually necessary. It is a good plant for a crevice or scree and makes a nice plant for the alpine house or cool greenhouse. It is a variable species and some forms are smaller with larger flowers and these are very worthwhile. The large forms may look rather gross and do not display their flowers very well. If grown in the scree the leaner conditions keep the plants more compact and show off their flowers better. Seed germinates well and it is easily propagated from cuttings or by division.

Sub-section Brevibracteata

Contains three species: *P. carniolica*, *P. latifolia* and *P. marginata*.

P. carniolica

This species is not as common in gardens as it should be, although it is quite often seen at the A.G.S. Shows. Some very nice colour forms have been in evidence recently on the show benches and a beautiful white form has been in cultivation in the past.

It requires more shade than many of the Auriculastrum group to grow well although it will survive in full sun. It usually does best in shade or partial shade and growing in a cool rich well drained soil. *P. carniolica* has also been successful in a shady peat bed used for Asiatic primulas. It seems to benefit from plenty of moisture at the roots especially when grown in full sun. At certain times of year the older leaves may go rather yellow but the plants grow out of it again. The reason for the yellowing is not understood.

It is quite easy to grow in pots in a shady position or in a well shaded part of the alpine house or frame (shaded in summer). It is quite a vigorous species and propagation is easy by division. Seed does not appear to set very readily in cultivation. Collected seed is occasionally offered in the exchanges.

P. latifolia (=P. viscosa)

This is a very variable but usually vigorous species. It grows quite well in a range of garden soils but does best in a soil which has had extra organic matter added. It prefers full sun provided that it does not become short of water in the summer. It is confined to non-calcareous soils in nature but does not object to alkaline conditions in cultivation. In the past some nurseries have supplied *P. hirsuta* under this name even though the two species are quite distinct (probably due to the fact that *P. viscosa* was the accepted name for *P. hirsuta* at one time). The flower colour is variable and so is the size of plant. There are several white forms in cultivation including one that received a Preliminary Commendation in 1978 (introduced by Henry and Margaret Taylor). As a pot plant *P. latifolia* is vigorous and reasonably free flowering. A John Innes No. 2 potting compost with extra peat will suit it. *P.latifolia* is propagated by seed, division or cuttings. The seed usually require chilling before germination will take place and the germination percentage is quite variable (but often on the low side).

P. marginata

This is the easiest of species for any type of garden soil providing there is adequate drainage. It is a long lived plant and there are a wide range of forms available in commerce. Most forms flower easily and well and are vigorous plants. It has been in cultivation a very long time having been introduced in 1777. It is shown off to the best extent when grown in a crevice in cliff or rocks but also makes a fine display in the scree or open garden. Old plants tend to become leggy showing lengths of bare stem. When plants do this they can be divided and replanted more deeply to hide the older stems if they are thought unsightly. One of the few drawbacks to growing *P. marginata* in the open is that it tends to lose much of the farina from its leaves. It makes a very fine pot plant for the alpine house or frame where, if not watered overhead too much, it retains the powdery white or yellow farina which makes the leaves look so much more interesting. The compost used in the pots is not too critical providing there is good drainage and sufficient nutrients (see composts). It is easily propagated by seeds, cuttings or division. Named cultivars and hybrids do not come true from seed and so these must be propagated by cuttings or division.

Sub-section Arthritica

This sub-section contains four species which can be treated in a similar way: *P. clusiana*, *P. glaucescens*, *P. spectabilis*, *P. wulfeniana*.

The members of this group are easy to grow in a range of garden soils. They have a reputation for shy flowering though this is not fully deserved. They require maximum sunlight and a rich gritty compost with plenty of moisture at their roots to make them flower well. Because of this, a rich scree or deep trough makes an ideal situation for them. They may also benefit from a weak liquid feed which is high in potassium (e.g. Phostrogen 10:10:27 at a rate of 5 ml. in 10 litres (1 teaspoonful in 2 gallons). Many early growers grew them in shady conditions where they flower less well. There are quite a number of clones being grown of each species (some of wild origin) and some seem to flower much more freely than others. It is worth growing these species from seed and selecting the best plants. All four species are easy from seed and they will usually flower one to three years after germination. The plants should be divided every two to three years to retain their vigour. All four can also be propagated by cuttings which are best taken in the summer months. They make good pot plants for the alpine house. They usually grow and flower reasonably well in a rich gritty compost such as 50% John Innes No. 2 potting compost and 50% small chippings or grit.

P. clusiana

This is probably the most widely grown of the four and the easiest to flower well. There is a vigorous large flowered form called *P. clusiana* 'Murray-Lyon Form'. This flowers well and the flowers are up to 4 cm. in diameter. It may possibly have another species in its make-up.

P. glaucescens

A vigorous species. It is usually shy flowering, however there are at least two free flowering clones that we know of. These grow strongly and flower well at least once a year, sometimes more. They benefit from regular division.

P. spectabilis

This is a species that will flower, but rarely flowers well. The size and colour of the flowers are rather variable on different forms, some are of poor colour and size. It may respond to a heavier mixture than for the other three, or benefit more from a liquid feed. There are several natural *P. spectabilis* hybrids being grown (they are quite close to *P. spectabilis*) which seem to flower better and have very attractive flowers.

P. wulfeniana

Possibly the least grown of the four though a very nice plant. It is usually quite vigorous but is shy flowering. The best position is probably a rich gritty limestone scree. Some clones seem to flower better than others. For some growers it seems to flower quite well, for others it never flowers. There appear to be no obvious reasons for this, other than clonal differences, though maybe this is not the complete answer.

Sub-section Erythrodrosum

This is a group of five species: *PP. apennina, daonensis, hirsuta, pedemontana* and *villosa*.

They are all of relatively easy culture in a sunny or partially shaded site with a well drained but moist soil. Rock crevices or rich scree seems to suit them. In warm dry areas they will require more shade. They are all easy to raise from seed, cuttings or division. Seed usually germinates better after a cold period (chilling). Sometimes the germination is delayed for two years or more and the germination percentage may be low. The colour and size of flowers are variable so good clones should be chosen and propagated by cuttings or division. All five species make good pot plants for the alpine house or frame.

P. apennina

This has never been common in cultivation. It seems to suffer more than the others from winter wet and so benefits from a layer of gravel around its neck or by being planted in a narrow crevice. It is rather shy flowering but when it does flower it is an attractive species. It should be regularly divided or cuttings taken to replace any plants lost.

P. daonensis

A range of plants are often cultivated under this name. The true species is quite rare in gardens. It seems to be a slow growing plant which does not flower as freely as *P. hirsuta* and *P. pedemontana*.

P. hirsuta

A very easy attractive species which does well in a range of soils and positions. The flower colour and size vary quite considerably. There is a very distinct form called *P. hirsuta* var. *exscapa* which has no visible peduncle and the flowers are sub-sessile in the umbel. There is also a lovely white form called *P. hirsuta* 'Nivea'.

P. pedemontana

This is another easy and rewarding species thought it seems to be slower growing than *P. hirsuta* and may take some time to become established. There are a number of very nice colour forms in cultivation including good white ones.

P. villosa

An easy species which should be treated in the same way as the others. *P. villosa* from the Cottian Alps seems to be more difficult to establish.

Sub-section Rhopsidium

This contains four species: *PP. allionii, integrifolia, kitaibeliana* and *tyrolensis*.

P. allionii

This was first collected in the Roya valley in 1901 and subsequently introduced into cultivation. It is considered to be an easy pot plant for the alpine house or frame but much more difficult outside. It can be long lived and specimens of over 30 years old have been known. There are many forms and cultivars, some being much more vigorous than others.

Under glass

Various composts may be used providing the drainage is really efficient. Several growers use a mixture of loam, leafmould and sand ($\pm$ gravel), whilst others use a John Innes potting compost (No. 1 or 2) with extra sand or chippings added. The compost is usually top dressed with about 1 cm. of chippings to keep the undersides of the leaves and the base of the stems as dry as possible. This reduces the possibility of fungal rots occurring. Careful watering is important. The plants are normally watered from below or water is added around the pot rim. It is important to keep the leaves dry, especially during the winter months. The compost should be kept moist but not too wet. The maximum ventilation available should be given at all times. In winter this reduces the incidence of botrytis and during the summer keeps the temperature at reasonable levels. Light shade is normally used from about April to September. Any dead flowers or leaves may become infected with fungus and should be carefully removed. If this is done with a slight sideways pull it causes less damage. Potting on is recommended when the leaves are getting close to the edge of the pot. Young plants are usually potted on each year, larger plants every two or three years. Propagation is by seed, division or cuttings. The seed usually germinates well but the resulting plants are variable. Division is best carried out any time after flowering and before August. The divisions can be given a little extra shade to allow them to become established. Cuttings taken in summer root easily in sharp sand (or peat plus sand) which is kept damp and shaded.

Outside

P. allionii can be grown successfully outside if protected from the wet. The siting is very important. In a crevice or tufa and protected by an overhang is probably the best position. A northerly aspect is better than any other as this reduces the problems of drying out. Any compost used should again be free draining. Some growers have successfully grown *P. allionii* outside unprotected from the weather in summer but covered with a piece of glass in winter.

P. integrifolia

This is a small but quite vigorous species which is restricted to acid conditions in the wild. It is quite easy to grow and it multiplies well but is shy flowering in cultivation. It seems to do best in moist conditions and full sun. In the wild it is often washed by snow-melt water when it is flowering. Propagation is easy by seed or division. The seed germinates well but germination may be delayed until the second year (seems to benefit from a cold period). Some of the forms which are grown are of rather a poor colour. One grower advocates planting this in the grass of the lawn to get it to flower better; another advocates planting in association with other plants such as *Gentiana verna* or *Campanula cochlearifolia*.

P. kitaibeliana

This is rare in cultivation and is considered a difficult species to grow. The main problem is that it seems to resent root disturbance and because of this it is difficult to establish. Once established it appears to grow better and flowers reasonably well but has a disconcerting habit of dying for no apparent reason. It is said to be better in the open garden rather than in pots in the alpine house. A scree or a well drained soil in partial shade may give the best chance of success. Propagation is also difficult. Division is not very satisfactory because of the problems of establishing the divided pieces. Seed is rarely set. The best chance is probably by cuttings.

P. tyrolensis
This is quite closely related to *P. allionii*. It is much easier to grow in the open garden than *P. allionii* and will withstand winters without any overhead protection (although it may grow rather more vigorously if protected by a pane of glass overhead in winter). Unfortunately it is much more shy flowering and when a plant does flower there is a tendency for it to produce only one or two flowering scapes. It is said to flower more easily in Scotland than in more southern parts of Britain. Different clones vary markedly in both their vigour and production of flowers but it is unusual to see a really well flowered plant. The best position is a scree or in a crevice containing a rich gritty compost. It is a valuable plant for the alpine house where it may be induced to flower a little better but not as freely as *P. allionii*. In a pot a rich gritty compost can be used with added peat and lime. It should be lightly shaded in the summer. Propagation is chiefly by cuttings or division as seed is not very freely produced in cultivation.

Sub-section Cyanopsis
This contains two species: *P. deorum* and *P. glutinosa*.

P. deorum
In nature it grows in bog conditions in high, wet meadows and by the side of small streams. It is uncommon in gardens. It requires much damper conditions than many in the Auriculastrum group but will grow reasonably well in a normal garden soil. It has always been shy flowering in gardens and even when flowers have been produced they have not compared very favourably with those in the wild. It can be grown in a shady moist peat bed or in a heavy well drained border soil in partial shade. The best plants that we know of are growing in a large trough in a compost formed from sphagnum moss in partial shade. Propagation is quite easy by the division of the crowns but the divided pieces seem to take a while to become established before they start to put on growth. Seed is occasionally set in cultivation and is sometimes available. *P. deorum* can also be grown in a pot in a peaty compost (e.g. 50% peat/50% John Innes No. 1). In pots the plants may benefit from standing in shallow water (1 cm.) for a couple of days a week or even (during the summer) permanently. Seed usually require a cold period before they will germinate. It can also be propagated by cuttings.

P. glutinosa
P. glutinosa is restricted to acid soils in nature and should be given acid conditions in cultivation (although it will tolerate a certain amount of lime). It is not a vigorous species and needs careful cultivation to keep it in good health. It requires a sunny position in a peaty acid soil (or peat bed) with plenty of moisture at the roots during the growing season. It is shy flowering in the wild and produces even fewer flowers in cultivation. The difficulty is to provide plenty of sunshine above

ground whilst providing abundant water for the roots underground. However, the soil should not become waterlogged as the plants suffer quickly as a result. It is much easier to grow in Scotland than the warmer drier areas of the South East of England (or on the Continent or in the U.S.A.). In warm areas the only way to prevent drying out is to give much more shade or very frequent irrigation. *P. glutinosa* can be successfully grown as a pot plant in a coarse peaty compost with frequent irrigation. It may be worth while to stand the pot in shallow water—2 cm.—several times a week in the summer for a few hours at a time. Both outside and under glass aphids are a problem with this species. A careful watch should be kept and the plants sprayed at the first sign of attack. Pirimicarb aerosol spray is the most convenient method of control. Propagation is by seed, division or cuttings. The seed requires chilling and germination is often delayed at least a year (two growers). The germination percentage is usually poor (often less than 10%). Careful division is a good means of propagation where multiple crowns have developed. Cuttings usually take longer to root compared to other species.

Sub-section Chamaecallis

This contains one species: *P. minima*.

P. minima

This is a lovely little species which is relatively easy to grow but is not very free flowering in cultivation. It has given rise to large numbers of hybrids and some of these are very close to the species. In fact quite a number of plants being grown as *P. minima* probably have some 'blood' of another species in them. Plants grown from seed collected where *P. minima* is pure (Czechoslovakia, Rumania, Bulgaria, Montenegro in Yugoslavia) seem to be more difficult to keep healthy. It grows on both limestone and granite in the wild, but one authority suggests that it flowers better in alkaline conditions in the garden. Another authority suggests that it flowers better if grown in association with other smaller plants such as *Gentiana verna*. We have not found a great deal of difference when growing it at different p.H's. Some clones appear to flower more freely than others though it is very unusual to see the true species covered in flower in the garden. Plants usually produce the odd flower or two at different times during the spring and summer. Some of the hybrids which are close to *minima* seem to be more floriferous. *P. minima* can also be grown as a pot plant for the alpine house or frame. A compost of John Innes potting No. 1 or 2 with added peat, gravel and lime seems to suit it. It may flower better if allowed to get rather pot bound and then fed with a liquid feed which is high in potassium (e.g. 'Phostrogen' 10:10:27). It is easily propagated by seed, division or cuttings. The seed requires chilling unless it is fresh. The germination percentage is usually quite low and the germination period may be spread over more than one year.

Section CUNEIFOLIA

There are two species in this section: *P. cuneifolia, P. suffrutescens.*

P. cuneifolia

This is considered to be a short lived species in cultivation (although in some cases it may persist for a number of years). Most of the plants in cultivation originate from Japan rather than Alaska. Outside it can be grown in a light loam with extra peat added, or in a peat bed. It prefers light to medium shade rather than full sun and should be kept moist during the summer. It should be covered in winter with a pane of glass to reduce the possibility of rotting. Because it only persists for a short time (1–3 years) seed should be sown each year to keep a supply of seedlings going. *P. cuneifolia* makes a worthwhile alpine house plant and can be grown in a peaty gritty compost. It is often more permanent as a pot plant under glass. Propagation is normally by seed although established plants can be divided. Seed germinates better after a cold period (chilling). The seedlings are quick growing and may flower during their first growing season.

P. suffrutescens

This is a distinct primula which is not common in cultivation. It deserves to be more widely grown as it is an attractive species. In the wild it is very floriferous but is much less so in cultivation and tends to produce flowers a few at a time. It can be grown outside in scree or trough conditions or in a light well drained soil with extra peat added. In the North of Britain it is best in a sunny sheltered position but in hotter areas it may benefit from light shade. A pane of glass over the plant in winter will reduce the possibility of winter rots but is not essential. *P. suffrutescens* makes a good pot plant for the alpine house or frame. A rich gritty compost seems to suit it (e.g. 2 parts John Innes No. 2 + 1 part peat and 1 part grit.) Propagation is by cuttings or seed. Soft cuttings 2–5 cm. long will root quickly in the summer in a compost of sand and peat. Seed when available usually germinates well and does not appear to require chilling prior to germination. Seed is not usually produced in quantity unless the plants are hand pollinated (thrum × pin).

Section FARINOSAE

Most members of this group are easily grown in a well drained soil with plenty of available moisture in the growing season. They are normally raised from seed although plants with multiple crowns can be divided. (The seeds of certain species are not very freely available). Some are short lived in cultivation and it is prudent to keep a reserve of young plants going to replace those lost. This is especially true of *PP. scotica, scandinavica, decipiens* (syn. *magellanica*) and *P. intercedens.* Most losses occur during the winter months due to rotting, or the crowns being lifted out of the soil during frost and being damaged or killed. It is better if these less permanent species can be kept as free as possible from excess moisture during the winter months (i.e. covered with a pane of glass.) Most of the more vigorous species stand up to the winter wet without sustaining any serious damage. If the frost does raise the crowns of the plants they should be carefully re-firmed in when it thaws. Most species grow well in sunny conditions providing they are never short of water in the summer. They usually flower well and produce abundant amounts of seeds. If it is fresh the seed of most species does not require chilling and germination is usually very good. With older seed which has been stored, germination is often delayed until a winter has occurred (occasionally two). Some species are not very showy and may be considered to be of botanical interest only (such as *P. stricta* and *P. egaliksensis*). Most members of this section make good pot plants. A gritty well drained compost suits them. They are usually more permanent when grown in a pot and protected from the worst of the winter weather. *P. scotica* and *P. decipiens* in particular make fine plants for the alpine house or frame.

This section contains 20 species from Europe and the Americas: *P. algida*, *P. borealis*, *P. egaliksensis*, *P. farinosa*, *P. frondosa*, *P. glacialis* (*P. auriculata*), *P. halleri*, *P. hunnewellii*, *P. incana*, *P. intercedens*, *P. laurentiana*, *P. luteola*, *P. decipiens* (*P. magellanica*), *P. mistassinica*, *P. nutans* (*P. sibirica*), *P. ossetica*, *P. scandinavica*, *P. scotica*, *P. specuicola*, *P. stricta*.

P. algida
A vigorous species which is easy to raise from seed. It does well in full sun or light shade in a well drained soil which does not dry out. It is quite permanent and can also be propagated by division. It is an attractive plant and well worth growing.

P. borealis
Very little is known about this in cultivation although from photographs in the wild it appears to be an attractive species. It should be tried in similar conditions to the rest of the group. We obtained seed of this species which was sown in February 1978. Several seeds germinated in April 1982(!) and we now have two small plants.

P. darialica
Most of the plants grown under this name belong to other species (usually *P. frondosa*). The true species appears not to be in cultivation. It is said to be close to *P. algida* and should be treated as such.

P. decipiens (*P. magellanica*)
This is a very worthwhile species which makes a fine plant for the garden or alpine house. It is easy to raise from seed. It seems to do best outside in a peat bed with some shade, although it will also grow in ordinary soil. In a pot it can be grown in a peaty compost (or John Innes plus added peat) in a shady frame or alpine house. Some very nice specimens have been seen on the show benches in recent years.

P. egaliksensis
This is a species of little garden value usually having long stems and disproportionately small flowers. It is rarely grown.
P. farinosa
It is reasonably happy in any well drained garden soil. A sunny position seems to suit it providing there is plenty of moisture at its roots. It has a reputation for being short lived but plants of 7–10 years of age are not so uncommon. It flowers well and sets abundant amounts of seed. There is quite a variation in colour and a lovely white form has been in cultivation in the past. There are some 'white' forms around at the present time but we have yet to see a really good one. In the wild it often grows in very wet conditions, so a wet area in the garden may also suit it providing that the water is not too stagnant. The seed germinates rapidly if fresh and seedlings often appear around the parent plants. Older plants can be carefully divided into individual crowns.
P. frondosa
This is an easy vigorous species which will persist and multiply in most garden soils. Self sown seedlings will often appear around the parent plants, and the larger plants are easily divided. It is a pleasing species which is more robust than *P. farinosa* and the colour of flowers is more consistent. It is happy in sun or partial shade and rarely suffers from winter wet. It is probably the most commonly grown species in its section.
P. glacialis (*P. auriculata*)
This is a vigorous species which is easy to raise from seed. It grows well in light shade in moist well drained soil. It is a variable species which is uncommon in cultivation.
P. halleri
This has been in cultivation for over 200 years. It is another easy and rewarding species which is firmly in cultivation. It is happy in sun or half shade, although it usually flowers better in a sunny position. It will probably be most permanent in a scree where excess moisture does not lodge around the crowns in winter.
P. hunnewellii
This is said to be closely related to *P. specuicola*. As far as we know it is not in cultivation and little is known about it.
P. incana
This appears to be very close to *P. farinosa* and should be treated in a similar way.
P. intercedens
This is very close to *P. mistassinica* and should have the same treatment as this species. It also produces young plants from its roots. It is often short lived in cultivation.
P. laurentiana
Many people grow other species under this name (e.g. *P. frondosa* and *P. farinosa*). It is a vigorous species which is usually larger and more robust than *P. farinosa*. The true plant is quite rare in cultivation

but plants we have grown from collected seed are strong growers and should do well outside in similar conditions to *P. farinosa*. They have so far been grown mainly in pots.

P. luteola

A vigorous species which grows and multiplies in most garden soils. It is quite happy in either sun or partial shade. It flowers well, having heads of showy yellow flowers. It is easy to raise from seed though the germination percentage is often less than for many Farinosae. It persists for quite a number of years and benefits from regular division.

P. mistassinica

This is a delicate plant which is uncommon in cultivation. It appears to be quite easy to grow and is unusual in producing plantlets from adventitious buds on the roots. The main plant is therefore often surrounded by several smaller plants. It should be treated in a similar way to *P. farinosa*. It can be propagated from seed or division.

P. nutans (*P. sibirica*)

This is a distinct species which is rarely seen in gardens. The plants should be kept moist at all times and seem to grow best in shade or partial shade. Propagation is by seed which germinates freely. In nature this plant is often found in salt marsh conditions and may be washed by the tide. Plants being grown from collected seed are doing well in shady acid conditions and some flowered eighteen months after germination.

P. ossetica

As far as we know this is not in cultivation.

P. scandinavica

This can be treated in the same way as *P. scotica*. It is usually short lived in the open garden.

P. scotica

This is a lovely little species which is easy to raise from seed. Germination is often delayed until the second year, but a high percentage germination usually occurs. It is usually short lived in the open garden. It will survive longer if grown in a pot under glass. Some growers tend to treat this as a biennial and sow some seed every year to keep a supply of plants going. The best position for it outside is probably in a trough or raised bed, where self sown seedlings may occur.

P. specuicola

Little is known about this species in cultivation. It is very rare both in the wild and in gardens. Collected seed has recently been distributed. Hopefully, the species will become established from this. There may be some doubt about its hardiness as it originates from hot cliffs in S.E. Utah.

P. stricta

A slender species with small flowers and of little garden value. It seems to persist reasonably well.

Section MEGASEAEFOLIA

Contains two species: *P. megaseaefolia* and *P. renifolia*.

P. megaseaefolia

This species is probably better treated as a pot plant for the cold or cool greenhouse rather than as a general garden plant. It is reasonably hardy outside but produces its flowers in mid-winter (October–March) and these are often spoiled by harsh weather (some plants may be killed in a harsh winter such as 1981–82). Outside it is usually grown in a soil which is high in peat or leaf mould and in a shady or semi-shaded spot. A sheltered spot is much better than one exposed to the cold winter winds. It makes quite a good plant for the peat bed under larger shrubs or trees.

It makes a good pot plant for the alpine house growing in a peaty compost. The flowers can be appreciated more here and they do not get damaged by the winter weather. Its main value is that it flowers at a time when there is a shortage of colour in the alpine house. It seems to be quite variable and some forms are very attractive. It is often attacked by aphids in summer (both inside and out) and the plants should be sprayed at the first sign of attack. Propagation is usually by division. Seed is not very often produced in cultivation. An artificial hybrid with *P. juliae* has been produced.

P. renifolia

This is a species only recently introduced into cultivation. Only a small number of plants are being grown in Britain at the moment and most of these are in pots. Composts based on John Innes have chiefly been used so far. e.g., John Innes No. 2+gravel or John Innes No. 2+gravel+leaf mould. It is a very attractive species and well worth growing.

Section NIVALES

The members of this group are difficult and rare in cultivation. The species can be raised from seed (not too easy) but the plants are difficult to maintain in good health for more than a year or two. They overwinter as large resting buds and these are susceptible to winter wet being very prone to rotting. The resting buds should be covered with a pane of glass and kept as dry as possible during the winter. They require plenty of moisture during the growing season and should not be allowed to get too dry. Outside the best site is probably in a peaty soil in light shade. They are easier to grow in the North of Britain than in the South. Propagation is by seed or careful division of the resting buds in spring when growth is just starting. Seed is only rarely available. Only three species from this large group are to be found in Europe and America. These are *P. bayernii*, *P. longipes* and *P. tschuktschorum*. They can be grown with difficulty, in pots in the alpine house. They are deep rooted and will require a good sized pot (6″+ (15 cm. +)). A peaty gritty compost should be used.

(See also the Nivales Section in the A.G.S. Guide, *Asiatic Primulas*, by Roy Green).

P. bayernii
This has been in and out of cultivation a number of times but has always been very rare.

P. longipes
This is a large, vigorous species in the wild. It has been in cultivation in the past but is now very rare. It is said to be very difficult outside but possible in the alpine house.

P. tschuktschorum
This is the most commonly grown species of the three, although the number of plants in cultivation is still small. Several growers have managed to grow this to flowering size and some have kept it going for a number of years. Most of the plants in cultivation are being grown in pots. Propagation is usually by seed which is set in cultivation. Germination is quite good though the seed usually requires chilling unless very fresh. It is a very attractive plant when grown well.

Section PARRYI

This section contains: *PP. angustifolia, capillaris, cusickiana, ellisiae, maguirei, nevadensis, parryi, rusbyi.*

The members of this group require plenty of moisture during their growing season and dry conditions during their dormant periods. A light well drained soil with extra organic matter added will suit them. In general they are considered to be quite difficult to cultivate outside but we have found *P. ellisiae* and *P. parryi* to be relatively easy. Some are more amenable to pot culture. *P. ellisiae* is the easiest species, *P. cusickiana* the most difficult. We have no experience of the rare species *PP. capillaris, maguirei, nevadensis* so cannot discuss their requirements. Propagation is normally by seed, although established plants can be divided. The seed usually germinates well and no chilling is thought to be required for fresh seed. With older seed better germination often occurs after a cold period.

P. angustifolia (inc. *P. brodheadae*)
This lovely little primula is related to *P. cusickiana* but is easier to grow. Quite a number of plants are in cultivation in Britain at the moment although most of these are being grown in pots. It is a slow growing species which benefits from a gritty open compost. Composts used vary from a John Innes plus limestone chippings mixture to a peat compost mixed with gravel. Gravel (or chippings) is placed around the crown of the plant to reduce the chance of rotting. The plants should be kept relatively dry in winter, gradually increasing the amount of water as growth starts in the spring. The plants should not be allowed to get too dry during their active growing season.

225

In the open garden *P. angustifolia* is more difficult and requires a well drained gritty soil in sun or partial shade. It is suitable for scree or trough culture. A pane of glass over the resting crown in winter will reduce the chance of winter rot. The usual method of propagation is by seed.

P. cusickiana

This is a beautiful primula having deep purple, pink or white flowers with a yellow eye. Unfortunately it is very difficult to grow. It has never been fully established in cultivation although individual growers have succeeded with it from time to time. It is very rare at the moment with only a very small number of growers having plants of it. The plants break into growth in spring, grow quickly for a few weeks and then go dormant for the summer and winter. It should be easier to grow on the European continent or in parts of the U.S.A. where a short moist spring is followed by a hot dry summer and a snow cover in winter. The difficulty of cultivation outside is in providing the very specialised requirements. It requires plenty of moisture during its short growing period and then dry conditions for the rest of the year. It is also difficult to grow in pots under glass. It should have a rich gritty mixture to which some chippings have been added. Watering is critical. It is best treated in the same way as the dionysias but given more water during its short growing season, (e.g. kept on the dry side during the summer and almost completely dry during the winter months). If the plants get too moist during the dormant period they may start into growth and this often leads to their death. It is slow growing so over potting should be avoided. Propagation is normally by seed when it is available. Germination is often reasonable but the problems start after this. In the first season the seeds produce cotyledons and then may go dormant until the second year. The plants often take five or more years to reach flowering size. Division is possible if the plants reach the stage of having multiple crowns.

P. ellisiae

This is the easiest species in the group. It is fully established in cultivation and frequently appears at the A.G.S. and S.R.G.C. shows. It has in the past won the Farrer medal. In the open it requires a rich well drained soil in full sun or light shade. A rich scree is also suitable. It requires plenty of moisture during the growing period and should not be allowed to get too dry at this time. It starts into growth in late spring, grows quickly and flowers a few weeks later in early summer. In hotter drier areas it is more difficult to keep healthy. In winter it becomes completely dormant with no sign of a resting bud. The dead leaves are usually left until the spring and then cut off near ground level. It will stand up to winter wet but a pane of glass over it will reduce the chance of rotting. It makes an excellent pot plant for the alpine house or frame. It is vigorous and usually requires a good sized pot, 5–6″ initially, 8–10″ later (13–25 cm.). The flower size and colour and petal shape vary quite considerably as does the size of plant. Good forms should be selected and propagated by division. A

John Innes No. 2 potting compost with extra peat and sand will suit it. When it goes dormant in the winter it should be kept fairly dry. *P. ellisiae* is easily raised from seed and established plants can be carefully divided.

P. parryi

This is a large vigorous species which does well in a rich loam with extra peat added or in a peat bed. It prefers light to medium shade and should have plenty of moisture during the growing season. It should never be allowed to get so dry that the leaves wilt. It does not object to either acid or alkaline conditions. Flowers are produced in the middle of summer in Britain although some growers have found it to be rather shy flowering. It is easily raised from seed and can also be divided. *P. parryi* is a deep rooted plant and requires a large pot (7–9" (17–23 cm.)) if it is to be used for pot culture. A peaty compost will suit it (50% John Innes No. 2 potting plus 50% peat). It appears to stand up to winter wet better than the other species in the section, although it benefits from a pane of glass over it.

P. rusbyi

This is rarer than *P. ellisiae* and not usually as vigorous. Plants being grown under this name are often *P. ellisiae*. *P. rusbyi* is related closely to *P. ellisiae* and should be treated in a similar way to that species. It usually starts into growth after *P. ellisiae* and flowers later in summer in Britain.

Section SREDINSKYA (GRANDIS)

This section only contains one species: *P. grandis.*

P. grandis

This is a large vigorous species with very small flowers. It is considered to be of botanical interest only, although the leaves are quite attractive. It is an easy species to grow in a damp shady place. It is propagated by seed or division.

Section VERNALES

Members of this group grow best in a medium to heavy loam with plenty of extra organic matter added (such as well rotted farm-yard manure, leaf mould or peat). If unsterilised leaf mould is used keep a look out for Primula Root Aphid. The species require plenty of moisture in spring and summer but excess moisture in winter is often harmful. A position with light to medium shade or with sun for only part of the day will suit them. In hot sunny areas a greater amount of shade should be given. They all benefit from regular division and a surface mulch is often beneficial. A mulch cuts down the water loss from the soil and reduces the weeds. It also encourages new roots to develop near the surface and prevents the plants becoming leggy and losing vigour. The plants also benefit from a top dressing of fertiliser containing nitrogen, phosphorus and potassium. One application of Growmore (7% N:7% P_2O_5:9% k_2O) granular fertiliser at a rate of 40–75 g./sq. m. (1–2 oz./sq. yd.) in spring can be used. For the double primroses and double polyanthus which are slow growing, a liquid feed can be used in addition to the granular fertiliser (e.g. Phostrogen 10:10:10 at a dilution of 5 ml. in 10 litres (1 teaspoonful in 2 gallons) or Chempak liquid fertiliser 20:20:20 (at 5 ml. in 10 litres) applied at a rate of 0·25–0·5 litres/plant (approximately $\frac{1}{2}$–1 pint per plant). Division is a good and common method of propagation and is the usual way of producing the cultivars and hybrids. All the species can be grown from seed. It is best to sow the seed fresh though sowing within 9–12 months usually gives good results. The seed should be left uncovered, or covered very lightly with gravel. Hybrids and cultivars generally do not come true from seed. Members of this group can be grown in pots but they usually do better in the open garden. A compost of 50% John Innes No. 2+50% peat would be suitable for growing in pots. They should not be left in the alpine house in the summer as they tend to be attacked by Red Spider mites.

P. amoena (*P. elatior* ssp. *meyeri*)

This species has been in cultivation since 1831. For most of the period since then it has been rare, although at the present time it does appear to be more common. It is occasionally available from commercial sources. Beware of other species or hybrids being grown under this name. Recently a number of collected plants and seeds have been introduced, so hopefully it will become firmly established from these. It appears to be quite easy to grow and benefits from regular division. Some stocks seem to lose vigour when they have been in cultivation for a time (probably due to virus infections and fungal attacks). The best way to retain healthy stocks is to keep the species going from seed as well as by dividing the parent plants. Hand pollinate pin plants with pollen from thrum plants. This species hybridises with related species so the chosen parents should be isolated before flowering starts.

PP. elatior, veris, vulgaris (inc. P. sibthorpii and P. abchasica.)

These are all vigorous plants which are easy to grow. *P. elatior* takes to pot culture better than the others. *P. elatior* ssp. *cordifolia* is a very attractive plant which is sometimes seen on the show benches. Cultural recommendations already mentioned should be followed. These species have crossed with each other and with others to give a large number of hybrids (see chapter on hybrids).

P. juliae

This is a dainty little species which is easy to grow. It prefers a rich damp soil in partial shade where it usually flowers and increases freely. It is usually propagated by division, using a sharp knife. Each crown is usually joined together by a length of rhizome which needs careful severing. Seed is not very freely produced unless a pin plant is hand pollinated with pollen from a thrum plant (should be isolated from other species before flowering starts). It hybridises freely with other members of the Vernales group. The hybrids produced by crossing *P. juliae* are usually grouped under the name *P. × pruhoniciana* (*P. × juliana*) (see chapter on hybrids).

MISCELLANEOUS

Little is known about the following species in cultivation: *P. afghanica, P. archibaldii, P. davisii, P. duckelmannii.*

Note that hybrids usually have cultivation requirements which are about the same as those of the parent species, and that in most cases they are easier to grow.

229

GLOSSARY

Acute—with a pointed end making an angle of less than 90°.

adpressed—pressed lengthwise close to a surface.

axil—the upper angle between the stem and leaf-stalk or leaf.

axillary—growing in an axil.

bract—a generally small leaf-like structure occurring as a cycle of several at the junction of peduncle and pedicels in an umbel.

calcareous—of rocks made up mainly (as in limestone or chalk) or partly of calcium carbonate.

calyx—the lower or outer cycle of flower parts made up of sepals, which in Primula are laterally fused to form a toothed cup.

campanulate—bell-shaped.

capitate—in primulas, with an umbel of a tight cluster of many flowers with only vestigial pedicels.

cartilaginous—of structures such as leaf margins, when translucent, usually whitish, firm, but flexible.

cilia (plural of cilium)—hairs, generally straight and stiff, along the margin of a structure.

ciliate—fringed with cilia.

ciliolate—fringed with very small cilia.

concave—of a surface when hollow.

cordate—heart-shaped.

corolla—the upper or inner cycle of flower parts made up of petals, which in Primula are fused at the base to form a tube.

crenate—generally of a leaf margin, with rounded teeth.

cuneate—wedge-shaped.

dentate—with pointed teeth.

denticulate—diminutive of dentate.

dichotomous key—an identification system which depends on a long branching sequence of either-or questions.

efarinose—totally devoid of farina.

elliptic—usually of leaves, when the length is 2 to 6 times the breadth, and the margins are evenly curved giving the greatest width at about mid-length.

emarginate—with a shallow broad notch at the tip.

entire—usually of leaves or petals, without toothing of any kind.

exannulate—without an annulus.

exserted—projecting out: the opposite of inserted.

farina—white to yellow powdery covering.

farinose—bearing farina, mealy.

floriferous—bearing flowers, usually with the implication that they are borne abundantly.

genera—plural of genus.

glabrous—hairless.

glandular hair—a hair tipped with a usually spherical gland.

globose, globular—of a spherical or rounded shape.

heteromorphic, heterostylous—with thrum- and pin-eyed flowers: that is, with flowers some of which have long styles reaching the mouth of the corolla tube, with anthers well within the tube, and the remainder have styles the tips of which lie below the anthers, all being within the tube.

hirsute—hairy, with fairly coarse hairs; shaggy, cf. pubescent.

homomorphic, homostylous—with flowers all of which have the same arrangement of style and anthers, usually within the tube.

igneous—of rocks, when they have been subjected to melting and recrystallisation.

inflorescence—the whole flowering organ, including the peduncle.

inter-specific hybrid—the result of a cross between two species from the same genus.

involute—when the margins of emergent juvenile leaves are rolled inwards, towards the upper surface.

lanceolate—of a leaf or bract, when the length is 4 to 6 times greater than the breadth, and is broadest below mid-length, like the blade of a lance.

limb—the combined corolla lobes.

linear—of a leaf or bract—narrow, with parallel sides.

lobe—a projecting part of a structure.

membraneous—thin, papery, frequently translucent.

mucronate—with a short pointed extension of the rounded tip of a leaf, bract or petal.

oblanceolate—as lanceolate, but broadest above mid-length.

obovate—as ovate, but broadest above mid-length.

obsolete—of a structure, when diminished to the point of having disappeared.

obtuse—blunt; of a leaf or bract tip, when it forms an angle greater than $90°$.

orbicular—circular in outline.

ovate—of a leaf, bract or petal, when the length is about $1\frac{1}{2}$ to 2 times the breadth, has well rounded ends, and is broadest below mid-length; egg-shaped.

ovoid—approximately egg-shaped.

pedicel—the stalk of a single flower, or the section of stalk within the umbel, and directly attached to the flower.

peduncle—the section of flower stalk below the umbel.

pendent—hanging, drooping.

phylogeny—the largely speculative history of the evolution of genera and species; the placing of genera and species into evolutionally related groups, and the whole into a probable evolutionary sequence; a kind of botanical 'family tree' . . .

polymorphic—of a species, when its form varies widely within populations.

pubescent—hairy or downy, usually with small fine hairs, cf. hirsute.

recurved—curved downwards or upwards.

reticulate—marked with a fine network, usually of veins.

revolute—when the margins of emergent juvenile leaves are rolled outwards, towards the lower surface, cf. involute.

rhizome—a generally horizontal stem, bearing roots along its length, and from one end of which the aerial parts develop; most rhizomes branch, and aerial parts grow from the branch tips.

rosulate—of a leaf rosette, in which the leaves are evenly distributed in a hemispherical, fairly tight cluster.

rugose—wrinkled, corrugated; usually the consequence of impressed veining on the upper surface of a leaf.

scale—in bud scales, usually pale or colourless modified leaves which serve as envelopes for the winter resting bud.

scape—in Primula, this term is equivalent to inflorescence.

schistose—schist-like: schist is a crystalline metamorphic rock in which the component minerals are oriented in a continuous succession of thin parallel planes. By contrast, granite shows no trace of layering.

sepal—the structural unit, five of which in Primula are fused to form the calyx.

serrate—of leaf margins which are saw-toothed, with the teeth pointing towards the leaf-tip.

sessile—without a stalk (of leaves and flowers), derived from the latin verb 'to sit'.

silicaceous—for our purposes, rocks which contain no calcium carbonate (limestone), and thus give rise to 'acid' soils.

spathulate—generally of an oblong leaf, when its blade is widest quite near its rounded tip, and tapers towards the stalk.

sub—as a prefix, denotes somewhat, not quite: thus for example, suborbicular.

synonymy—in biology, where one Species has been given two or more names by various Authors: Usually the invalid names are viewed as synonyms of the valid name. Abbrev. syn.

systemic—related to pesticides. The chemical enters the conducting tissues of the plant and is spread throughout. A pest feeding on any part of the plant will take up the chemical and be affected by it.

truncate—ending very abruptly, as if cut straight across: of tip or base of leaf.

umbel—a type of many flowered inflorescence in which the pedicels all arise from one point.

undulate—of a leaf or petal margin, wavy.

variety—of a species in the wild, this denotes a distinct, stable population with a form different from that of other, geographically quite separate, populations.

vectors—carriers of virus diseases which transmit them from plant to plant.

vesicular—covered with tiny bladders or air-filled cavities.

winged petiole—a leaf stalk with thin longitudinal membranes in the same plane as the leaf blade, and merging with it.

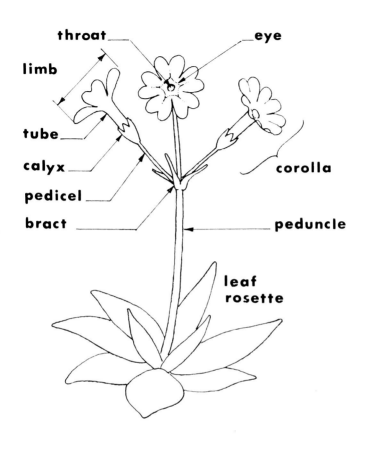

throat   eye

limb

tube

calyx

pedicel

bract

corolla

peduncle

leaf
rosette

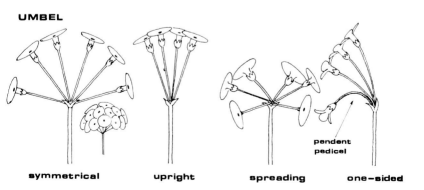

UMBEL

pendent
pedicel

symmetrical   **upright**   **spreading**   **one-sided**

233

CALYX

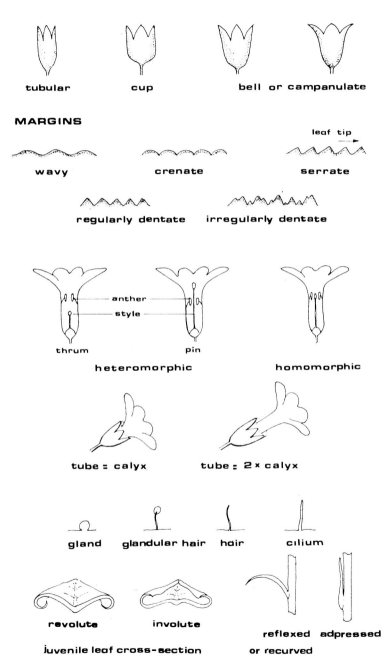

tubular   cup   bell or campanulate

MARGINS

leaf tip →

wavy   crenate   serrate

regularly dentate   irregularly dentate

anther
style

thrum   pin

heteromorphic   homomorphic

tube = calyx   tube = 2 × calyx

gland   glandular hair   hair   cilium

revolute   involute   reflexed adpressed

juvenile leaf cross-section   or recurved

234

exannulate

annulate

short rhizome

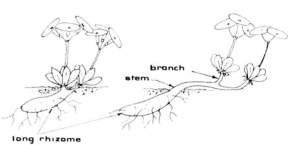

long rhizome

branch

stem

235

BIBLIOGRAPHY

This list contains the main sources used, and is not comprehensive.

Bulletin of the Alpine Garden Society (Bull.)
Journal of the Scottish Rock Garden Club.
Bulletin of the American Rock Garden Society.
Bulletin of the American Primrose Society.
Curtis's Botanical Magazine (Published by the Royal Horticultural Society up to 1970, and since then by the Royal Botanic Gardens at Kew).

Abrams L., *Illustrated Flora of the Pacific States*, Stanford Univ. Press 1955.

Corsar K. C., *Primulas in the Garden*, Lindsay Drummond, London 1948.

Davies P. H., *Flora of Turkey*, Edinburgh Univ. Press 1978.

Farrer R., *The English Rock Garden*, Nelson, London 1919.

Fedorov A. A., *Primulaceae*. In: Flora of the U.S.S.R., Vol. XVIII, Engl. transl. Jerusalem 1967.

Genders R., *Primroses*, John Gifford, London 1959.

Green R., *Asiatic Primulas*, the Alpine Garden Society 1976.

Hitchcock C. L. et al., *Vascular Plants of the Pacific North-West*, Univ. of Washington 1969.

Hulten E., *Atlas of Distribution of Vascular Plants in Scandinavia*, Stockholm 1950.

Hulten E., *Flora of Alaska and neighbouring Territories*, Stanford Univ. Press 1968.

Lüdi W., *Primulaceae*. In: Hegi G., Flora von Mittel Europa, part V3, C. Hanser Verlag, München 1927.

McWatt J., *Primulas of Europe*, Country Life 1923.

Valentine D. H. and Kress A., *Primulaceae*. In: Flora Europaea, vol. III, Cambridge Univ. Press 1972.

Widmer E., *Die Europaeischen Arten der Gattung Primula*, Verlag Oldenbourg, München 1891.

Watson J. W., *Pictorial Dictionary of the cultivated Species of the Genus Primula*, Bulletin of the American Primrose Society, 1967, *25*, No. 3.

Sir W. Wright-Smith and H. R. Fletcher, the Genus Primula:
    Sections Cuneifolia, Floribundae, Parryi, and Auricula, *Transactions of the Royal Society of Edinburgh*, LXI, part III, 1947–48 (No. 22).
    Section Vernales, *Transactions of the Botanical Society of Edinburgh*, XXXIV, part IV, 1946–47.
    Section Farinosae, *Transactions of the Royal Society of Edinburgh*, LXI, part I, 1942–43 (No. 1).
    Section Nivales, Ibid., LX, part II, 1941–42 (No. 17).

SYNONYMY IN EUROPEAN AND AMERICAN PRIMULA SPECIES

algida Adam
= *auricula* Ledeb., *bungeana* C. A. Mey., *caucasica* Koch, *farinosa* M. Bieb., *farinosa* var. *algida* Traut., var. *armena* Koch, var. *caucasica* Koch, var. *luteo-farinosa* Regel, var. *multiflora* Koch, var. *pauciflora* Koch, *hookeri* Freyn *et* Stint, *longifolia* M. Bieb, *luteo-farinosa* Rupr.

allionii Lois.
= *glutinosa* All.

amoena M. Bieb.
= *altaica* Hort., *elatior* Ledeb., *elatior* var. *amoena* Duby, *elatior* var. *dubia* Regel, *elatior* subsp. *meyeri* (Rupr.) Valentine *et* Ramond.

angustifolia Torr.
= *brodheadae* Jones, *parryi* Pax.

apennina Widmer
= *hirsuta* Arc., *villosa* Parl., *villosa* Jacq. var. *apennina* (Widmer) Fiore.

auricula L.
= *lutea* Vill., *alpina* Salisb., *crenata* Fuss, *balbisii* Lehm., *ciliata* Moretti, *nivalis* Donn ex Reichb., *bellunensis* Venzo, *dolomitis* Hort., *obristi* Stein, *similis* Stein, *serratifolia* Rochel.

auriculata Lam.
= *farinosa* var. *longifolia* Koch, *longifolia* Curtis, *macrophylla* Koch, *nivalis* Adam, *tournefortii* Rupr., *pycnorhiza* Ledeb.

bayernii Rupr.
= *nivalis* var. *bayernii* (Rupr.) Regel, *nivalis* var. *farinosa* Ledeb.

borealis Duby
= *farinosa* var. *mistassinica* (Michx) Pax, *chamissonis* E. Busch, *hornemanniana* Hook., *mistassinica* Cham. *et* Schlechtd., *parvifolia* Duby, *sibirica* var. *borealis* Duby, *sibirica* var. *mistassinica* (Michx.) Kurtz, *tenuis* Small.

carniolica Jacq.
= *freyeri* Hoppe, *grandiflora* Bast., *integrifolia* Scopoli, *jellenkiana* Freyer, *multiceps* Freyer.

clusiana Tausch.
= *clusii* Wies. *ex* Gaud., *integrifolia* L., *spectabilis* Mert. *et* Koch, *spectabilis* var. *ciliata* Koch.

cortusoides L.
= *dentata* Donn, *dentiflora* Andrews.

cuneifolia Ledeb.
= *minima* Mertens.

cusickiana Gray
= *angustifolia* var. *cusickiana* Gray.

daonensis Leyb.
= *cadinensis* Porta, *plantae* Brügger, *poliana* Brügger, *oenensis* Thomas *ex* Gamli, *stelviana* Vulp., *villosa* var. *daonensis* Leyb.

egaliksensis Wormsk.
= *borealis* Gray, *egaliccensis* Lehm., *egalikensis* Hulten, *sibirica* Hook.

egaliksensis f. *violacea* Fern.
= *farinosa* var. *groenlandica* Pax, *farinosa* subsp. *groenlandica* (Warming) W.W.Sm. *et* Forr., *groenlandica* (Warming) Balf. f., *sibirica* var. *arctica* Fern., *stricta* var. *groenlandica* Warming.

elatior (L.) Hill
= *alpestris* Schur, *ambigua* Salisb., *benkoiana* Borbas, *brachycalyx* Opitz, *carpathica* (Griseb. *et* Schenck) Fuss, *columnae* Schur, *cordifolia* Rupr., *crenata* Salz., *dambialis* C. Richter, *elatior* Baum., *elatior* Beck, *flüggeana* Lehm., *fragrans* E. H. L. Krause, *glabrescens* Arv.-Touvet, *hispanica* Wilmott, *inodora* Gilib., *intricata* Gordon *et* Gren., *intricata* Janka, *intricata* Will.

	et Lange, *laterifolia* Goupil, *leucophylla* Pax, *leudrensis* Porta, *lofthousei* Harr., *montana* Opitz, *montana* Schur, *oblongifolia* Schur, *pachyscapa* Goiran, *pallasii* Lehm., *perreiniana* Flügge, *pseudoelatior* Kusn., *rhododendricola* Sennen, *ruprechtii* Kusn., *subarctica* Schur, *tommasinii* Lange, *unicolor* Nolte, *veris* Oeder, *veris* var. *elatior* L.
ellisiae Poll. *et* Cockerell	=*rusbyi* Pax.
farinosa L.	=*auricula* Hill, *nivalis* Turcz.
frondosa Janka	=*algida* Janka, *farinosa* Gris., *farinosa* var. *turcica* Friv.
glaucescens Moretti	=*calycina* Duby, *laevigata* Duby *ex* Reichb., *longobarda* Porta.
grandis Trautv.	=*Sredinskya grandis* (Trautv.) Fed.
halleri J. F. Gmel.	=*longiflora* All.
hirsuta All.	=*ciliata* Schrank, *confinis* Schott, *decora* Sims, *decipiens* Stein *ex* Pax, *exscapa* Regetsch *et* Heer, *nelsonii* Hort. *ex* Stein, *nivalis* Hort., *pallida* Schott, *pubescens* Lois., *rubra* J. F. Gmel., *villosa* Curtis, *viscosa* Vill., *viscosa* f. *frigida* Widmer.
incana Jones	=*americana* Rydb., *dealbata* Engelm. *ex* Gray, *farinosa* var. *genuina* Pax, *farinosa* subsp. *incana* (Jones) W. W. Sm. *et* Forr.
integrifolia L.	=*candolleana* Reichb., *incisa* Lam.
intercedens Fern.	=*farinosa* f. *americana*, *farinosa* Nutt, *farinosa* subsp. *intercedens* (Fern.) W. W. Sm. *et* Forr., *pusilla* Hook.
kitaibeliana Schott	=*integrifolia* Vis., *viscosa* Waldst. *et* Kit.
latifolia Lapeyr.	=*alpina* Lois., *graveolens* Hegetsch., *hirsuta* Vill., *viscosa* All.
laurentiana Fern.	=*farinosa* var. *americana* Fern., var. *macropoda* Fern., var. *incana* St. John, *pusilla* Sweet.
longipes Freyn *et* Sint.	=*nivalis* var. *longipes* Kusn.
longiscapa Ledeb.	=*altaica* Turcz, *farinosa* subsp. *davurica* var. *intermedia* Pax, *farinosa* subsp. *intermedia* Sims, *farinosa* var. *longiscapa* Koch, *intermedia* Sims.
luteola Rupr.	=*auriculata* var. *luteola* (Rupr.) Regel.
magellanica Lehm.	=*decipiens* Duby, *farinosa* Gray, *farinosa* var. *magellanica* (Lehm.) Hook., *magellanica* Hook.
marginata Curtis	=*auricula* All., *crenata* Lam., *microcalyx* Lehm.
minima L.	=*sauteri* Schultz.
mistassinica Michx	=*hornemanniana* Hook., *maccalliana* Wiegand, *pusilla* Goldie, *sibirica* var. *mistassinica* (Michx) Kurtz.
nutans Georgi	=*finnmarchica* Jacq., *integrifolia* Oeder, *intermedia* Ledeb., *rotundifolia* Pallas, *sibirica* Jacq.
parryi Gray	=*mucronata* Greene.
pedemontana Thomas	=*bonjeani* Huguenin, *glandulosa* Bonjean, *latifolia* var. *pedemontana* Arc., *pubescens* Reichb., *villosa* var. *glandulosa* Duby, *viscosa* var. *pedemontana* Hort.
rusbyi Greene	= ?*serra* Small.
scandinavica Bruun	=*scotica* var. *scandinavica* Bruun.
scotica Hook.	=*farinosa* subsp. *scotica* (Hook.) W. W. Sm. *et* Forr., *farinosa* var. *pygmaea* Pax.

spectabilis Tratt.

=*baldensis* Goiran *ex* Parl., *carniolica* Poll., *calycina* Reichb., *glaucescens* Reichb., *integrifolia* Tausch., *longifolia* Pollini, *parlatorii* Porta, *polliniana* Moretti, *weldeniana* Reichb.

stricta Hornemann

=*farinosa* var. *groenlandica* Pax, *farinosa* var. *mistassinica* Pax, *farinosa* var. *stricta* (Horn.) Wahlen., *glabrescens* F. Nyl., *hornemanniana* Lehm., *mistassinica* Gray.

tschuktschorum Kjellm.

= ?*arctica* Koidzumi, *nivalis* var. *pumila* Ledeb., *pumila* Ledeb.

tyrolensis Schott

=*allionii* Koch.

veris Linn.

=*columnae* Ten., *cordifolia* Schur, *coronaria* Salisb., *discolor* Schur, *domestica* Hoffmannsegg, *foliis rugosis* Gmelin, *horticola* Domin., *inflata* Duby, *inflata* Lehm., *intermedia* Facchini, *legionensis* Wilmott, *legueana* Camus, *macedonica* Adamovic, *macrocalyx* Bunge, *macrocalyx* Schur, *montana* Reuter, *odorata* Gilib., *officinalis* (Linn.) Hill, *pannonica* Kerner, *praticola* Fritsch, *pseudoacaulis* Caruel, *pyrenaica* Miegeville, *suaveolens* Bertol., *suaveolens* Radde, *sylvestris* Scop., *tommasinii* var. *columnae* Caruel, *travnicensis* Wiesbaur, *uralensis* Fischer, *variabilis* Caruel, *variiflora* Beck, *velenovskyi* Fritsch, *veris* M. Bieb., *veris* Bubani, *bosniaca* Beck, *brevistyla* DC.

villosa Jacq.

=*commutata* Schott, *cottia* Widmer, *hirsuta* Reichb., *simsii* Sweet, *villosa* Parl.

vulgaris Hudson

=*abchasica* Sosn., *acaulis* Hohenacker, *acaulis* (L.) Hill, *amoena* var. *acaulis* M. Bieb., *amoena* var. *sibthorpii* Koch, *bicolor* Rafinesque, *caulescens* (Koch) Pax, *grandiflora* Lam., *heterochroma* Stapf., *hybrida* Schrank, *komarovii* Losin., *pseudoacaulis* Schur, *sibthorpii* Hoffmannsegg, *uniflora* Gmel., *veris* var. *acaulis* Linn., *vernalis* Salisb., *woronowi* Losin.

wulfeniana Schott

=*calycina* Reichb., *clusiana* E. Weiss, *carniolica* Wulfen, *baumgarteniana* Degen, *glaucescens* Reichb., *integrifolia* Reichb., *spectabilis* Josch.

capillaris Holmgren, *comberi* W. W. Sm., *darialica* Rupr., *dealbata* Schwz, *deorum* Velen., *glacialis* Adam, *glutinosa* Wulfen, *hunnewellii* Fern., *juliae* Kusn., *maguirei* L. O. Williams, *megaseaefolia* Boiss., *nevadensis* Holmgren, *ossetica* Kusn., *palinuri* Petagna, *renifolia* Volg., *specuicola* Rydb., and *suffrutescens* Gray have no synonyms.

239

ALPHABETICAL LIST OF SYNONYMS OF EUROPEAN AND AMERICAN SPECIES

abchasica Sosn. = *vulgaris*
acaulis (L.) Hill = *vulgaris*
acaulis Hohenacker = *vulgaris*
algida Janka = *frondosa*
allionii Koch = *tyrolensis*
alpestris Schur = *elatior*
alpina Lois. = *latifolia*
alpina Salisb. = *auricula*
altaica Hort. = *amoena*
altaica Turcz = *longiscapa*
ambigua Salisb. = *elatior*
americana Rydb. = *incana*
amoena var. acaulis M. Bieb. = *vulgaris*
amoena var. sibthorpii Koch = *vulgaris*
angustifolia var. cusickiana A. Gray = *cusickiana*
arctica Koidzumi = ?*tschuktschorum*
auricula All. = *marginata*
auricula Hill = *farinosa*
auriculata Ledeb. = *algida*
auriculata var. luteola (Rupr.) Regel = *luteola*

balbisii Lehm. = *auricula*
baldensis Gorran ex Parl. = *spectabilis*
baumgarteniana Degen = *wulfeniana*
bellunensis Venzo = *auricula*
benkoiana Borbas = *elatior*
bicolor Rafin. = *vulgaris*
bonjeani Huguenin = *pedemontana*
borealis Gray = *egaliksensis*
bosniaca Beck = *veris*
brachycalyx Opitz = *elatior*
brevistyla DC = *veris*
*brodheadae Jones = *angustifolia*
bungeana C. A. Mey = *algida*

cadinensis Porta = *daonensis*
calycina Duby = *glaucescens*
calycina Reichb. = *spectabilis* and *wulfeniana*
candolleana Reichb. = *integrifolia*
carniolica Poll. = *spectabilis*
carniolica Wulfen = *wulfeniana*
carpathica (Gris. et Sch.) Fuss = *elatior*
caucasica Koch = *algida*
caulescens (Koch) Pax = *vulgaris*
chamissonis E. Busch = *borealis*
ciliata Moretti = *auricula*
ciliata Schrank = *hirsuta*
clusiana E. Weiss = *wulfeniana*

*Often misspelt *broaheadae*

clusii Wies. ex Gaud. = *clusiana*
columnae Schur = *elatior*
columnae Ten. = *veris*
commutata Schott = *villosa*
confinis Schott = *hirsuta*
cordifolia Rupr = *elatior*
cordifolia Schur = *veris*
coronaria Salisb. = *veris*
cottia Widmer = *villosa*
crenata Fuss = *auricula*
crenata Lam. = *marginata*
crenata Salz. = *elatior*

dambialis C. Richter = *elatior*
dealbata Engelm. ex Gray = *incana*
decipiens Duby = *magellanica*
decipiens Stein ex Pax = *hirsuta*
decora Sims = *hirsuta*
dentata Donn. = *cortusoides*
dentiflora Andrews = *cortusoides*
discolor Schur = *veris*
dolomitis Hort. = *auricula*
domestica Hoffmsg = *veris*
elatior Baum. = *elatior*

elatior Beck = *elatior*
elatior Ledeb. = *amoena*
elatior var. amoena Duby = *amoena*
elatior var. dubia Regel = *amoena*
egalikensis Hulten = *egaliksensis*
egaliccensis Lehm. = *egaliksensis*
exscapa Hegetsch. et Heer = *hirsuta*

farinosa Bieb. = *algida*
farinosa Gray = *magellanica*
farinosa Gris. = *frondosa*
farinosa M.Bieb. = *algida*
farinosa Nutt = *intercedens*
farinosa var. algida Traut. = *algida*
farinosa var. americana Fern. = *laurentiana*
farinosa var. armena Koch = *algida*
farinosa var. caucasica Koch = *algida*
farinosa subsp. davurica var. intermedia Pax = *longiscapa*
farinosa subsp. groenlandica (Warming) W. W. Sm. et Forr. = *egaliksensis* var. *violacea*
farinosa var. groenlandica Pax = *stricta*
farinosa var. incana St. John = *laurentiana*
farinosa subsp. incana (Jones) W. W. Sm. et Forr. = *incana*

240

farinosa subsp. *intercedens* (Fern.) W. W. Sm. *et* Forr. = *intercedens*
farinosa subsp. *intermedia* Sims = *longiscapa*
farinosa var. *longifolia* Koch = *auriculata*
farinosa var. *longiscapa* Koch = *longiscapa*
farinosa var. *luteo-farinosa* Regel = *algida*
farinosa var. *macropoda* Fern. = *laurentiana*
farinosa var. *magellanica* (Lehm.) Hook. = *magellanica*
farinosa var. *mistassinica* Pax = *stricta*
farinosa var. *mistassinica* (Michx) Pax = *borealis*
farinosa var. *multiflora* Koch = *algida*
farinosa var. *pauciflora* Koch = *algida*
farinosa var. *pygmaea* Pax = *scotica*
farinosa subsp. *scotica* (Hook.) W. W. Sm. *et* Forr. = *scotica*
farinosa var. *stricta* (Horn.) Wahler = *stricta*
farinosa var. *turcica* Friv. = *frondosa*
finnmarchica Jacq. = *nutans*
flüggeana Lehm. = *elatior*
foliis-rugosis Gmelin = *veris*
fragrans E. H. L. Kraus = *elatior*
freyeri Hoppe = *carniolica*

glabrescens Arv.-Touvet = *elatior*
glabrescens F. Nyl. = *stricta*
glandulosa Bonjean = *pedemontana*
glaucescens Reichb. = *spectabilis* and *wulfeniana*
glutinosa All. = *allionii*
grandiflora Bast. = *carniolica*
grandiflora Lam. = *vulgaris*
graveolens Hegetsch. = *latifolia*
groenlandica (Warming) Balf. f. = *egaliksensis*

heterochroma Stapf. = *vulgaris*
hirsuta Arc. = *apennina*
hirsuta Reichb. = *villosa*
hirsuta Vill. = *latifolia*
hispanica Wilmott = *elatior*
hookeri Freyn *et* Stint = *algida*
hornemanniana Hook. = *borealis* and *mistassinica*
hornemanniana Lehm. = *stricta*
horticola Domin. = *veris*
hybrida Schrank = *vulgaris*

incisa Lam. = *integrifolia*
inflata Duby = *veris*
inflata Lehm. = *veris*
inodora Gilib. = *elatior*
integrifolia L. = *clusiana*
integrifolia Oeder = *nutans*
integrifolia Reichb. = *wulfeniana*

integrifolia Scopoli = *carniolica*
integrifolia Tausch. = *spectabilis*
integrifolia Vis. = *kitaibeliana*
intermedia Facch. = *veris*
intermedia Ledeb. = *nutans*
intermedia Sims = *longiscapa*
intricata Gord. *et* Gren. = *elatior*
intricata Janka = *elatior*
intricata Will. *et* Lange = *elatior*
jellenkiana Frey. = *carniolica*
komarovii Losin. = *vulgaris*
laevigata Duby *ex* Reichb. = *glaucescens*
laterifolia Goupil = *elatior*
latifolia var. *pedemontana* Arc. = *pedemontana*
legionensis Wilmott = *veris*
legueana Camus = *veris*
leucophylla Pax = *elatior*
leudrensis Porta = *elatior*
lofthousei Harr. = *elatior*
longiflora All. = *halleri*
longifolia Curtis = *auriculata*
longifolia M. Bieb. = *algida*
longifolia Pollini = *spectabilis*
longobarda Porta = *glaucescens*
lutea Vill. = *auricula*
luteo-farinosa Rupr. = *algida*

maccalliana Wiegand = *mistassinica*
macedonica Adamovic = *veris*
macrocalyx Bunge = *veris*
macrocalyx Schur = *veris*
macrophylla Koch = *auriculata*
magellanica Hook. = *magellanica*
microcalyx Lehm. = *marginata*
minima Mertens = *cuneifolia*
mistassinica Cham. *et* Schlechtd. = *borealis*
mistassinica Gray = *stricta* Hornem.
montana Opitz = *elatior*
montana Reuter = *veris*
montana Schur = *veris*
mucronata Greene = *parryi*
multiceps Frey. = *carniolica*

nelsonii Hort. *ex* Stein = *hirsuta*
nivalis Donn *ex* Reichb. = *auricula*
nivalis Hort. = *hirsuta*
nivalis Turcz. = *farinosa*
nivalis var. *bayernii* (Rupr.) Regel = *bayernii*
nivalis var. *farinosa* Ledeb. = *bayernii*
nivalis var. *longipes* Kusn. = *longipes*
nivalis var. *pumila* Ledeb. = *tschuktschorum*
oblongifolia Schur = *elatior*
obristi Stein = *auricula*
odorata Gilib. = *veris*
oenensis Thomas *ex* Gamli = *daonensis*
officinalis (L.) Hill = *veris*

pachyscapa Goiran = *elatior*
pallasii Lehm. = *elatior*
pallida Schott = *hirsuta*
pannonica Kerner = *veris*
parlatorii Porta = *spectabilis*
parvifolia Duby = *borealis*
perreiniana Flügge = *elatior*
plantae Brügger = *daonensis*
poliana Brügger = *daonensis*
polliniana Moretti = *spectabilis*
praticola Fritsch = *veris*
pseudoacaulis Caruel = *veris*
pseudoacaulis Schur = *vulgaris*
pseudoelatior Schur = *elatior*
pubescens Lois. = *hirsuta*
pubescens Reichb. = *pedemontana*
pumila Ledeb. = *tschuktschorum*
pusilla Goldie = *mistassinica*
pusilla Sweet = *laurentiana*
pycnorhiza Ledeb. = *auriculata*
pyrenaica Miegèville = *veris*

rhododendricola Sennen = *elatior*
rotundifolia Pallas = *nutans*
rubra J. F. Gmel. = *hirsuta*
ruprechtii Kusn. = *elatior*
rusbyi Pax = *ellisiae*

sauteri Schultz = *minima*
scotica var. *scandinavica* (Hook.)
  Bruun = *scandinavica*
serra Small = ?*rusbyi*
serratifolia Rochel = *auricula*
sibirica Hook. = *egaliksensis*
sibirica Jacq. = *nutans*
sibirica var. *arctica* Fern. = *egaliksensis*
  f. *violacea*
sibirica var. *borealis* Duby = *borealis*
sibirica var. *mistassinica* (Michx)
  Kurtz = *borealis* and *mistassinica*
sibthorpii Hoffmsg = *vulgaris*
similis Stein = *auricula*
simsii Sweet = *villosa*

spectabilis Josch. = *wulfeniana*
spectabilis Mert. *et* Koch = *clusiana*
spectabilis var. *ciliata* Koch = *clusiana*
stelviana Vulp. = *daonensis*
stricta (Horn.) Wahlen. = *stricta*
stricta var. *groenlandica* Warming =
  egaliksensis f. *violacea*
suaveolens Bertol. = *veris*
suaveolens Radde = *veris*
subarctica Schur = *elatior*
sylvestris Scop. = *veris*

tenuis Small = *borealis*
tommasinii Lange = *elatior*
tommasinii var. *columnae* Caruel =
  veris
tournefortii Rupr. = *auriculata*
travnicensis Wiesbaur = *veris*

unicolor Nolte = *elatior*
uniflora Gmel. = *vulgaris*
uralensis Fischer = *veris*

variabilis Caruel = *veris*
variiflora Fritsch = *veris*
veris M. Bieb. = *elatior*
veris Bubani = *elatior*
veris Oeder = *elatior*
veris var. *acaulis* L. = *vulgaris*
veris var. *elatior* L. = *elatior*
vernalis Salisb. = *vulgaris*
villosa Curtis = *hirsuta*
villosa Parl. = *apennina* and *villosa*
villosa Jacq. var. *apennina* (Widmer)
  Fiore = *apennina*
villosa var. *daonensis* Leyb. = *daonensis*
villosa var. *glandulosa* Duby =
  pedemontana
viscosa All. = *latifolia*
viscosa Vill. = *hirsuta*
viscosa Waldst. *et* Kit. = *kitaibeliana*
viscosa f. *frigida* Widmer = *hirsuta*
weldeniana Reichb. = *spectabilis*
woronowi Losin. = *vulgaris*

APPENDIX III

SYNONYMY IN NATURALLY OCCURRING EUROPEAN HYBRIDS

A. Auriculastrum Section

× *discolor* Leybold   (auricula × daonensis) = *portae* Huter, *daonensis* var. *judicariae* Widmer.

× *facchinii* Schott   (spectabilis × minima) = *dumoulinii* Stein, *floerkeana* Facch., *fratensis* Gusmus, *fumana* Gusmus, *varians* Gusmus, *valbonae* Gusmus, *macciassonica* Dalla T. *et* S., *magiassonica* Porta.

×*floerkeana* Schrad. (glutinosa × minima)=*biflora* Huter, *huteri* Kerner, *salisburgensis* Floerke, *permixta* Gusmus, *puberula* Schott, *minima* var. *hybrida* Reichb.

×*forsteri* Stein (hirsuta × minima)=*bilekii* Sünd., *brennia* Gusmus, *diversa* Gusmus, *kellereri* Widmer, *pseudoforsteri* Gusmus, *steinii* Obrist., *venalensis* Gusmus.

×*heerii* Brügg. (hirsuta × integrifolia)=*assimilis* Sünd., *davosiana* Sünd., *globulariaefolia* Gusmus, *trisannae* Gusmus, *montafonensis* Gusmus, *laggeri* Sünd., *thomasiana* Sünd., *integrifolia* var. *gavarnensis* Widmer.

×*intermedia* Port. (clusiana × minima)=*caesarea* Farrer, *floerkeana* Salzer, *fallax* Gusmus, *monticola* Gusmus, *portenschlagii* Beck, *spinulosa* Gusmus, *wettsteinii* Wiem.

×*lempergii* F. Buxb. (auricula × clusiana)=*clusiana* Reichb., *integrifolia* Lehm., *admontensis* Gusmus, *churchilli* Gusmus, *clusiana* var. *crenigera* Beck.

×*muretiana* Moritzi (latifolia × integrifolia)=*dinyana* Lagger.

×*pubescens* Jacq. (auricula × hirsuta)=*alba* Hoffmsg, *alpina* Schleicher, *aretotis* Kerner, *helvetica* Donn, *intermedia* Van Houtte, *kerneri* Göbl *et* Stein, *nivalis* Hort., *peyritschii* Stein, *rhaetica* Gaud.

×*pumila* Kerner (daonensis × minima)=*alpigena* Dalla T. *et* S., *coronata* Porta, *widmerae* (Pax) Dalla T. *et* S.

×*truncata* Lehm. (villosa × minima)=*flatnitzensis* Gusmus, *laxii* Gusmus, *jiraseckiana* Tratt., *sturii* Schott, *variiformis* Gusmus.

×*venzoides* (wulfeniana × tyrolensis)=*penzoi*.

×*venusta* Host. (auricula × carniolica)=*jelenkae* Gusmus, *idriana* Gusmus.

×*vochinensis* Gusmus (wulfeniana × minima)=*deschmannii*, *kankeriana*, *mutata*, *serrata*, *serratifolia* Gusmus (all five).

B. Vernales Section

×*digenea* Kerner (elatior × vulgaris)=*anisiaca* Stapf., *caulescens* Pax, *falkneriana* Porta, *pseudoacaulis* Schur.

× *media* Peterm. (elatior × veris) – hybr. with *veris* subsp. *veris*=*glabrescens* Arv.-Touvet, *lateriflora* Goupil, *leudrensis* Porta, *sileniflora* H. Schmidt, *sordida* Beck, *tommasinii* Lange, *unicolor* Nolte; hyb. with *veris* subsp. *canescens*=*fallax* C. Richter; hybr. with *veris* subsp. *columnae*=*brevifrons* Borbas; hyb. with *veris* subsp. *macrocalyx*=*goppertiana* Pax.

×*variabilis* Goupil (veris × vulgaris) – hybr. with *veris* subsp. *veris*=*flagellicaulis* Kerner 2, *brevistyla* DC 1, *intermedia* Facch. 2, *legueana* Gusmus 1, *radiciflora* La. *et* Mort. 3, *sanctae coronae* Beck 3; hybr. with *veris* subsp. *canescens*= *austriaca* Wettst. 2, *gaisbergensis* Pax 1, *richteri* Pax 3, *wiesbaurii* Pax 3, hybr. with *veris* subsp. *columnae*= *ambigua* Beck 3, *bosniaca* Beck, *?, brandisii* Wies. 3, *macedonica* Adam 1, *schmidelyi* Gremli *? ternoviana* Kerner 2, *tomentosa* Pax 3, *tommasinii* Godr. *et* Gren. 1, *travnicensis* Wies. *?*; hybr. with *veris* subsp. *macrocalyx*= *cupularis* Pax *?*.

N.B.   1 = hybrids close to *veris*
2 = intermediate
3 = hybrids close to *vulgaris*

The following ten hybrids have no synonyms: *berninae, bowlesii, carueli, crucis, escheri, juribella, kolbiana, miniera, obovata* and *seriana*.

ALPHABETICAL LIST OF NAMES AND SYNONYMS OF NATURAL HYBRIDS

The valid names are in **heavy** type

admontensis Gusmus= ?aur. × clus.
alba Hoffmsg=aur. × hirs.
alpigena Dalla T. *et* S.=daon. × min.
alpina Schleicher=aur. × hirs.
ambigua Beck= ver. subsp. col. × vulg.
anisiaca Stapf.=elat. × vulg.
arctotis Kerner=aur. × hirs.
assimilis Sünd.=hirs. × integr.
austriaca Wettst.=ver. subsp. can. × vulg.

berninae Kerner=lat. × hirs.
biflora Huter=glut. × min.
bilekii Sünd.=hirs. × min.
bosniaca Beck= ver. subsp. col. × vulg.
bowlesii Farrer=lat. × ped.
brandisii Wies.=ver. subsp. col. × vulg.
brennia Gusmus=hirs. × min.
brevifrons Borbas=elat. × ver. susp. col.
brevistyla DC=ver. × vulg.

caesarea Farrer=clus. × min.
carueli Porta=glauc. × spect.
caulescens Pax=elat. × vulg.
churchilli Gusmus= ?aur. × clus.
clusiana Reichb. = ?aur. × clus.
clusiana var. *crenigera* Beck=? aur × clus.
coquozi Palez
coronata Porta=daon. × min.
crucis Bowles=latif. × marg.
cupularis Pax=ver. subsp. macr. × vulg.

daon. var. *judicariae* Widmer =aur × daon.
davosiana Sünd.=hirs. × integr.
deschmannii Gusmus=wulf. × min.
digenea Kerner=elat. × vulg.
dinyana Lagger=latif. × integr.
discolor Leybold=aur. × daon.
diversa Gusmus=hirs. × min.
dumoulinii Stein=spect. × min.

escheri Brügg=aur. × integr.

facchinii Schott=spect. × min.
falkneriana Porta=elat. × vulg.
fallax Gusmus=clus. × min.
fallax C. Richter=elat. × ver. subsp. can.
flagellicaulis Kerner=ver. × vulg.
flatnitzensis Gusmus=vill. × min.
floerkeana Schrad.=glut. × min.

floerkeana Salzer=clus. × min.
floerkeana Facch.=spect. × min.
forsteri Stein=hirs. × min.
fratensis Gusmus=spect. × min.
fumana Gusmus=spect. × min.

gaisbergensis Pax=ver. subsp. can. × vulg.
glabrescens Arv.-Touvet=elat. × ver.
globulariaefolia Gusmus=hirs. × integr.
göbelii Kerner=aur. × vill.
goebelii Ludi, *goebli* Ingw., *göblii* Mountf.=*göbelii* Kerner
goppertiana Pax=elat. × ver. subsp. macr.

heerii Brügg.=hirs. × integr.
helvetica Donn=aur. × hirs.
hugueninii Reichb.= ?integr. × glut.
huteri Kerner=glut. × min.
hybrida (anon)=aur. × vill.

idriana Gusmus=aur. × carn.
incerta Gusmus=hirs. × integr.
integrifolia Lehm.= ?aur. × clus.
integrifolia var. *gavarnensis* Widmer= hirs. × integr.
intermedia Facch.=ver. × vulg.
intermedia Port.=clus. × min.
intermedia Van Houtte=aur. × hirs.

jelenkae Gusmus=aur. × carn.
jiraseckiana Tratt.=vill. × min.
juribella Sünd.=tyr. × min.

kankeriana Gusmus=wulf. × min.
kellereri Widmer=hirs. × min.
kerneri Göbl. *et* Stein=aur. × hirs.
kolbiana Widmer=daon. × latif.

laggeri Sünd.=hirs. × integr.
lateriflora Goupil=elat. × ver.
laxii Gusmus=vill. × min.
lebliana Gusmus= ?aur. × wulf.
legueana Gusmus=ver. × vulg.
lempergii F. Buxb.= ?aur. × clus.
leudrensis Porta=elat. × ver.
macciassonica Dalla T. *et* S.=spec. × min.
macedonica Adam=ver. subsp. col. × vulg.
magiassonica Porta=spec. × min.
media Pet.=elat. × ver.
miniera (anon.)=all. × marg.
minima var. *hybrida* Reichb.=glut. × min.

montafonensis Gusmus = hirs. × integr.
monticola Gusmus = clus. × min.
murbeckii = elat. × (× variabilis)
muretiana Moritzi = latif. × integr.
mutata Gusmus = wulf. × min.
nivalis Hort. = aur. × hirs.
obovata Huter = aur. × tyr.
oenipontina = aur. × latif.
penzoi = wulf. × tyr.
permixta Gusmus = glut. × min.
peyritschii Stein = aur. × hirs.
portae Huter = aur. × daon.
portenschlagii Beck = clus. × min.
pseudoacaulis Schur. = elat. × vulg.
pseudoforsteri Gusmus = hirs. × min.
puberula Schott = glut. × min.
pubescens Jacq. = aur. × hirs.
pumila Kerner = daon. × min.
radiciflora La. *et* Mort. = ver. × vulg.
rhaetica Gaud. = aur. × hirs.
richteri Pax = ver. subsp. can. × vulg.
salisburgensis Floerke = glut. × min.
salisii Brügg = hirs. × latif.
sanctae coronae Beck = ver. × vulg.
schmidelyi Gremli = ver. subsp. can. ×
  vulg.
seriana Widmer = daon. × hirs.
serrata Gusmus = wulf. × min.
serratifolia Gusmus = wulf. × min.
sileniflora H. Schm. = elat. × ver.
sordida Beck = elat. × ver.

spinulosa Gusmus = clus. × min.
steinii Obrist. = hirs. × min.
sturii Schott = vill. × min.
tauernensis (anon.) = aur. × vill.
ternoviana Kerner = ver. subsp. col. ×
  vulg.
thomasiana Sünd. = hirs. × integr.
tomentosa Pax = ver. subsp. col. × vulg.
tommasinii Lange = elat. × ver.
tommasinii Godr. *et* Gren. = ver.
  subsp. col. × vulg.
travnicensis Wies. = ver. subsp. col. ×
  vulg.
trisannae Gusmus = hirs. × integr.
truncata Lehm. = vill. × min.
unicolor Nolte = elat. × ver.
valbonae Gusmus = spec. × min.
variabilis Goup. = ver. × vulg.
varians Gusmus = spec. × min.
variiformis Gusmus = vill. × min.
venalensis Gusmus = hirs. × min.
venusta Host. = aur. × carn.
venzoides (anon.) = wulf. × tyr.
vochinensis Gusmus = wulf. × min.
weldeniana Reichb. = ?aur. × spect.
wettsteinii Wiem. = clus. × min.
widmerae (Pax) Dalla T. *et* S. = daon. ×
  min.
widmeriana Sünd. = aur. × latif.
wiesbaurii Pax = veris subsp. can. ×
  vulg.

INDEX

Page numbers in **bold** type refer to major text articles. Numbers preceeded by a
bold **P** refer to the coloured plates which will be found between pages 158 and 159.